The Lyle
Price Guide
to
DOULTON

Mick Yewman

The Lyle
Price Guide
to
DOULTON

While every care has been taken in the compiling of information contained in this volume the publishers cannot accept any liability for loss, financial or otherwise, incurred by reliance placed on the information herein.

All prices quoted in this book are based on forty years of experienced dealing backed by accurate and up-to-date reports obtained from a variety of auctions in various countries during the twelve months prior to publication and are converted to dollars at the rate of exchange prevalent at the time of sale.

British Library Cataloguing in Publication Data

The Price guide to Doulton.
  1. Royal Doulton ware — Prices
  2. Art auctions
  I. Yewman, M.
338.4'3738   NK4210.D67

ISBN 0-86248-058-2

SBN 0-86248-058-2

Printed by Hazell Watson & Viney Limited, Aylesbury, Bucks.
Bound by Dorstel Press Limited, Harlow, Essex.

CONTENTS

The publishers wish to express their sincere thanks to the following for their involvement and assistance in the production of this volume:—

TEXT BY LIZ TAYLOR
EDITED BY TONY CURTIS

JANICE MONCRIEFF
KAREN DOUGLASS
NICHOLA FAIRBURN
ANNETTE CURTIS
MARGARET ANDERSON
TANYA FAIRBAIRN
SALLY DALGLIESH
FRANK BURRELL
ROBERT NISBET
EILEEN BURRELL

ACKNOWLEDGEMENTS

CHARLES YORK
JOCELYN LUKINS
BOB DIMMACK
RITA DIMMACK
TOM POWER
FRED DEARDEN
BILL & LILY BRETT
GILLIAN DENMARK
JOHN MacFARLANE
ANGELA SMITH (Collectors Fayre)
KEITH DUNN (Photographer)
KEN WHITBREAD (Photographer)
FRANK SPARKS (Photographer)
CHRISTOPHER DENVIR (Greater London Photographic Library)
P. HATFIELD (Lambeth Archives Dept.)
JENNY BOTTGER (Press Officer, London Fire Brigade HQ, Lambeth)
FRANCIS BROOKER (Archivist, London Fire Brigade HQ, Lambeth)
FLORENCE MARY YEWMAN
DOROTHY GREEN
DORIS AMES
BERYL BURGESS (Toby Jug Museum, St. Ives, Cornwall)
ABRIDGE AUCTION ROOMS, Market Place, Abridge, Essex
and a special thanks to DAVID COPE of 'Stand Even', Doulton Specialists, Kidsgrove, Stoke-on-Trent, without whose sincere help and advice this book would not have been possible.

The History of DOULTON

"**B**etter to bear with singularity than crush individuality" said Henry Doulton when critics complained about the variable output of his pottery studio.

He knew that the artists and potters who worked for him were producing treasures for ordinary people at reasonable prices and also for future generations of collectors. Even though some of the hundreds of thousands of designs and individual items that were produced under the Doulton name were calculated to appeal to the bizarre and overdecorated taste of the High Victorians, there were many others of such high quality and originality that they have never lost their artistic quality and appeal.

A study of the trade catalogues of the Doulton Company gives a staggering glimpse into the enormous range of their products and the free scope which both John and Henry Doulton gave to the people who worked for them.

There never was a style 'trademark' in Doulton, each potter and artist was free to interpret influences and fashions in their own way and the result was an upsurge of creative talent which has never been equalled by any commercial enterprise in Britain.

In its Lambeth factory the company provided an opportunity for artistic creation and self expression to an army of men and women who otherwise would have lived and died in obscurity without exercising their enormous talents. Men like George Tinworth, an illiterate who became an R.A., or Frank Butler who was deaf and dumb and whose expertise at creating beautiful pieces of pottery enthralled visitors to the Doulton works, owed everything to the liberal minded attitudes of John and particularly Henry Doulton.

The Studio also provided an outlet for the talents of artistic women and paved the way for more employment equality between the sexes. The names of Hannah and Florence Barlow, Louisa Davis and the two Elizas, Simmance and Sayers would never be remembered today if it had not been for the fact that they were allowed and encouraged to work at Lambeth.

It is to the credit of Henry Doulton in particular that this creativity burst into life for he was the archetypal Victorian business man, forward thinking, energetic and entrepreneurial who took over a well established business and turned it into a world famous name.

He was not however a woolly minded do-gooder for his company first of all had to turn out a profit but still he was prepared, for the sake of an ideal, to sponsor and finance a pottery studio side by side with the money making commercial factory. In the 1860's the Lambeth Studio made a loss for several years until the public began to appreciate the quality and enormous originality of the work that was being produced there.

Doultons' premises, formerly Stiff & Sons, on the corner of Broad St. (now Black Prince Road) and the Albert Embankment, circa 1909.

The original site of the Doulton factory on the Albert Embankment is now the headquarters of the London Fire Brigade built in 1937.

Hannah B. Barlow, 1871-1913.

Florence E. Barlow, 1873-1909.

The Doulton story began with Henry's father John, a native of Fulham who was reputed to be the best thrower of pint pots in London. He worked as an apprentice with John Dwight, called 'the father of English pottery', who was carrying on the ancient tradition of saltglaze pottery making in Fulham. In 1815 young John, who had saved the considerable sum of £100, went into partnership in a pottery with a widow called Jones and a journeyman called Watts. They were established at Vauxhall, opposite the gate of the famous Vauxhall Pleasure' Gardens, once the haunt of the fashionable beaux and belles of 18th century London.

The widow disappeared from the scene fairly quickly but Watts and Doulton continued in business. It is said that in the beginning their pottery sign board had "Watts and Doulton" on one side and "Doulton and Watts" on the other but after a short time they called themselves only Doulton and Watts until 1853 when Mr Watts retired.

By this time the firm had moved to Lambeth High Street, to a property with a large garden which was to become the nucleus of the famous Lambeth Pottery Works. It was to stay there until 1956 when it closed down because of rising transport costs and the clean air legislation. In its 19th century heyday however it made a fine sight on the south bank of the Thames because the original works were rebuilt as an Italianate Palace, modelled on the Palazzo Vecchia of Florence on the advice of Henry Doulton's friend, John Ruskin of "The Stones of Venice" fame. The 233 foot high factory chimney was disguised as a campanile.

While John Doulton and his original partners were running the business they concentrated on making earthenware beer bottles, chimney pots, ridge tiles and garden vases. Now and again however they would produce a good selling pot 'figure'; for example the model of George IV's unfortunate Queen Caroline which they made in 1820 and also figures of contemporary heroes including Nelson and even of enemies like Napoleon, which were very much in demand with the poorer class of customers at the time.

In 1832 while the country was afire with enthusiasm for the Reform Bill which extended the male franchise, Doulton and Watts, like several other companies, brought out what are known as Reform flasks. They were really stone glazed bottles for gin but the upper half was modelled on the figure of a popular politician of the time. Because they were designed for such a utilitarian purpose few of those flasks still exist but the

11

few that do are highly prized – and priced – by collectors.

By the time Watts left the firm and it became Doulton and Company, Henry, John's second son had joined his father in spite of his parents' wish that he become a Baptist preacher. The lure of pottery making was too much for Henry. His father proudly exhibited outside the door of their works a vast pottery urn which was Henry's handiwork. It was reputed to be the largest stoneware vessel in the world and could hold 300 gallons. However, it also seems likely that the lure of business made preaching pale into insignificance for the energetic Henry who turned out to be a prime example of Victorian enterprise and ingenuity.

No idea was too novel for him to give it serious consideration. Edwin Chadwick, the pioneer of improved sanitation, was a friend of Henry's and persuaded him that a better sewage and water supply system was the only way of freeing Britain's crowded cities of the scourge of cholera that stalked them every summer. Chadwick's theories originally must have seemed the theorising of a crank for at the beginning of the 19th century even doctors believed that the cholera infection was spread through the air – they never guessed it was water borne. Henry Doulton however listened to Chadwick and was one of the first to start making earthenware sewage and water pipes. Many of the drainpipes and conduits made during Henry Doulton's lifetime are still in use beneath city streets today.

He designed a self-adjusting joint for water pipes and before long was extending the firm's product lines into baths, lavatories, washbasins and other sanitary fitments to cope with the new 'bathroom' craze which was to sweep the country. This branch of the business was to culminate in a magnificent order for fitting out the bathrooms of the Savoy Hotel in London with 237 specially designed baths.

At the height of their production the Doulton Works were turning out one fifth of the sewer pipes made in Britain at a rate of ten miles a week and exporting them all over the world.

Ever inventive, Henry took a chemistry course and also designed air tight jars for keeping food and a screw top bottle. He recognised the enormous potential of the new industries and inventions that were to transform Victorian Britain into the modern age and devised chemical resistant earthenware for use in telephone and electrical systems.

The Prince of Wales with Henry Doulton, 1885.

It was Henry's idea to install steam power in the factory to drive the potters' wheels and by doing so he put his firm in the forefront of the pottery industry because it was a good ten years before any competitor followed his example.

The development of the company into art pottery would not have been possible without the sound financial base provided by the industrial and sanitary side. By the 1860's however John and Henry Doulton were presiding over a company of enormous capacity and world fame. At the time when their finances were beginning to be established on a very stable basis, Henry was prepared to take a chance and found a Pottery Studio in the corner of his works.

In doing so he was responding to a prevalent theory among the intelligentsia that art and industry should be able to co-exist. That theory was continued and fostered by the Doulton Company right till the end of the First World War and to a lesser extent after as well but by the 1930's the new generation of studio potters were rejecting the Victorian ideas of a creative collaboration between art and industry.

Henry Doulton was first approached by John Sparkes, head of the newly formed Lambeth School of Art, in the late 1850's with the proposition that some of the students should be allowed to try their hand at potting. At first the idea met with little response from John Doulton but his son was to return to it later and set aside a corner of the factory for a few Lambeth School of Art students. It is noticeable that many of them were people who would have worked at lowly or manual trades without this opportunity. Tinworth, a universally acknowledged artistic genius, was a wheelwright before Sparkes took him up and he and the famous Barlows were among the first intake to the Lambeth Studio.

Henry Doulton was ahead of his time too in his ability as a publicist for he was quick to realise the value of the exhibitions which were organised all over the world in the 19th century and, having an acute sense of what was going to be important, he never missed an opportunity to display his firm's goods. This was the medium that presented the work of his studio potters to the world.

Henry had joined his father's firm in 1835 and when the Great Exhibition was unveiled in Hyde Park in 1852, Doulton and Company exhibited but the pieces on show were all industrial items except for a figure of Old Father Time and some terracotta garden vases.

By 1862 however the Lambeth Studio had been established in a small way and in the London Exhibition of that year Doulton's exhibited their first piece of art pottery – a reproduction of a 16th century Rhenish salt cellar.

In the Paris Exhibition of 1867 however the work of George Tinworth was on the Doulton stand and it created a sensation which was followed at the London International Exhibition of 1871 where the robust and virile work of Hannah and Arthur Barlow was first displayed. Queen Victoria was so impressed by the Doulton ware in the exhibition that she ordered some to be sent to Buckingham Palace.

The Doulton name had now begun to have another meaning than just pipes and conduits. At the Vienna Exhibition of 1873 a distinctive cobalt blue glaze which the company was using was given the official name of 'Doulton blue' and in the Philadelphia Centennial Exhibition of 1876, which perhaps marked the zenith of the Lambeth Pottery, they won five first class awards. There was such a great interest in the pieces from the American public that a cult for Doulton began which continues to this day. American collectors are among the most enthusiastic and knowledgeable in the world. Their original enthusiasm was only intensified by the Chicago International Exhibition of 1893 where the firm showed 1,500 items from its Lambeth and its recently acquired Burslem factory.

Some of the items displayed over the years were of such magnificence that they stopped the public in its tracks. For example for the Glasgow Exhibition of 1888 Doulton's made an Indian pavilion of glazed and enamelled terracotta with stained glass windows which had also been manufactured by the company. The firm's success at international exhibitions continued into the 20th century for at the Brussels Exhibition of 1958 they were the winners of the only Gold Medal awarded to a British pottery manufacturer.

They expanded rapidly throughout the 19th century and in 1877 Henry Doulton bought an earthenware factory called Pinder Bourne and Company in Burslem, Staffordshire. In spite of antagonism and opposition from rival potteries there who regarded him as a southern incomer and upstart, he set about energising the new acquisition with his own brand of magic and in 1882 the name was changed to Doulton and Company, Burslem. His firm now had major factories in London and in Staffordshire where they were able to draw on the long established potting skills of the local population. It was in Burslem that Doulton's began to manufacture bone china in 1885 when a new wing was built onto the factory for that purpose. As in Lambeth, a Studio for creative artists and potters was established and the variety of their output was truly dazzling.

Sir Henry Doulton died in 1897, loaded with honours and success. He was given the Albert Medal by the Royal Society of Arts in 1885 and in 1887 he was knighted by Queen Victoria, the first potter ever to be awarded the honour of a knighthood.

Part of his achievement was the creation of an artistic environment that encouraged individual creation. It must have been exhilarating to be on the staff of the Studios belonging to Doulton because their artists were given a free hand, there was no official guidelines about what sort of thing they should be turning out, no production line theories of any kind.

This manner of handling artists produced results. Not only did they create exactly the sort of thing that the mass of the public wanted to buy but they also produced in enormous volume. Hannah Barlow, at her peak, made 30 different original pieces every week and hundreds of thousands of other individual pieces were turned out by the rest of the Doulton artists. They signed their work with their initials or monograms and took a personal pride in their creations, a pride that was fostered and encouraged by their employer.

Eliza Simmance, 1873-1928.

Alberta L. Green, 1878-1887.

St. Margaret's Bay, by the talented Linnie Watt.

Linnie Watt, 1875-1890.

When the staff of the Lambeth Studio expanded from a handful of people to 200 by 1880 and later doubled by the end of the century, the firm enjoyed a world dominance in decorative pottery. Both factories were constantly trying to devise new ways of firing and producing exotic glazes or experimenting with new colours. C. J. Noke who joined Doulton from the Worcester Pottery in 1889 and later became the Artistic Director of Burslem, concentrated on producing a range of experimental transmutation glazed wares as good as those made by Sevres, Copenhagen or Dresden. He devised the Titanian glaze which gave a Copenhagen style look to pottery. Noke also experimented in recreating some of the Oriental techniques of the past and his work resulted in the famous Flambé, Sung, Chinese jade and Chang pottery. In the 1890's he also guided the firm into one of its most successful lines, the production of figure models. The first of these, a range of Shakespearian characters, were shown at the Chicago Exhibition in 1893.

As the Lambeth Studio was getting into full swing Henry Doulton converted a group of workers' houses into individual studios where his protégès were encouraged to work

A terracotta panel by George Tinworth depicting the Doulton Studio.

The entrance to Doulton House on the corner of Lambeth High Street and Black Prince Road (formerly Broad St.) which housed the offices and artists' studios.

without managerial interference and this policy proved to be a hothouse for talent. Creativity was allowed its head and pieces were produced with leaves or lace pressed into the glaze as the artists' fancies took them. The potters also devised new techniques like *pâte sur pâte*, as used by Florence Barlow and Eliza Simmance, and their work reflects the styles and fashions of the day. Doulton designs over the years show the influence of Japanese and Primitive art as well as the rising Art Nouveau which they were among the first to popularise, producing a range of distinctive items for Liberty's.

The First World War brought a running down to the Lambeth Studio but it survived on a reduced scale under J. H. Nott, producing some notable items including a range of Persian inspired designs. The Second World War however marked its death knell and though it produced the well designed range of blue plaques for the LCC which mark houses in London where famous people lived, and the Festival of Britain brought a surge of short lived energy, the Studio finally closed in 1956. That closure marked a 90 year long association between art and industry in Lambeth. Burslem however continued and carried on the success story.

Another interesting aspect of the Doulton story is the fact that while they had a famous name for producing decorative pottery they were also turning out a huge variety of other products. Not only did they continue to make sanitary and industrial goods, but they had a huge output of garden ornaments, especially in the 19th century when the age of the public park began. They made drinking fountains, garden seats, urns, edgings, pots and sundials for every sort of garden from that of a stately home to the suburban villa. After the First World War the spacious age of gardening declined but the Doulton artists then turned their attention to creating decorative things for the smaller garden including garden gnomes but

some of the imaginative artefacts installed in urban housing estates of the 1920's and '30's were produced for them by academic sculptors like Gilbert Bayes.

The firm also specialised in architectural work and was particularly well known for decorative tiles which were used both to beautify the interiors and exteriors of buildings. The famous Oyster Bar in Edinburgh's Café Royal is a lovely example of Doulton tile work and many hospital wards, especially children's wards, throughout the country were decorated with tile pictures. Those that survive today are highly prized.

The great upsurge in building in the latter half of the 19th century gave the company an enormous boost and they found that terracotta was an invaluable building and decorative material. Designs made in terracotta could be easily mass reproduced and it was also longer lasting and less liable to atmospheric pollution damage than stone. Examples of terracotta work by Doulton's can still be seen on London's Savoy Hotel and Royal Court Theatre.

Doulton's also made a huge range of advertising wares and collectors now look out for things like model feet they produced for Dr Scholl's; for ceramic|pump handles; ashtrays and stoneware whisky bottles. For many years these were a profitable sideline of a multifacetted business which today continues its diversification with ceramics for the aerospace and textile industries.

Today Doulton and Co. is part of the Pearson Group and is still the largest producer of ceramic products in the U.K. with interests in glass, industrial and sanitary wares, engineering and building materials as well as producing the world famous Royal Doulton decorative pieces and tableware at Burslem. The artists in the Doulton factory continue the long artistic tradition laid down by their distinguished predecessors. They are still carrying on Henry Doulton's dream-making collectors' pieces for future generations.

ADVERTISING WARES

Before the advent of plastics, ceramics were used on an enormous scale for the production of advertising items.

Doultons were involved with the beer and spirit trade from the beginning of the 19th century and they produced all manner of promotional items for these industries ranging from public house tiled or terracotta frontages and ceramic beer pump handles to ashtrays and spittoons for public bars.

Some of the other advertising artefacts produced by the company included perfume bottles moulded like figures and plaques painted with portraits of Queen Victoria advertising soap or toothpaste.

One of the more unusual advertising commissions came Doulton's way in the 1950's when they were asked to make a Toby jug depicting the American industrialist Clifford Cornell, head of the Cleveland Flux Company of Ohio. He was a great fan of Winston Churchill and commissioned Doulton to make a Toby jug of him imitating the one they had recently produced of Churchill. Another oddity was a moulded white china foot which was made to advertise Dr Scholl's Zino pads.

The collecting of Doulton ceramic advertising ware is a growing field and items are eagerly sought out by enthusiasts.

Bulldog with the Union Jack draped over his back, 4in. high, c.m.l. & c. $150 £100

English Setter and Pheasant, HN2529, 8½in. high, c.m.l. & c. $240 £160

ANIMAL FIGURES

Before 1912 only a few animal figures were produced by the Doulton potteries but among them were the highly successful Flambe Ware figures.

However by the time of World War One, Charles J. Noke launched a new line, very realistic figures of animals and birds which proved to be highly popular with the buying public.

In the beginning they were used to decorate ashtrays, bookends and other household objects but later they began to be produced as freestanding figures in their own right. Great care was taken to model and paint them as close to reality as possible.

In 1936 limited numbers of earthenware figures of goats, calves and deer were made by artist Raoh Schorr but one of the first series which were produced in large numbers for an eager public was the Championship Dog range, which was launched in 1939. At least 41 models were made and many of them are still in production.

The Chatcull Range of animal figures was started in 1940 with figures modelled by artist Joe Ledger who named the series after his home, Chatcull Hall. Most of these are now out of production.

In 1973 yet another artist, Robert Jefferson started animal figure modelling and his Jefferson range of limited editions still continues today.

ART POTTERY

The most astonishing aspect of Doulton Art Pottery is its range and the variety of styles and techniques introduced by the company.

These were developed in the Lambeth Studios established by Henry Doulton from 1867 onwards. The Studio was financed by the far more prosaic side of the business, sanitary and chemical ceramics.

Henry Doulton provided creative artists with the opportunity of expressing themselves in pottery and it is to his credit that he allowed their talents and eccentricities full flowering. There was never any attempt to impose a 'house style' on them.

"The personal is the true vivifying element in art," he said.

The first big name in Art Pottery was that of George Tinworth who began making little models of mice and children, mainly for his own amusement. Many of those were never exhibited.

He was followed by over 400 enthusiastic artists who worked at Lambeth over the years. They not only experimented with the sort of sculptures that could be produced in pottery but also in the intricacy of decorative painting and devised a great range of glazing and firing techniques.

One of the innovators in this respect was William Rix among whose discoveries was a way of reproducing the marbling effect found in 18th century 'agate' wares. Charles J. Noke at Burslem was to carry on the Rix tradition, producing the famous Flambe and Chang glazes among others.

CARRARA WARE . . .

. . . got its name because it looks like Italian Carrara marble and is a dense off-white stoneware with a slightly transparent crystalline matt glaze which is occasionally crackled. The effect was achieved by using more Cornish china clay than usual in the mixture. It was mainly produced between 1887 and 1903 but some examples were still being made in the 1920's when it had a short lived revival.

CHANG WARE . . .

. . . was named after a Chinese master potter of the Sung Dynasty and it was an effort by Doulton to produce glazes which old Chinese potters had also tried to create. The first Chang pottery appeared in 1925 and was characterised by thick textured layers of

Chang Ware powder bowl by Cecil Noke and Harry Nixon, 6in. high. $975 £650

19

flowing glaze in lustrous colours which gave a lava like appearance. It was used on vases, some of them festooned with dragons or lizards.

CHINESE JADE . . .

. . . In 1920, after years of experimentation, Charles J. Noke achieved his ambition of reproducing jade in ceramic. His simulated jade was used to make libation cups, figures and bowls and examples of it are now very rare because only a limited number of pieces were successfully made.

CROWN LAMBETH . . .

. . . is a fine earthenware remarkable for the richness and transparency of the decorations. It was decorated by hand painting on biscuit ware and after glazing, was re-fired and re-painted several times. Crown Lambeth was first shown in the Chicago Exhibition of 1893 and was much admired but production ceased after 1903 because heavy kiln losses meant the line was a loss maker.

CRYSTALLINE WARE . . .

. . . the surface of the glaze sparkled because zinc oxide was mixed in the glaze compound and it was kept in a high kiln temperature for long periods. It was invented by Cuthbert Bailey who left Doulton's in 1907 but examples of crystalline ware were produced till 1914 when production ceased because of the expense caused by the high number of failures in firing.

CYPRUS WARE . . .

. . . In 1878 Cyprus was annexed to Britain by the Treaty of Berlin and Doulton's celebrated the occasion by introducing Cyprus Ware. It is recognisable by the lotus and hatched designs, based on ancient vases excavated on the island of Cyprus about the time of the Annexation. Not a great number of pieces were made and the name is mainly found on Lambeth Faience vases and bowls produced during 1879.

FLAMBE . . .

. . . the name describes the streaky, flame like effect of the deep blood red glaze which

Flambe elephant with trunk down, 12in. high, circa 1930. $825 £550

was produced by mixing copper oxide and other minerals and allowing certain amounts of oxygen to be admitted to the kiln during firing. The technique was first discovered by Bernard Moore, a chemist and innovator who worked in conjunction with Doulton at the turn of the century. After two years' experimentation the first examples of Flambe were shown at the St Louis Exhibition of 1904 and it had a huge appeal. Although it is expensive to make, Flambe is still being produced.

IMPASTO . . .

. . . the unusual effect of Impasto is achieved by fusing two harmonious pigments and firing with very little gloss. Colour was applied to raw clay and potters used a small amount of relief to add to reality. Impasto colours were browns, yellows, greens and blues and its production in the last quarter of the 19th century coincided with one of the most artistic periods of the Lambeth Pottery. The first piece was brought out of the kiln during a visit from Princess Alexandra in February 1879 and it continued in production until 1914, though the numbers produced dwindled after 1906.

MARQUETERIE WARE . . .

. . . this is the rarest of the Lambeth wares. Invented in 1886, it was patented in 1887 under the joint names of Doulton and Rix, and was a simulation of the different coloured wood inlays made by cabinetmakers. This was achieved in pottery by cutting thin slices of coloured clay in various patterns. Marqueterie Ware was produced in large quantities until 1906 when it ceased because of heavy production costs.

MORRISIAN WARE . . .

. . . derives its name from the decorations of Morris dancers with which it was decorated. It was made between 1901 and 1924 at Lambeth and some items were designed by A. Pierce. Other items, not marked as Morrisian but with the same sort of decoration, were painted with figures of golfers in 17th century costume.

PERSIAN WARE . . .

. . . was based on Eastern designs with blue, green and orange colouring. Persian ware was produced between 1884 and 1912 and was influenced by the work of William de Morgan. It was used in tiles and panels for wall decoration as well as in pottery. The painting on a white slip coating was done before the glazing and firing.

SUNG . . .

. . . is remarkable for the mottled and veined effect of the glaze produced by high temperatures during firing. The first examples of Sung were exhibited at the British Industry Fair at the Crystal Palace in 1920 and they were of animal and figure models. One of the best known is the elephant and the lustrous green Buddha. Each piece was signed by Charles J. Noke who developed the glaze.

TITANIAN WARE . . .

. . . the name derives from titanium oxide which gives this ware its characteristic smoky blue colour. It was developed by Charles J. Noke during the early years of World War One and was often decorated with transfer printings of birds of paradise or, during the 1920's when the Tutankhamen fever was at its height, with Egyptian designs. Artists involved were Allen, Raby, Tittensor and Henri.

VELLUMA WARE . . .

. . . was only produced between 1911 and 1914 and as a consequence is extremely rare. The offwhite glaze has a parchment like texture, hence the name. The earthenware shapes were brought from Burslem and painted at Lambeth with transfers from etchings by A. E. Pearce and W. Rowe. The designs are usually landscapes or figure subjects.

CHARACTER JUGS

The first Royal Doulton Character Jug, titled 'John Barleycorn Old Lad' was produced in the early 1930's from a design and model by Charles Noke. As the popularity of the jugs grew, many new characters were introduced including 'Sairey Gamp', 'Parson Brown', 'Dick Turpin' and 'Old Charley'. Some of these jugs are still in production today but many of the earlier designs were discontinued in the sixties.

One of the first to be withdrawn was the Churchill character jug made during the Battle of Britain and designed as a Loving Cup by C. J. Noke. It is cream coloured with two black handles and bears the inscription 'Winston Churchill Prime Minister of Britain 1940'. It was withdrawn after only eighteen months however because, it is said, Churchill himself was not pleased with the likeness. Because so few were produced this jug is an extremely rare and desirable item, coveted by collectors throughout the world, and a fair estimate of its price at auction today is between five and ten thousand pounds.

Churchill, character jug (as loving cup), large, designed by C. J. Noke, introduced 1940, withdrawn 1942, AS D6170.

John Barleycorn, character jug, large, designed by C. J. Noke, introduced 1934, withdrawn 1960, AS D5327.

Drake, character jug (hatless) large version, designed by H. Fenton, AS D6115, introduced 1940, withdrawn 1941.

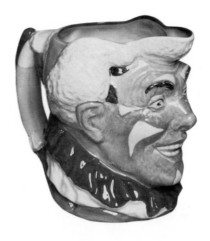

Another notable jug is the 'Drake' designed by Mr H. Fenton and introduced in 1940. In the first version the rim is the character's hair but in later versions the rim is his hat. The earlier jug, known as 'The Hatless Drake', bears the inscription 'Drake He Was A Devon Man' and production was limited. Today the hatless version can sell for around £2,000 but the hatted version is less sought after and sells for only about £60.

H. Fenton was also the designer of the red haired, brown haired and white haired clowns. The first two were introduced in 1937 and withdrawn in 1942. Today in auction they can sell for around £1,750. The white haired version, which was introduced in 1951 and withdrawn in 1955, sells for between £550 and £650. In the 1950's however it sold for under £5.

Other favourite jugs are the Cockney costermonger and his wife ''Arry and 'Arriet', introduced in the mid 1940's and withdrawn by 1960. The ''Arry' is usually predominantly brown in colour but if there are buttons on his hat and collar he is known as a 'Brown Pearly Boy'; a version with a blue collar and white buttons is the 'Blue Pearly Boy'. The latter is the most rare and sells for around £2,250.

''Arriet' too is predominantly brown with a green hat and handle, but if she has a blue collar and a maroon hat she is 'Blue Pearly

Clown, character jug (white hair), large, designed by H. Fenton, introduced 1951, withdrawn 1955, AS D6322.

Clown, character jug (red hair), large, designed by H. Fenton, introduced 1937, withdrawn 1942, AS D5610.

Very rare black haired Clown, designed by H. Fenton, possibly unique – could make as much as £12,000 ($18,000) at auction.

'Arry, character jug, large, designed by H. Fenton, introduced in 1947, withdrawn 1960, AS D6207.

'Arry, character jug, (Blue Pearly Boy), large, designed by H. Fenton, introduced 1947, withdrawn 1955.

Old King Cole musical jug with yellow crown, D6014, issued 1939.

Girl', which is extremely rare and can command a price of between £3,500 and £4,500.

Small details such as the colours of buttons, triangles or hair can represent the difference between hundreds and thousands of pounds for an item. Each jug bears the Doulton backstamp and is numbered according to the firm's numbering system which greatly assists collectors.

TOBY JUGS

The name 'Toby' has long associations with conviviality and it was used by Shakespeare in his Toby Belch and by Laurence Sterne in his character Uncle Toby in 'Tristram Shandy'. Today it has come to signify a jug made like a seated male figure in a tricorn hat with a pipe or a mug of beer on his knee. This is particularly due to the creations of Doulton who took up and developed the long history of the Toby jug and made it beloved by a vast collecting public.

From 1815 when John Doulton first set up his business, the firm made Toby jugs but the earliest examples were only brown salt glazed as they had been for centuries. In 1925 however coloured Toby jugs were added to the range by Harry Simeon and their potential was immediately recognised by Charles J. Noke who made their colours even more vivid and developed them into one of the company's best selling lines.

One of the distinguishing marks of the Toby jug is that one corner of his tricorn hat is always used as a pourer for the beverage he carries.

FIGURES

The first highly skilled figure maker who worked for Doulton was George Tinworth, the Lambeth sculptor, but his figure output was small.

However in 1889 Charles J. Noke left the Royal Worcester Company where he was already showing his prodigious talent as a

Flower Seller's Children, designed by L. Harradine, HN1206, 8¼in. high, introduced 1926, withdrawn 1949. $375 £250

Roseanna, designed by L. Harradine, HN1926, introduced 1940, withdrawn 1959, 8in. high. $195 £130

sculptor and went to work for Doulton's at Burslem. The son of an antique dealer who appreciated the fine vases and figures made by Derby, Bow, Chelsea, Meissen and Sevres, he was fired with the ambition of recreating the once greatly admired Staffordshire figure making industry. For the Chicago Exhibition of 1893 he made several figures including 'Jack Point' and 'Lady Jester'.

During the next five years more figures followed including Noke's 'Pierrot'; 'Geisha' and the double figures 'Oh Law!' and 'Double Jester'. The latter figure today sells for £1,700 because it was only produced in small numbers.

These figures, though finely modelled, were of dull colours and did not sell well so Noke's figure making was suspended until around 1912 when he re-introduced a figure range which was released to the public in 1913 after Queen Mary, on a visit to Burslem, exclaimed "What a Darling!" at the sight of a figure called 'Bedtime' modelled by Charles Vyse.

'Bedtime' was re-christened 'Darling' and proved to be one of the most popular Doulton figures ever produced. It is still in production.

The colours of the new figures were bolder and a group of very talented sculptors worked on them. One of the most notable was Harry Tittensor, (1914-21), a local art master, His 'Europa and The Bull' today sells for £2,000 and his 'Princess Badoura' for a remarkable £6,500.

The work of Leslie Harradine, who began his career at the Lambeth Studio before emigrating to Canada but returned to work at Burslem after World War One, was filled with vitality. His 'Contentment' and 'The Goose Girl' showed his ability to capture movement and he also had a great talent for picking subjects which caught the public fancy. His 'Old Balloon Seller' is still in production today and is one of the most popular Doulton figures ever.

The quality of the range which now

Folly, designed by L. Harradine, HN1750, 9in. high, introduced 1936, withdrawn 1949.
$675 £450

Jester, (first version), designed by C. J. Noke, HN45, introduced 1915, withdrawn 1938, 10in. high. *$750 £500*

Belle o' the Ball, designed by L. Harradine, HN1997, introduced 1947, withdrawn 1978. $135 £90

numbers over 2,000 is superb. Limited editions of figures and wall masks were produced by Richard Garbe, an R.A. and Professor of Sculpture at the Royal College of Art who modelled for Doulton's between 1934 and 1939. His 'West Wind', which today fetches a price of £1,900, was produced in an edition of only 25 and originally sold for just over £8. Most of his wall masks, made of special porcelain with an ivory glaze, were in editions of 100.

Figure making still continues at Burslem with more than 200 still in production. The star of our times is Margaret (Peggy) Davies who was born and brought up in the pottery district of Burselm and, after studying at Burslem College of Art, began work as an assistant to Clarice Cliff. Her association with Doulton began in 1939 and she has worked for them ever since, producing a vast range of figures ranging from her Kate Greenaway children to period characters from English history and a modelled head of Queen Elizabeth II.

Her work is notable for meticulous research which can be clearly seen in the 'Indian Brave' (today's price £3,500). She takes great care in researching her subject, studying the anatomy of animals and people, as well as ensuring that all costume details are absolutely correct. Her 'Matador and The Bull' is a good example of this and today the figure sells for £2,000 to collectors. Her group, produced in an edition of 12, entitled 'The Marriage of Art and Industry', (today's price £2,500), showing a man and a woman, the tree of knowledge and doves of peace, was centrepiece for the Doulton stand at the Brussels Exhibition of 1958. It helped them win the only Grand Prix awarded to a pottery firm at the exhibition.

Even figures which are still in production can command large prices among collectors. An example is St George by W. K. Harper. This is the third version of St George produced by Doulton and was introduced in 1978. Its price at auction is £3,000.

KINGSWARE

In 1899 a new method of stoneware production was introduced at Burslem which involved applying colour slips of subdued greens, yellows and reddish browns to the interior of plaster moulds in which a

A pair of Kingsware beakers decorated with landscape scenes, 4in. high. $52 £35

design was impressed. When another brown slip was poured in the colours fused to give a deep and soft effect to the embossed design.

Kingsware was mostly used for the production of pottery flasks to hold whisky and they were produced in enormous quantities, usually in editions of 1,000, for firms like John Dewar and Sons of Perth; Bullock Lade; Greenlees and Watson and the Hudson's Bay Company.

The glaze was most commonly a dark treacle brown but more unusual was a paler yellow called the 'Kingsware yellow glaze'.

The flasks were embossed with designs emphasising the pleasures of drinking and figures like Falstaff and the Sporting Squire were especially popular. These were often modelled by Arthur Bailey who worked between 1912 and 1932.

Some of the flasks had silver fittings and they are more likely to have survived than the everyday specimens.

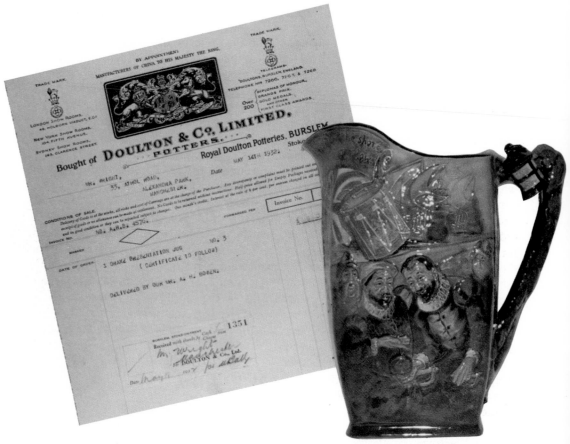

Sir Francis Drake jug, designed by Noke & Fenton, issued in 1933 in a limited edition of 500, together with the original invoice for the Drake jug, dated May 14th 1932 for £1. 5 shillings.

LIMITED EDITION LOVING CUPS AND JUGS

One of Charles J. Noke's greatest talents was giving the public what it wanted and in 1930 he hit upon the idea of producing a range of limited editions of loving cups and jugs, ornately embossed and decorated to a certain theme.

They were modelled on the slip cast relief jugs which had been made in Staffordshire during Victorian times but were much more intricate and colourful.

The first one produced was 'The Master of Foxhounds Presentation Jug'. It was modelled in low relief with rich glowing colours painted by William Grace and it set the style of the lip and handle of the jug or cup continuing the theme.

The following year 'The Regency Coach Jug' appeared and it was followed by a new one each year including the 'Dickens Dream Jug'; 'The Shakespeare Jug' and 'Robin Hood and His Merry Men'. The maximum number in each edition was 1,000 and each jug or cup bore a certificate of authenticity.

Some were produced to coincide with significant dates like the one made in 1932 for George Washington's birth bicentenary which was designed for the American market. In 1953 a loving cup was issued for the coronation of Queen Elizabeth II by Cecil Noke and in 1977 another edition of only 250 was produced by Richard Johnson for her Silver Jubilee.

SERIES WARE

"Adorn yet serve some useful purpose" was the reasoning behind the very successful introduction of Series Ware which was the brain child of Charles J. Noke who joined Doulton's in 1889.

He realised that standard pottery shapes could be decorated with popular images and sold as 'novelty art wares' to the general public who were not able to afford the more expensive creations of individual artists.

Designs, many of them by Noke himself, were transfer printed onto plates, jugs, bowls, mugs and tea sets. Refined earthenware or bone china was used and the transfer prints were handcoloured which gave the technique the name of 'print and tint'.

The first series issued was the 'Isthmian Games' in 1889 and it was followed by a new theme almost every year till World War Two. They include Olde Worlde England, characters from legend, song or story, motoring scenes, characters from Dickens and hunting scenes. Collectors could buy everything from tooth brush holders to dinner plates with their favourite theme and the craze for collecting them continues today.

In the 1970's Doulton's revived Series Ware when they issued sets of plates for special events and anniversaries called "Collectors' International".

Moorish Gateway, a Series Ware rack plate, designed by H. Allen, introduced 1926, withdrawn 1945, D4601, 9½in. diam. $27 £18

STONEWARE

The production of saltglazed stoneware had been carried on at Lambeth for centuries when John Doulton first went into the pottery business there in 1815.

At first his firm continued the prevalent output of cheap mass produced items like bottles, jugs and barrels and it was not until John's son Henry joined the business that more complex modelling and detail began to be introduced.

It was Henry who diversified into architectural stoneware and who started to turn his Lambeth Pottery into a centre for the production of decorative stoneware.

In 1866 he took into the company a group of students from the Lambeth School of Art and in the Paris Exhibition of 1867 their work was highly acclaimed.

The people who produced decorative stoneware at this time included the three famous Barlows, Frank Butler, George Tinworth and many others including women like Eliza Simmance. At first designs were fairly simple and incised but this led on to 'pâté sur pâté' work which involved building up a raised outline by delicate brushwork and to far more sophisticated designs of incised and carved stylised foliage which were a precursor of the Art Nouveau styles.

Stoneware manufacture ceased entirely at Lambeth in 1956 and had only been on a limited scale there since 1914 but today there is a great resurgence of interest in it among collectors.

ARTHUR BARLOW (1871-78) . . .

. . . died sadly young while his talent was in its full flowering. He was one of the first students to be accepted from the Lambeth School of Art by Henry Doulton in his Lambeth Pottery Works. Arthur Barlow's work is distinctive because of its subtle colours and his flowing use of the foliate scroll.

FLORENCE BARLOW (1873-1909) . . .

. . . was the third member of the Barlow family to work for Henry Doulton. After 1877 she made an arrangement with her more famous sister Hannah that she would only paint birds and leave the animals to Hannah. Florence was a skilled exponent of the 'pâté sur pâté' technique but throughout her career her style stayed relatively unchanged.

Doulton Lambeth stoneware vase by Hannah Barlow, with a frieze of incised goats, 10½in. high.   *$330 £220*

HANNAH BARLOW (1871-1913) . . .

. . . was the most famous Doulton artist who maintained an incredible level of output and variety throughout her career. Like her brother and her sister Florence she was a student at Lambeth School of Art, and when she made history by being the first female artist to be employed by Henry Doulton, she paved the way for hundreds of women who came after her. Some of her best pieces were paintings of animals for which she had a strong affection and she maintained a small private zoo at her home. Her best period was between the 1870's and the late 1880's. It is interesting to note that Hannah actually lost the use of her right hand early in her career and retrained herself to use her left.

FRANK BUTLER (1872-1911) . . .

. . . became one of the best known personalities of the art world during the last quarter of the 19th century when the press discovered that he was a deaf mute who could create things of fascination and beauty from clay. He was one of the early stoneware designers working at Lambeth and often went to exhibitions where he worked in front of the public on the company's stand. His greatest talent was for folding soft clay into myriad shapes and the Indian Pavilion used as a centrepiece for Doulton's exhibit in the Glasgow Exhibition was his work. His peak was between 1872 and 1890 but when the Art Nouveau fashion developed he adopted it with enthusiasm, adapting his designs to the new styles.

LESLIE HARRADINE (1902-1915) . . .

. . . was a gifted artist with a great flair for capturing movement, who modelled at Lambeth from 1902 until 1915 when he emigrated to Canada. He returned to Britain after serving in World War One and for the rest of his life freelanced for Doulton's at Burslem producing some of their most notable figures including the Old Balloon Seller and the Beggar's Opera series. He is best known for his series of Dickens' characters, produced at a rate of about two a month for almost 40 years, and for his set of spirit flasks modelled on 20th century politicians in the same way as the Reform Flasks of 1832 were modelled on the politicians of that time.

EDITH LUPTON (1876-?) . . .

. . . her early work was incised stylised foliage but, after 1880, she turned to 'pâté sur pâté' and pierced vases. Her death is recorded in 1896 but it is not known exactly when she stopped working for Doulton though she is thought to have still been producing work in 1892.

MARK MARSHALL (1879-1912) . . .

. . . a gifted stoneware modeller who produced imaginative dragons, lizards and grotesque creatures, some of them moulded and some in limited editions. He was much influenced by the Art Nouveau movement and translated its ideas into pottery.

ELIZA SIMMANCE (1873-1928) . . .

. . . first assisted on the production of Barlow vases and silicon pieces but after 1900 her work became much more free and all her pieces thereafter were signed. Her output was enormous and her most characteristic work shows finely incised 'pâté sur pâté' decorations of flowers and blossoms.

GEORGE TINWORTH (1866-1913) . . .

. . . was the illiterate son of a Walworth wheelwright who became an artistic genius with a world famous reputation. He studied sculpture at Lambeth School of Art and was one of the first students to work for Henry Doulton who quickly recognised his talents. He produced many terracotta panels with religious themes as well as humorous figures of people and animals and incised and painted vases and jugs.

Saltglaze tile panel in low relief by George Tinworth, 4in. by 5¾in. $135 £90

BIBELOTS . . .

. . . were small trifles which could be given as presents. They range from ring trays and inkwells to match strikers and bookends. They were produced in very large numbers and, though many of them were the work of major artists, they are nearly always unsigned.

COMMEMORATIVE WARE . . .

. . . large numbers of these were produced to mark historical events like centenaries and military actions during the 19th and early 20th centuries. Many of the designs were by John Broad and most had applied, moulded decorations.

DOULTON AND SLATER'S WARE

. . . is also known as 'Chine' and is easily recognised because it was decorated by lace pressed into the stoneware body while still soft. It was then glazed, decorated and gilded with applied motifs. The technique was the invention of John Slater who was Art Director at Burslem between 1887 and 1914.

MINIATURES . . .

. . . were very popular during the last quarter of the 19th century because they made amusing gifts. They were scaled down glazed stoneware copies of popular lines of vases and jugs and great care was taken to ensure the proportions were true. Many of the miniatures were decorated by major artists.

NATURAL FOLIAGE WARE . . .

. . . was produced by pressing real leaves into soft clay and the impressions were joined by twigs which were incised before the vase was glazed. This Ware was produced between 1886 and 1936.

SILICON WARE . . .

. . . is a hard, smooth, high fired stoneware with a thin glaze. It was produced in the greatest quantities between 1880 and 1912 and decorated by some of the most famous Doulton artists. Carved, pierced, gilt or lustre painted Silicon Ware can be found in

Doulton Lambeth Silicon Ware ewer, 7in. high.
$50 £35

considerable quantities and the predominant colours are light blue and white on buff or brown bodies.

SIMULATED WARE . . .

. . . is a type of ware in which silicon bodies have been painted to look like some other material. For example there are pottery cricket balls or cast iron weights as well as jugs that look as if they were made of copper with painted on joints and rivets and a lustre glaze. They were even given a coating of simulated verdigris. Very popular when they first appeared, were leatherwork jugs with black silicon bodies that had a dark textured surface stitched with imitation waxed threads. This range was produced from 1887, when the simulated copper first appeared, until around 1910.

SPORTING SUBJECTS . . .

. . . comprise a series of stoneware mugs and jugs decorated with relief figures of famous sportsmen. They were introduced in 1880 and the figures were the work of John Broad. One of the best examples is his W. G. Grace jug showing the famous cricketer in eight different poses.

ADVERTISING WARES

A match box holder and ashtray manufactured for Bass, 3½in. high, circa 1908. $65 £45

Small character jug liqueur flask made for W. Walklate Ltd. depicting 'Poacher', 4in. high.
$55 £38

A stoneware matchstriker and ashtray made for Schweppes.
$60 £40

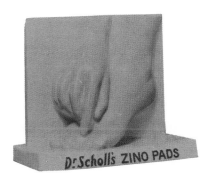

Charrington Toby jug inscribed 'Toby Ale', 9¼in. high.
$180 £120

Display model for Dr Scholl's Zino Pads, circa 1930. $100 £65

Ashtray made for DCL Scotch Whisky depicting a bottle of whisky. $54 £36

Doulton whisky jug made for Charles Wilkinson & Co., featuring Burns Cottage, Ayr. $90 £60

Pick-Kwik character jug with the writing 'Pick-Kwik, Derby, Sells Dewar's Whiskey', circa 1984. $60 £42

A small 'Auld Lang Syne' whisky flagon depicting an Inn scene, 4in. high. $50 £35

Doulton Lambeth stoneware match-holder and striker for John Dewar & Sons. $60 £40

Small character jug liqueur flask made for W. Walklate Ltd. depicting 'Falstaff', 4in. high. $55 £38

Match-holder and striker advertising 'Sir Edward Lee's Old Scotch Whisky', with the slogan 'As supplied to the House of Commons'. $60 £40

'Zodiac' plate, a limited edition of 500 made for Batchelor's, circa 1980. $30 £20

Pick-Kwik character jug depicting Buz Fuz, circa 1983, limited edition of 2000. $60 £42

Early 20th century 'Big Ben Scotch Whisky' jug. $135 £90

Stoneware water jug manufactured for Whitbread, 5in. high, circa 1900. $50 £35

Counter display sign for Grossmith's perfume, 'Tsang Ihang' the perfume of Tibet, circa 1923. $675 £450

Jim Beam whiskey character jug depicting 'Uncle Sam', 5in. high, circa 1984. $60 £40

ADVERTISING WARES

Stoneware matchstriker and holder made for Worthingtons, 4in. high, circa 1900. $65 £45

A 'Nursery Rhyme' biscuit box made for Huntley & Palmer's in the form of a commode, 5½in. high, circa 1905. $270 £180

'Bull Dog Guinness' figure for Robt. Porter & Co. Ltd. of London. $150 £100

Pick-Kwik flagon depicting Micawber with the lettering 'Dewar's', circa 1983. $70 £46

Counter displaying sign for 'Stauffers Watches' depicting a begging dog, 8in. high, circa 1929. $190 £125

Character jug depicting Pickwick made for 'Jim Beam Whiskey, 3¾in. high, circa 1984. $55 £38

A Royal Doulton Bell's whisky decanter, c.m.l. & c. $15 £10

A bone china plaque depicting Queen Victoria made for Vinolia Soap 'For Delicate Skins', circa 1897. $50 £35

Charrington Toby jug inscribed 'One Toby leads to another', 9¼in. high. $200 £130

35

Small character jug liqueur flask made for W. Walklate Ltd. depicting 'Rip Van Winkle', 4in. high. $55 £38

Stoneware tug boat made for the Trafalgar Towing Co., circa 1925. $200 £130

Ashtray for 'Apollinaris' table water. $55 £38

An interesting 'Colonel Bogey Whisky' jug depicting a golfer, 7½in. high. $525 £350

Display sign of a Beefeater for Illustrated London News, 8in. high. $1275 £850

Stoneware footed tankard for 'Beefex'. $50 £35

Stoneware plaque designed for Green King Breweries, circa 1933. $225 £150

Pick-Kwik flagon depicting Micawber with the printed words 'Pick-Kwik De Luxe Whisky', circa 1983. $60 £40

Stoneware bottle made for Dewar Whisky depicting their premises in Piccadilly. $100 £65

ADVERTISING WARES

Display sign for 'Army Club Cigarettes' depicting the bust of a soldier. $120 £80

Counter display sign for Yardley's Old English Lavender perfume, circa 1925. $600 £400

'Glen Garry Old Highland Whisky' jug with blue lettering, 7½in. high. $90 £60

Doulton & Slater's patent whisky jug made for Dewars of Perth, 8in. high. $100 £70

'The McCallum', a large Kingsware character jug made for D. & J. McCallum Whisky Distillers, circa 1930. $2175 £1450

Stoneware match-holder and striker made for John Dewar & Sons. $60 £40

Hip flask in the form of a book made for John Dewar's Whisky, circa 1910. $180 £120

Scotsman and Irishman whisky flasks in a wooden tantalus designed for Asprey & Co. of New Bond St., London. $5250 £3500

Whisky flask in the form of a crow made for National Distillers of Kentucky, circa 1954. $200 £130

Stoneware ashtray advertising Silver Seal Port. $100 £70

Green glazed stoneware candlestick made for Allied Newspapers, circa 1935. $420 £280

A small stoneware hot water bottle designed for Dewar's Perth Whisky, 4in. long. $75 £50

A caviare jar made for J. Pepler & Co., Pall Mall, 4in. high. $45 £30

A Royal Doulton figural bottle for Sandiman's Port, 10¼in. high, circa 1920-1956, c.m.l. & c.
$55 £38

Stilester, blue Stilton cheese container made for John Barker & Co. of Kensington, 5in. high.
$55 £38

Stoneware flower vase bearing the logo of the Orient Line Shipping Co., circa 1950.
$30 £20

Pick-Kwik character jug, 4in. high, made in a limited edition of 2000, circa 1982. $60 £42

'Spare a coin for the poor and crippled bairns', money box for the Ragged School Union.
$65 £45

ANIMAL FIGURES

Character Dog, head turned, HN2508, 2½in. high, withdrawn 1985. $30 £20

English Setter, HN1050, 3¾in. high, c.m., withdrawn 1985. $39 £26

Irish Setter, HN1055, 5¼in. high, withdrawn 1985. $38 £25

Persian Cat, HN999, 5in. high, c.m.l. & c., withdrawn 1985. $48 £32

Cocker Spaniel & Pheasant, HN1138, 5¼in. high, withdrawn 1985. $45 £30

Cocker Spaniel, HN1036, 5in. high, c.m., withdrawn 1985. $63 £42

Character Dog, standing, HN2509, 2½in. high, withdrawn 1985. $30 £20

Character Kitten, cleaning paw, HN2583, 2in. high, c.m., withdrawn 1985. $27 £18

French Poodle, HN2631, 5½in. high, c.m.l. & c., withdrawn 1985. $24 £16

Cairn, sitting, K11, 2¼in. high, c.m., withdrawn 1985. $33 £22

Scottish Terrier, begging, K10, 3½in. high, withdrawn 1985. $33 £22

Collie, HN1059, 3½in. high, c.m.l. & c., withdrawn 1985. $33 £22

Cocker Spaniel, K9, 2½in. high, c.m.l. & c., with-drawn 1985. $48 £32

Character Kitten, HN2584, 1¾in. high, c.m., with-drawn 1985. $27 £18

Three Terrier Puppies, in a basket, HN2588, 2¾in. high, c.m.l. & c., withdrawn 1985. $27 £18

Scottish Terrier, sitting, K18, 2¼in. high, c.m., withdrawn 1985. $33 £22

Character Dog, bone in mouth, HN1159, 3¾in. high, withdrawn 1985. $30 £20

Character Dog, running, tail up, HN2510, 3in. high, withdrawn 1985. $30 £20

Baltimore Oriole, HN2542, 4in. high, withdrawn 1985. $38 £25

Character Dog, with brown ball, HN1103, 2½in. high, withdrawn 1985. $30 £20

Welsh Corgi, HN2559, 3½in. high, c.m., withdrawn 1985. $24 £16

Siamese Cat, standing, HN2660, 5¼in. high, c.m., withdrawn 1985. $36 £24

Character Dog, with plate, HN1158, 3in. high, withdrawn 1985. $30 £20

River Hog, HN2663, 3½in. high, c.m.l. & c., withdrawn 1985. $120 £80

Puppy in a Basket, HN2585, 2in. high, withdrawn 1985. $27 £18

Cocker Spaniels, asleep, HN2590, 1¾in. high, c.m.l. & c., withdrawn 1985. $27 £18

Labrador, HN2667, 5in. high, c.m., withdrawn 1985. $33 £22

Fox Terrier, small, HN1014, withdrawn 1985. $27 £18

Rough Haired Terrier, HN1014, 4in. high, c.m., withdrawn 1985. $33 £22

Cocker Spaniel, HN1020, 5¼in. high, c.m., withdrawn 1985. $27 £18

ANIMAL FIGURES

Character Dog, on back, HN1098, 2¼in. high, withdrawn 1985. $30 £20

Dachshund, HN1128, 3¾in. high, c.m., withdrawn 1985. $30 £20

Bulldog, white, small, HN1074, 3¼in. high, withdrawn 1985. $45 £30

Boxer, HN2643, 6½in. high, withdrawn 1985. $33 £22

Character Dog, standing, tail straight, HN2511, 3¾in. high, withdrawn 1985. $30 £20

Character Dog, yawning, HN1099, 4¼in. high, withdrawn 1985. $30 £20

Golden Crested Wren, HN2613, 4in. high, withdrawn 1985. $120 £80

English Setter and Pheasant, HN2529, 8½in. high, c.m.l. & c., withdrawn 1985. $240 £160

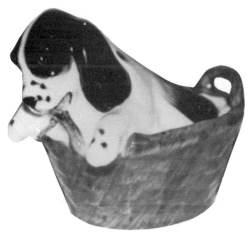

Cocker Spaniel, in a basket, HN2586, 2¾in. high, c.m.l. & c., withdrawn 1985. $30 £20

Siamese Cat, Sitting, HN2655, 5¼in. high, withdrawn 1985. $27 £18

English Setter, HN1049, 7¾in. x 12¼in., c.m., withdrawn 1985. $165 £110

Collie, medium, HN1058, 5¼in. high, withdrawn 1985. $38 £25

Pride of the Shires, HN2528, 9in. high, withdrawn 1985.
$210 £140

Peacock, HN2577, 4in. high, withdrawn 1985.
$75 £50

Huntsman Fox, HN6448, 4½in. high, c.m.l. & c., withdrawn 1985.
$30 £20

Bulldog, with the Union Jack draped over his back, 4in. high, c.m.l. & c..
$150 £100

Royal Doulton model of a rhinoceros, by Leslie Harradine, 6¼in. high.
$825 £550

Tiger on Rock, a Royal Doulton Prestige figure, HN2639, 11½ x 14in., c.m.l. & c. $975 £650

ART POTTERY

Doulton crackleglaze plate with shaped edge. $27 £18

Doulton crackleglaze Deadwood teapot. $48 £35

Doulton Burslem Royles Patent self pouring teapot, circa 1900. $115 £75

A Doulton Lambeth coffee pot painted with a purple iris, circa 1879. $330 £220

Doulton Art Pottery jardiniere with a blue ground and applied flowers, 8¾in. high. $90 £60

An oviform pate-sur-pate vase decorated with birds by Florence Barlow, 15in. high. $525 £350

Doulton jug of tapered cylindrical form decorated with a bird on a branch, by Florence Barlow, circa 1890. $300 £200

Doulton Burslem Royles Patent self pouring teapot, circa 1900. $115 £75

A Doulton Burslem baluster vase painted with an Edwardian lady, by H. G. Theaker, 10¼in. high. $500 £330

A Holbein Ware vase with silver rim, 9in. high. $240 £160

Royal Doulton vase of flattened shape, 6¾in. high. $390 £260

Royal Doulton Art Pottery vase, 9in. high, circa 1910. $150 £100

Doulton Lambeth Carrara Ware vase with flared neck by Josephine Durtnall, 16in. high. $570 £380

A Doulton Crown Lambeth two-handled vase and cover decorated with panels of wild flowers by Emma Harrison, circa 1889. $430 £285

Doulton Lambeth vase by Florence Barlow, decorated in pate-sur-pate with an owl, 12½in. high. $375 £250

Doulton Lambeth ewer by Hannah Barlow, decorated with a pate-sur-pate frieze of dogs, 11in. high. $300 £200

Royal Doulton bowl, Japanese Fan, designed by H. Tittensor, introduced 1921, withdrawn 1938. $450 £300

Royal Doulton vase painted by Ethel Beard, 13in. high. $180 £120

ART POTTERY

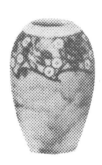

A Royal Doulton Art Pottery vase decorated with stylised flowers, 8in. high, circa 1910. $90 £60

A Royal Doulton jug decorated with a maiden wearing a flowing dress, 10½in. high. $225 £150

A fine hand painted vase with bird and flower decoration, 11in. high. $600 £400

CHANG

Royal Doulton Chang vase by C. J. Noke and Harry Nixon, 7½in. high, circa 1930. $1800 £1200

Royal Doulton Chang vase by Noke and Moore, 7½in. high, circa 1935. $825 £550

Royal Doulton Chang vase by Noke and Nixon, 8¾in. high. $1500 £1000

A Chang vase by Noke and Nixon, 5in. high. $900 £600

Royal Doulton Chang bowl by Nixon and Noke, circa 1930. $1500 £1000

A Royal Doulton Chang vase by Nixon and Noke, 9¼in. high, circa 1925. $1800 £1200

CHANG

A Chang bowl by Noke and
Nixon, 8in. diam. $900 £600

A Chang vase by Noke and
Nixon, 8in. high. $1,450 £950

A Chang vase by Noke and
Nixon, 5in. high.$1,200 £800

A Chang vase by Noke and
Nixon, 11in. high.
$1,950 £1,300

A Chang vase by Noke and
Nixon, 10in. high.
$4125 £2750

A Chang vase by Noke and
Nixon, 10in. high.
$1,800 £1,200

A Chang vase by Noke and
Nixon, 10in. high.
$1,875 £1,250

A Chang vase by Noke and
Nixon, 7in. high.$1,200 £800

A Chang vase by Noke and
Nixon, 10in. high.
$1,725 £1,150

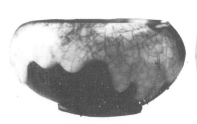

A Chang bowl by Noke and
Nixon, 5in. high.
$1,275 £850

A Chang vase by Noke and
Nixon, 7in. high.
$1,320 £880

A Chang bowl by Noke and
Nixon, 8in. diam.
$1,725 £1,150

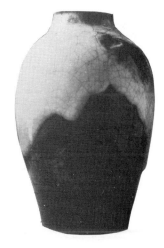

A Chang vase by Noke and
Nixon, 8in. high. $1,450 £950

The Chang Potter lamp base by
Noke and Nixon, 10½in. high.
$4,200 £2,800

A Chang vase by Noke and Nixon,
10in. high. $1,800 £1,200

A Chang vase by Noke and
Nixon, 7in. high.
$1,350 £900

A Chang vase by Noke and
Nixon, 8in. high. $1,350 £900

A Change vase by Noke and
Nixon, 10in. high.
$1,650 £1,100

CHANG

Royal Doulton Chang vase by Noke and Nixon, 10¼in. high. $1275 £850

Royal Doulton Chang vase by Nixon and Noke, 5¾in. high, circa 1920. $750 £500

A Chang vase by Noke and Nixon, 9in. high. $1500 £1000

CHINESE JADE

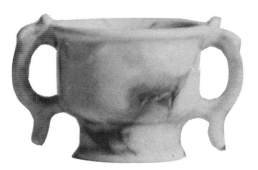

A Chinese jade model of a fish in white and green by Noke, 3¼in. high. $1000 £675

Royal Doulton Chinese jade two-handled bowl in white and green, 3½in. high. $480 £320

Royal Doulton Chinese jade vase by Nixon, 7½in. high, circa 1930. $600 £400

FAIENCE

Royal Doulton faience vase by John H. McLennan, decorated with panels representing Earth and Water, 13½in. high. $270 £180

A pair of Doulton Lambeth faience oil lamp bases decorated by Esther Lewis, 10¼in. high. $675 £450

A Doulton Lambeth faience vase painted with stylised flowers, by Emily Gillman, 9¼in. high. $130 £85

FAIENCE

A Doulton Lambeth faience
wall plaque decorated with
fruit and foliage, 13¾in. diam.
$180 £120

Doulton Lambeth faience vase
decorated with daffodils and
narcissi, 10½in. high. $120 £80

Doulton Lambeth faience vase
with the artist's monogram for
Mary Butterton, circa 1880.
$270 £180

Doulton Lambeth faience vase
by Mary Capes, decorated with
flowers, circa 1878. $210 £140

A Doulton Lambeth faience
coffee service painted with
azaleas, dahlias and dog roses,
circa 1879. $330 £220

One of a pair of Doulton faience
vases decorated by Katherine
Smallfield, 12½in. high.
$450 £300

A large Doulton Lambeth
faience plaque by Florence
E. Lewis, 15½in. diam., circa
1880. $270 £180

Pair of Doulton Lambeth faience
vases decorated with sprays of
leaves and flowers by Mary M.
Arding, 14¾in. high, circa 1880.
$420 £280

Doulton faience moon flask
decorated with leaves and wild
flowers, 14¼in. high. $480 £360

FAIENCE

Doulton Lambeth faience wall plaque by Helen A.
Arding, circa 1880. $210 £140

Doulton Lambeth faience two-handled vase decorated
with a band of wild flowers by Margaret M. Challis,
7½in. high, circa 1880. $125 £85

A pair of Doulton faience vases, by Fanny Stable,
decorated with dragons amongst clouds, 11½in.
high, circa 1879. $675 £450

Royal Doulton faience vase and cover by Ada
Dennis, Esther Lewis and Mary Denley, 24in.
high, circa 1885. $3750 £2500

FAIENCE

A large Doulton faience moon flask decorated with flowers and fruit, 14¼in. high. $480 £360

Doulton Lambeth faience wall plaque, 'Old Cottage, Bromley, Kent', by Esther Lewis, 14¾in. diam., circa 1882. $315 £210

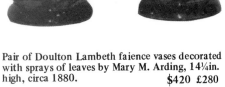

Doulton Lambeth faience water jug decorated with flowers, 7½in. high. $72 £48

Pair of Doulton Lambeth faience vases decorated with sprays of leaves by Mary M. Arding, 14¼in. high, circa 1880. $420 £280

FLAMBE

A Royal Doulton flambe ashtray with elephant heads on the corners, by Moore, 3½in. wide. $165 £110

Hare, a Royal Doulton flambe figure, 656A, introduced 1973, 1¾in. long. $24 £16

Rhinoceros, a Royal Doulton flambe figure, 615, introduced 1973, 9½in. long. $340 £225

Royal Doulton flambe jardiniere decorated with a desert scene. $420 £280

Royal Doulton flambe model of a collie dog, 7¾in. high, circa 1926. $450 £300

The Dragon, a Royal Doulton flambe figure, 2085, introduced 1973, 7½in. high. $285 £190

A Royal Doulton flambe figure of a crab, 4½in. wide. $375 £250

Royal Doulton flambe model of a terrier, 5¼in. high, circa 1930. $255 £170

FLAMBE

Pig Dish, 2½in. high x 4½in. long, silver mounted, circa 1927. $450 £300

Tiger, snarling, HN225, 2½in. high x 9in. long, circa 1930. $375 £250

Guinea Fowl, Model 69, 3in. high. $180 £120

Pomegranate, 2¾in. high. $225 £150

Monkeys, embracing, Model 486, 5½in. high.
$210 £140

Fox, sitting, head down, Model 12A, 3in. high, circa 1912. $180 £120

Cat, sitting, Model 2259, 11½in. high, circa 1977, c.m.l. & c. $120 £80

Pigs, three at trough, 2in. high x 4in. wide.
$480 £320

FLAMBE

Mallard, Model 654, 4in. high, designed by Noke, introduced 1920, withdrawn 1961. $285 £195

Fox, slinking, full length, Model 29, 2½in. high x 12in. long. $180 £120

Leaping Salmon, Model 666, 12in. high, designed by Noke, introduced 1940, withdrawn 1950. $450 £300

Buddha, smiling, 4in. high, circa 1926. $470 £320

Monkey, dunce's cap, HN972, 5½in. high. $450 £300

Penguin, double, Model 103, HN133, 6in. high, circa 1929. $180 £120

Pigeons, two fantail, Model 46, 3¾in. high. $300 £200

Elephant, trunk raised, Model 489, 7in. high, designed by Noke, introduced 1930, withdrawn 1961. $405 £270

FLAMBE

Tiger, Model 1809, 5½in. long. $210 £140

Scotch Terrier, 4in. high. $165 £110

Fish, group of, Model 682, 6½in. high, circa 1921.
$405 £270

Pelican, beak up, Model 109, 4½in. high, circa
1929. $345 £230

Mouse, on cube, Model 1164, HN255, 2½in. high,
circa 1908. $300 £200

Fox, sitting, head up, Model 102, 9½in. high,
designed by Noke, introduced 1962, withdrawn
1965. $255 £170

Elephant, trunk down, 12in. high, circa 1930.
$825 £550

Bull, 7in. long, circa 1930. $480 £320

HOLBEIN WARE

Royal Doulton Holbein Ware globular vase, signed by W. Nunn, 11in. high. $600 £400

A large Royal Doulton Burslem Holbein Ware jardiniere decorated with four cavaliers playing cards, 13¼in. high, signed W. Nunn. $675 £450

IMPASTO

A Doulton Lambeth Impasto vase decorated with chrysanthemums, by Rosa Keen, 11in. high. $250 £165

A Doulton Lambeth Impasto jardiniere decorated with wild flowers by Rosa Keen, 10½in. high. $210 £140

Doulton Lambeth Impasto Ware jug by Kate Rogers, decorated with white flowers, 8in. high. $225 £150

A Doulton Lambeth Impasto wall plaque decorated with chrysanthemums, by Frances Linnell, 14½in. diam., circa 1882. $170 £115

MORRISIAN WARE

Doulton Burslem Morrisian Ware tobacco jar and cover decorated with a band of dancing girls, 5½in. high. $80 £55

Doulton Burslem Morrisian Ware teapot with a frieze of girls dancing, 8in. high. $130 £85

PERSIAN WARE

Royal Doulton Persian design octagonal shaped teapot, introduced 1917, withdrawn 1942. $60 £40

Royal Doulton Persian design octagonal jardiniere, introduced 1917, withdrawn 1942. $90 £60

Doulton Lambeth circular wall plate in the Persian style by William Rowe, 20in. diam., circa 1878.
$410 £275

Royal Doulton Persian design vase of square section, introduced 1917, withdrawn 1942.
$60 £40

Royal Doulton Sung model of a
rabbit, 4in. long, circa 1928.
$450 £300

Royal Doulton Sung vase decorated with a leopard in a mountainous landscape, 6¾in. high.
$190 £125

Royal Doulton Sung bowl decorated with stylised flowers, 9in.
diam., circa 1920. $450 £300

Royal Doulton Sung vase by
Noke, decorated with a peacock
painted by A. Eaton, 10½in.
high. $450 £300

A large Royal Doulton Sung
vase by Arthur Eaton, decorated
with dragons amongst clouds,
13 in. high, circa 1930.
              $1200 £800

Royal Doulton Sung vase decorated by A. Eaton, 14½in. high.
$1050 £680

A Royal Doulton Sung vase
and cover, circa 1926, 13in.
high. $500 £330

A Royal Doulton Sung vase
by Noke, 6¾in. high, circa 1928.
              $600 £400

Royal Doulton Sung vase by
Charles Noke and Fred Moore
10¼in. high, circa 1930.
              $390 £260

SUNG

Royal Doulton Sung vase painted with fish swimming among weeds, 6¼in. high, circa 1930. $225 £150

A Royal Doulton Sung ashtray by Charles Noke and Fred Moore, 3¾in. square. $190 £125

A Royal Doulton Sung vase by Charles Noke and Fred Moore, 7in. high, circa 1930.$225 £150

A tall Royal Doulton Sung vase by Charles Noke and F. Allen, 11½in. high, circa 1930. $480 £320

Royal Doulton Sung vase signed by A. Eaton, 5¾in. high. $1080 £720

Royal Doulton Sung vase decorated with a peacock by Arthur Eaton, 8½in. high, circa 1925. $825 £550

Royal Doulton Sung vase by Noke, decorated with flying birds, 8¾in. high. $750 £500

Royal Doulton Sung bowl decorated with a band of geometric ornament, 8in. diam., circa 1925. $375 £250

Royal Doulton Sung tobacco jar and cover of hexagonal form, 6¼in. high, circa 1930. $225 £150

TITANIAN WARE

Royal Doulton Titanian Ware salad bowl with 'Bird of Paradise' design, introduced 1922, withdrawn 1935. $82 £55

Royal Doulton Titanian vase by Harry Allen decorated with a long eared owl, 13in. high. $525 £350

Royal Doulton Titanian Ware sugar bowl and cover, 4¼in. high, circa 1922. $36 £24

A Royal Doulton Titanian bowl decorated with a dragon, 14½in. diam. $150 £100

Royal Doulton Titanian figure, 'The Smiling Buddha', by Noke, issued in 1921, withdrawn 1938. $900 £600

A Royal Doulton Titanian Ware teapot, 6½in. high, circa 1922. $42 £28

A Royal Doulton Titanian Ware teapot, 6½in. high, circa 1920. $45 £30

Royal Doulton Titanian figure of 'Blighty', 11½in. high, circa 1919. $600 £400

Royal Doulton Titanian Ware plate with 'Bird of Paradise' design, 10in. diam., introduced 1922, withdrawn 1935. $52 £35

CHARACTER JUGS

ANNE BOLEYN D6644
Designer: D. Tootle
Size: Large
Issued: 1975-
Price: $69 £28

ANNE BOLEYN D6650
Designer: D. Tootle
Size: Small
Issued: 1980-
Price: $37 £15

ANNE BOLEYN D6651
Designer: D. Tootle
Size: Mini
Issued: 1980-
Price: $25 £10

ANNE OF CLEVES D6653
Designer: M. Abberley
Size: Large
Issued: 1980-
Price: $69 £28

ANNIE OAKLEY D6732
Designer: S. Taylor
Size: Medium
Issued: 1985-
Price: $49 £20

ANTHONY AND CLEOPATRA D6728
Designer: M. Abberley
Size: Large
Issued: 1985-
Price: $137 £55

APOTHECARY D6567
Designer: M. Henk
Size: Large
Issued: 1963-1983
Price: $57 £38

APOTHECARY D6574
Designer: M. Henk
Size: Small
Issued: 1963-1983
Price: $37 £25

APOTHECARY D6581
Designer: M. Henk
Size: Mini
Issued: 1963-1983
Price: $30 £20

ARAMIS D6441
Designer: M. Henk
Size: Large
Issued: 1956-
Price: $69 £28

ARAMIS D6454
Designer: M. Henk
Size: Small
Issued: 1956-
Price: $37 £15

ARAMIS D6508
Designer: M. Henk
Size: Mini
Issued: 1960-
Price: $25 £10

ANN BOLEYN

ANNE OF CLEVES

ANNIE OAKLEY

ANTHONY AND CLEOPATRA

APOTHECARY

ARAMIS

'ARD OF EARING D6588
Designer: D. Biggs
Size: Large
Issued: 1964-1967
Price: $675 £450

'ARD OF EARING D6591
Designer: D. Biggs
Size: Small
Issued: 1964-1967
Price: $525 £350

'ARD OF EARING D6594
Designer: D. Biggs
Size: Mini
Issued: 1964-1967
Price: $675 £450

'ARRIET D6208
Designer: H. Fenton
Size: Large
Issued: 1947-1960
Price: $150 £100

'ARRIET D6236
Designer: H. Fenton
Size: Small
Issued: 1947-1960
Price: $67 £45

'ARRIET D6250
Designer: H. Fenton
Size: Mini
Issued: 1947-1960
Price: $60 £40

'ARRIET D6256
Designer: H. Fenton
Size: Tiny
Issued: 1947-1960
Price: $112 £75

'ARRY D6207
Designer: H. Fenton
Size: Large
Issued: 1947-1960
Price: $150 £100

'ARRY D6235
Designer: H. Fenton
Size: Small
Issued: 1947-1960
Price: $67 £45

'ARRY D6249
Designer: H. Fenton
Size: Mini
Issued: 1947-1960
Price: $60 £40

'ARRY D6255
Designer: H. Fenton
Size: Tiny
Issued: 1947-1960
Price: $120 £80

ATHOS.D6439
Designer: M. Henk
Size: Large
Issued: 1956-
Price: $69 £28

'ARD OF EARING   'ARRIET

PEARLY BOY (Blue) also
known as 'ARRY.

'ARRY   ATHOS

CHARACTER JUGS

ATHOS D6452
Designer: M. Henk
Size: Small
Issued: 1956-
Price: $37 £15

ATHOS D6509
Designer: M. Henk
Size: Mini
Issued: 1960-
Price: $25 £10

AULD MAC D5823
Designer: H. Fenton
Size: Large
Issued: 1937-
Price: $42 £28

AULD MAC D5824
Designer: H. Fenton
Size: Small
Issued: 1937-
Price: $37 £15

AULD MAC D6253
Designer: H. Fenton
Size: Mini
Issued: 1937-
Price: $25 £10

AULD MAC D6257
Designer: H. Fenton
Size: Tiny
Issued: 1946-1960
Price: $135 £90

BACCHUS D6499
Designer: M. Henk
Size: Large
Issued: 1959-
Price: $69 £28

BACCHUS D6505
Designer: M. Henk
Size: Small
Issued: 1959-
Price: $37 £15

BACCHUS D6521
Designer: M. Henk
Size: Mini
Issued: 1960-
Price: $25 £10

BEEFEATER D6206
Designer: H. Fenton
Size: Large
Issued: 1947-
Price: $69 £28

BEEFEATER D6233
Designer: H. Fenton
Size: Small
Issued: 1947-
Price: $37 £15

BEEFEATER D6251
Designer: H. Fenton
Size: Mini
Issued: 1947-
Price: $25 £10

AULD MAC

BEEFEATER

BACCHUS

BEEFEATER (GR on handle)
D6206
Designer: H. Fenton
Size: Large
Issued: 1947-1953
Price: $67 £45

BEEFEATER (GR on handle)
D6233
Designer: H. Fenton
Size: Small
Issued: 1947-1953
Price: $37 £25

BEEFEATER (GR on handle)
D6251
Designer: H. Fenton
Size: Mini
Issued: 1947-1953
Price: $37 £25

BENJAMIN FRANKLIN
D6695
Designer: E. Griffiths
Size: Small
Issued: 1982-
Price: $42 £28

BLACKSMITH D6571
Designer: D. Biggs
Size: Large
Issued: 1963-1983
Price: $52 £35

BLACKSMITH D6578
Designer: D. Biggs
Size: Small
Issued: 1963-1983
Price: $37 £25

BLACKSMITH D6585
Designer: D. Biggs
Size: Mini
Issued: 1963-1983
Price: $37 £25

BOOTMAKER D6572
Designer: D. Biggs
Size: Large
Issued: 1963-1983
Price: $52 £35

BOOTMAKER D6579
Designer: D. Biggs
Size: Small
Issued: 1963-1983
Price: $37 £25

BOOTMAKER D6586
Designer: D. Biggs
Size: Mini
Issued: 1963-1983
Price: $30 £20

BUFFALO BILL D6735
Designer: S. Taylor
Size: Medium
Issued: 1985-
Price: $49 £20

BUZ FUZ D5838
Designer: L. Harradine &
           H. Fenton
Size: Intermediate
Issued: 1938-1948
Price: $127 £85

BLACKSMITH

BOOTMAKER

BUFFALO BILL

CHARACTER JUGS

BUZ FUZ D5838
Designer: L. Harradine &
           H. Fenton
Size: Small
Issued: 1948-1960
Price: $75 £50

CAPTAIN AHAB D6500
Designer: G. Sharpe
Size: Large
Issued: 1959-1985
Price: $52 £35

CAPTAIN AHAB D6506
Designer: G. Sharpe
Size: Small
Issued: 1959-1985
Price: $30 £20

CAPTAIN AHAB D6522
Designer: G. Sharpe
Size: Mini
Issued: 1960-1985
Price: $22 £15

CAP'N CUTTLE D5842
Designer: L. Harradine
Size: Intermediate
Issued: 1938-1945
Price: $112 £75

CAP'N CUTTLE D5842
Designer: L. Harradine
Size: Small
Issued: 1948-1960
Price: $75 £50

**CAPTAIN HENRY MORGAN
D6467**
Designer: G. Sharpe
Size: Large
Issued: 1958-1982
Price: $52 £35

**CAPTAIN HENRY MORGAN
D6469**
Designer: G. Sharpe
Size: Small
Issued: 1958-1982
Price: $37 £25

**CAPTAIN HENRY MORGAN
D6510**
Designer: G. Sharpe
Size: Mini
Issued: 1960-1982
Price: $30 £20

CAPTAIN HOOK D6597
Designer: M. Henk & D. Biggs
Size: Large
Issued: 1965-1971
Price: $390 £260

CAPTAIN HOOK D6601
Designer: M. Henk & D. Biggs
Size: Small
Issued: 1965-1971
Price: $360 £240

CAPTAIN HOOK D6605
Designer: M. Henk & D. Biggs
Size: Mini
Issued: 1965-1971
Price: $345 £230

CAP'N CUTTLE   CAPTAIN HENRY MORGAN

CAPTAIN HOOK

CARDINAL D5614
Designer: C. Noke
Size: Large
Issued: 1936-1960
Price: $90 £60

CARDINAL D6033
Designer: C. Noke
Size: Small
Issued: 1939-1960
Price: $57 £38

CARDINAL D6129
Designer: C. Noke
Size: Mini
Issued: 1940-1960
Price: $45 £30

CARDINAL D6258
Designer: C. Noke
Size: Tiny
Issued: 1947-1960
Price: $135 £90

CATHERINE HOWARD D6645
Designer: P. Gee
Size: Large
Issued: 1978-
Price: $69 £28

CATHERINE HOWARD D6692
Designer: P. Gee
Size: Small
Issued: 1984-
Price: $37 £15

CATHERINE HOWARD D6693
Designer: P. Gee
Size: Mini
Issued: 1984-
Price: $25 £10

CATHERINE OF ARAGON D6643
Designer: A. Maslankowski
Size: Large
Issued: 1975-
Price: $69 £28

CATHERINE OF ARAGON D6657
Designer: A. Maslankowski
Size: Small
Issued: 1981-
Price: $37 £15

CATHERINE OF ARAGON D6658
Designer: A. Maslankowski
Size: Mini
Issued: 1981-
Price: $25 £10

CATHERINE PARR D6664
Designer: M. Abberley
Size: Large
Issued: 1981-
Price: $69 £28

CARDINAL D6129   CARDINAL D6033

CATHERINE HOWARD

CHARACTER JUGS

CAVALIER D6114
Designer: H. Fenton
Size: Large
Issued: 1940-1960
Price: $90 £60

CAVALIER D6173
Designer: H. Fenton
Size: Small
Issued: 1941-1960
Price: $90 £60

CAVALIER D6114
Designer: H. Fenton
Size: Large (with goatee beard)
Issued: 1940-1942
Price: $1800 £1200

CHURCHILL (White) D6170
Designer: C. Noke
Size: Large
Issued: 1940-1941
Price: $7500 £5000

CLARK GABLE D6709
Designer: S. Taylor
Size: Large
Issued: 1984-
Price: $3300 £2200

CLOWN D5610
Designer: H. Fenton
Size: Large (Red Haired)
Issued: 1937-1942
Price: $2250 £1500

CLOWN D5610
Designer: H. Fenton
Size: Large (Brown Haired)
Issued: 1937-1942
Price: $2625 £1750

CLOWN D6322
Designer: H. Fenton
Size: Large (White Haired)
Issued: 1951-1955
Price: $825 £550

CLOWN D5610
Designer: H. Fenton
Size: Large (Black Haired)
Issued: 1937-1942
Price: $18000 £12000

CHIEF SITTING BULL AND GEORGE ARMSTRONG CUSTER D6712
Designer: M. Abberley
Size: Large
Issued: 1984-
Price: $112 £75

D'ARTAGNAN D6691
Designer: S. Taylor
Size: Large
Issued: 1982-
Price: $69 £28

CAVALIER

THE WHITE CHURCHILL

CLARK GABLE

THE RED HAIRED CLOWN

THE WHITE HAIRED CLOWN

THE BLACK HAIRED CLOWN

DAVY CROCKET/SANTA ANNA D6729
Designer: M. Abberley
Size: Large
Issued: 1985-
Price: $97 £65

DICK TURPIN (First version) D5485
Designer: C. Noke & H. Fenton
Size: Large
Issued: 1935-1960
Price: $90 £60

DICK TURPIN (First version) D5618
Designer: C. Noke & H. Fenton
Size: Small
Issued: 1936-1960
Price: $52 £35

DICK TURPIN (First version) D6128
Designer: C. Noke & H. Fenton
Size: Mini
Issued: 1940-1960
Price: $45 £30

DICK TURPIN (Second version) D6528
Designer: D. Biggs
Size: Large
Issued: 1960-1981
Price: $52 £35

DICK TURPIN (Second version) D6535
Designer: D. Biggs
Size: Small
Issued: 1960-1981
Price: $30 £20

DICK TURPIN (Second version) D6542
Designer: D. Biggs
Size: Mini
Issued: 1960-1961
Price: $30 £20

DICK WHITTINGTON D6375
Designer: G. Blower
Size: Large
Issued: 1953-1960
Price: $300 £200

DOC HOLLIDAY D6731
Designer: S. Taylor
Size: Medium
Issued: 1985-
Price: $49 £20

DON QUIXOTE D6455
Designer: G. Blower
Size: Large
Issued: 1960-
Price: $69 £28

DON QUIXOTE D6460
Designer: G. Blower
Size: Small
Issued: 1960-
Price: $37 £15

DICK TURPIN
(First version)

DICK TURPIN
(Second version)

DICK WHITTINGTON

DON QUIXOTE D6511
Designer: G. Blower
Size: Mini
Issued: 1960-
Price: $25 £10

DRAKE D6115
Designer: H. Fenton
Size: Large (Hatless)
Issued: 1940-1941
Price: $3000 £2000

DRAKE D6115
Designer: H. Fenton
Size: Large
Issued: 1940-1960
Price: $90 £60

DRAKE D6174
Designer: H. Fenton
Size: Small
Issued: 1941-1960
Price: $52 £35

FALCONER D6533
Designer: M. Henk
Size: Large
Issued: 1960-
Price: $69 £28

FALCONER D6540
Designer: M. Henk
Size: Small
Issued: 1960-
Price: $37 £15

FALCONER D6547
Designer: M. Henk
Size: Mini
Issued: 1960-
Price: $25 £10

FALSTAFF D6287
Designer: H. Fenton
Size: Large
Issued: 1950-
Price: $69 £28

FALSTAFF D6385
Designer: H. Fenton
Size: Small
Issued: 1950-
Price: $37 £15

FALSTAFF D6519
Designer: H. Fenton
Size: Mini
Issued: 1960-
Price: $25 £10

FARMER JOHN D5788
Designer: C. Noke
Size: Large
Issued: 1938-1960
Price: $90 £60

FARMER JOHN D5789
Designer: C. Noke
Size: Small
Issued: 1938-1960
Price: $60 £40

DON QUIXOTE

DRAKE (Hatless)

DRAKE

FALCONER

FALSTAFF

FARMER JOHN

FAT BOY D5840
Designer: L. Harradine &
         H. Fenton
Size: Intermediate
Issued: 1938-1948
Price: $112 £75

FAT BOY D5840
Designer: L. Harradine &
         H. Fenton
Size: Small
Issued: 1948-1960
Price: $67 £45

FAT BOY D6139
Designer: L. Harradine &
         H. Fenton
Size: Mini
Issued: 1940-1960
Price: $52 £35

FAT BOY D6142
Designer: L. Harradine &
         H. Fenton
Size: Tiny
Issued: 1940-1960
Price: $82 £55

FIREMAN D6697
Designer: R. Tabbenor
Size: Large
Issued: 1984-
Price: $87 £35

FORTUNE TELLER D6497
Designer: G. Sharpe
Size: Large
Issued: 1959-1967
Price: $375 £250

FORTUNE TELLER D6503
Designer: G. Sharpe
Size: Small
Issued: 1959-1967
Price: $270 £180

FORTUNE TELLER D6523
Designer: G. Sharpe
Size: Mini
Issued: 1960-1967
Price: $270 £180

FRIAR TUCK D6321
Designer: H. Fenton
Size: Large
Issued: 1951-1960
Price: $270 £180

GAOLER D6570
Designer: D. Biggs
Size: Large
Issued: 1963-1983
Price: $52 £35

GAOLER D6577
Designer: D. Biggs
Size: Small
Issued: 1963-1983
Price: $30 £20

GAOLER D6584
Designer: D. Biggs
Size: Mini
Issued: 1963-1983
Price: $27 £18

FAT BOY   FRIAR TUCK

FORTUNE TELLER

CHARACTER JUGS

GARDENER D6630
Designer: D. Biggs
Size: Large
Issued: 1973-1981
Price: $57 £38

GARDENER D6634
Designer: D. Biggs
Size: Small
Issued: 1973-1981
Price: $42 £28

GARDENER D6638
Designer: D. Biggs
Size: Mini
Issued: 1973-1981
Price: $37 £25

GEORGE HARRISON D6727
Designer: S. Taylor
Size: Medium
Issued: 1984-
Price: $50 £20

GEORGE WASHINGTON D6669
Designer: S. Taylor
Size: Large
Issued: 1982-
Price: $69 £28

GEORGE WASHINGTON/ KING GEORGE III
Designer: M. Abberley
Size: Large
Issued: 1986
Price: $137 £55

GERONIMO D6733
Designer: S. Taylor
Size: Medium
Issued: 1985-
Price: $49 £20

GLADIATOR D6550
Designer: M. Henk
Size: Large
Issued: 1961-1967
Price: $405 £270

GLADIATOR D6553
Designer: M. Henk
Size: Small
Issued: 1961-1967
Price: $270 £180

GLADIATOR D6556
Designer: M. Henk
Size: Mini
Issued: 1961-1967
Price: $240 £160

GOLFER D6623
Designer: D. Biggs
Size: Large
Issued: 1971-
Price: $42 £28

GONDOLIER D6589
Designer: D. Biggs
Size: Large
Issued: 1964-1969
Price: $345 £230

GARDENER

GEORGE WASHINGTON

GERONIMO

GLADIATOR

GOLFER

GONDOLIER

CHARACTER JUGS

GONDOLIER D6592
Designer: D. Biggs
Size: Small
Issued: 1964-1969
Price: $300 £200

GONDOLIER D6595
Designer: D. Biggs
Size: Mini
Issued: 1964-1969
Price: $330 £220

GONE AWAY D6531
Designer: G. Sharpe
Size: Large
Issued: 1960-1982
Price: $52 £35

GONE AWAY D6538
Designer: G. Sharpe
Size: Small
Issued: 1960-1982
Price: $37 £25

GONE AWAY D6545
Designer: G. Sharpe
Size: Mini
Issued: 1960-1982
Price: $22 £15

GRANNY D5521
Designer: H. Fenton &
          M. Henk
Size: Large
Issued: 1935-1983
Price: $52 £35

GRANNY D6384
Designer: H. Fenton &
          M. Henk
Size: Small
Issued: 1953-1983
Price: $30 £20

GRANNY D6520
Designer: H. Fenton &
          M. Henk
Size: Mini
Issued: 1960-1983
Price: $27 £18

**GRANNY (Toothless version)
D5521**
Designer: H. Fenton &
          M. Henk
Size: Large
Issued: 1935
Price: $1050 £700

GROUCHO MARX D6710
Designer: S. Taylor
Size: Large
Issued: 1984-
Price: $87 £35

GUARDSMAN D6568
Designer: M. Henk
Size: Large
Issued: 1963-1983
Price: $52 £35

GONE AWAY

GRANNY D5521

GRANNY (Toothless version)

CHARACTER JUGS

GUARDSMAN D6575
Designer: M. Henk
Size: Small
Issued: 1963-1983
Price: $37 £25

GUARDSMAN D6582
Designer: M. Henk
Size: Mini
Issued: 1963-1983
Price: $27 £18

GULLIVER D6560
Designer: D. Biggs
Size: Large
Issued: 1962-1967
Price: $360 £240

GULLIVER D6563
Designer: D. Biggs
Size: Small
Issued: 1962-1967
Price: $270 £180

GULLIVER D6566
Designer: D. Biggs
Size: Mini
Issued: 1962-1967
Price: $300 £200

GUNSMITH D6573
Designer: D. Biggs
Size: Large
Issued: 1963-1983
Price: $52 £35

GUNSMITH D6580
Designer: D. Biggs
Size: Small
Issued: 1963-1983
Price: $37 £25

GUNSMITH D6587
Designer: D. Biggs
Size: Mini
Issued: 1963-1983
Price: $27 £18

HAMLET D6672
Designer: M. Abberley
Size: Large
Issued: 1982-
Price: $87 £35

HAMPSHIRE CRICKETER D6739
Designer: H. Sales
Size: Medium
Issued: 1985
Price: $57 £38

HENRY V D6671
Designer: R. Tabbenor
Size: Large
Issued: 1982-
Price: $87 £35

HENRY VIII D6642
Designer: E. Griffiths
Size: Large
Issued: 1979-
Price: $69 £28

GULLIVER

GUNSMITH

HENRY VIII

77

CHARACTER JUGS

HENRY VIII D6647
Designer: E. Griffiths
Size: Small
Issued: 1979-
Price: $37 £15

HENRY VIII D6648
Designer: E. Griffiths
Size: Mini
Issued: 1979-
Price: $25 £10

IZAAC WALTON D6404
Designer: G. Blower
Size: Large
Issued: 1953-1982
Price: $52 £35

JANE SEYMOUR D6646
Designer: M. Abberley
Size: Large
Issued: 1979-
Price: $69 £28

JARGE D6288
Designer: H. Fenton
Size: Large
Issued: 1950-1960
Price: $225 £150

JARGE D6295
Designer: H. Fenton
Size: Small
Issued: 1950-1960
Price: $180 £120

JESTER D5556
Designer: C. Noke
Size: Small
Issued: 1936-1960
Price: $72 £48

JIMMY DURANTE D6708
Designer: D. Biggs
Size: Large
Issued: 1985-
Price: $52 £35

JOCKEY D6625
Designer: D. Biggs
Size: Large
Issued: 1971-1975
Price: $225 £170

JOHN BARLEYCORN D5327
Designer: C. Noke
Size: Large
Issued: 1934-1960
Price: $90 £60

JOHN BARLEYCORN D5735
Designer: C. Noke
Size: Small
Issued: 1937-1960
Price: $57 £38

JOHN BARLEYCORN D6041
Designer: C. Noke
Size: Mini
Issued: 1939-1960
Price: $45 £30

IZAAC WALTON

JANE SEYMOUR

JARGE

JIMMY DURANTE

JOCKEY

JOHN BARLEYCORN

CHARACTER JUGS

JOHN DOULTON D6656
Designer: E. Griffiths
Size: Small
Issued: 1980
Price: $57 £38

JOHN LENNON D6725
Designer: S. Taylor
Size: Medium
Issued: 1984-
Price: $50 £20

JOHN PEEL D5612
Designer: H. Fenton
Size: Large
Issued: 1936-1960
Price: $90 £60

JOHN PEEL D5731
Designer: H. Fenton
Size: Small
Issued: 1937-1960
Price: $52 £35

JOHN PEEL D6130
Designer: H. Fenton
Size: Mini
Issued: 1940-1960
Price: $45 £30

JOHN PEEL D6259
Designer: H. Fenton
Size: Tiny
Issued: 1947-1960
Price: $135 £90

JOHNNY APPLESEED D6372
Designer: H. Fenton
Size: Large
Issued: 1953-1969
Price: $255 £170

LAWYER D6498
Designer: M. Henk
Size: Large
Issued: 1959-
Price: $69 £28

LAWYER D6504
Designer: M. Henk
Size: Small
Issued: 1959-
Price: $37 £15

LAWYER D6524
Designer: M. Henk
Size: Mini
Issued: 1960-
Price: $25 £10

LOBSTER MAN D6617
Designer: D. Biggs
Size: Large
Issued: 1968-
Price: $69 £28

LOBSTER MAN D6620
Designer: D. Biggs
Size: Small
Issued: 1968-
Price: $37 £15

JOHN DOULTON

LAWYER

JOHNNY APPLESEED

LOBSTER MAN D6652
Designer: D. Biggs
Size: Mini
Issued: 1980-
Price: $25 £10

LONG JOHN SILVER D6335
Designer: M. Henk
Size: Large
Issued: 1960-
Price: $69 £28

LONG JOHN SILVER D6386
Designer: M. Henk
Size: Small
Issued: 1960-
Price: $37 £15

LONG JOHN SILVER D6512
Designer: M. Henk
Size: Mini
Issued: 1960-
Price: $25 £10

LORD NELSON D6336
Designer: G. Blower
Size: Large
Issued: 1952-1969
Price: $240 £160

LOUIS ARMSTRONG D6707
Designer: D. Biggs
Size: Large
Issued: 1984-
Price: $87 £35

LUMBERJACK D6610
Designer: M. Henk
Size: Large
Issued: 1967-1983
Price: $52 £35

LUMBERJACK D6613
Designer: M. Henk
Size: Small
Issued: 1967-1983
Price: $37 £25

MACBETH D6667
Designer: M. Abberley
Size: Large
Issued: 1982-
Price: $87 £35

MAD HATTER D6598
Designer: M. Henk
Size: Large
Issued: 1965-1983
Price: $52 £35

MAD HATTER D6602
Designer: M. Henk
Size: Small
Issued: 1965-1983
Price: $37 £25

MAD HATTER D6606
Designer: M. Henk
Size: Mini
Issued: 1965-1983
Price: $27 £18

LOBSTER MAN   LONG JOHN SILVER

LORD NELSON   LUMBERJACK

MACBETH   MAD HATTER

MAE WEST D6688
Designer: C. Davidson
Size: Large
Issued: 1983-1985
Price: $52 £35

MARK TWAIN D6654
Designer: E. Griffiths
Size: Large
Issued: 1980-
Price: $69 £28

MARK TWAIN D6694
Designer: E. Griffiths
Size: Small
Issued: 1983-
Price: $37 £15

MEPHISTOPHELES D5757
Designer: H. Fenton
Size: Large
Issued: 1937-1948
Price: $1350 £900

MEPHISTOPHELES D5758
Designer: H. Fenton
Size: Small
Issued: 1937-1948
Price: $775 £550

MERLIN D6529
Designer: G. Sharpe
Size: Large
Issued: 1960-
Price: $69 £28

MERLIN D6536
Designer: G. Sharpe
Size: Small
Issued: 1960-
Price: $37 £15

MERLIN D6543
Designer: G. Sharpe
Size: Mini
Issued: 1960-
Price: $25 £10

MIKADO D6501
Designer: M. Henk
Size: Large
Issued: 1959-1969
Price: $285 £190

MIKADO D6507
Designer: M. Henk
Size: Small
Issued: 1959-1969
Price: $255 £170

MIKADO D6525
Designer: M. Henk
Size: Mini
Issued: 1960-1969
Price: $262 £175

MINE HOST D6468
Designer: M. Henk
Size: Large
Issued: 1958-1982
Price: $45 £30

MEPHISTOPHELES

MERLIN

MIKADO

CHARACTER JUGS

MINE HOST D6470
Designer: M. Henk
Size: Small
Issued: 1958-1962
Price: $33 £22

MINE HOST D6513
Designer: M. Henk
Size: Mini
Issued: 1960-1982
Price: $27 £18

MONTY D6202
Designer: H. Fenton
Size: Large
Issued: 1946-
Price: $69 £28

MR MICAWBER D5843
Designer: L. Harradine and
H. Fenton
Size: Intermediate
Issued: 1938-1948
Price: $112 £75

MR MICAWBER D5843
Designer: L. Harradine and
H. Fenton
Size: Small
Issued: 1948-1960
Price: $57 £38

MR MICAWBER D6138
Designer: L. Harradine and
H. Fenton
Size: Mini
Issued: 1940-1960
Price: $45 £30

MR MICAWBER D6143
Designer: L. Harradine and
H. Fenton
Size: Tiny
Issued: 1940-1960
Price: $90 £60

MR PICKWICK D6060
Designer: L. Harradine and
H. Fenton
Size: Large
Issued: 1940-1960
Price: $90 £60

MR PICKWICK D5839
Designer: L. Harradine and
H. Fenton
Size: Intermediate
Issued: 1938-1948
Price: $112 £75

MR PICKWICK D5839
Designer: L. Harradine and
H. Fenton
Size: Small
Issued: 1948-1960
Price: $57 £38

MR PICKWICK D6245
Designer: L. Harradine and
H. Fenton
Size: Mini
Issued: 1947-1960
Price: $45 £30

MINE HOST   MR MICAWBER

MR PICKWICK

MR PICKWICK D6260
Designer: L. Harradine and
           H. Fenton
Size: Tiny
Issued: 1947-1960
Price: $112 £75

MR QUAKER D6738
Designer: H. Sales
Size: Large
Issued: 1985
Price: $337 £225

NEPTUNE D6548
Designer: M. Henk
Size: Large
Issued: 1961-
Price: $69 £28

NEPTUNE D6552
Designer: M. Henk
Size: Small
Issued: 1961-
Price: $37 £15

NEPTUNE D6555
Designer: M. Henk
Size: Mini
Issued: 1961-
Price: $25 £10

NIGHT WATCHMAN D6569
Designer: M. Henk
Size: Large
Issued: 1963-1983
Price: $52 £35

NIGHT WATCHMAN D6576
Designer: M. Henk
Size: Small
Issued: 1963-1983
Price: $42 £28

NIGHT WATCHMAN D6583
Designer: M. Henk
Size: Mini
Issued: 1963-1983
Price: $30 £20

NORTH AMERICAN INDIAN D6611
Designer: M. Henk
Size: Large
Issued: 1967-
Price: $69 £28

NORTH AMERICAN INDIAN D6614
Designer: M. Henk
Size: Small
Issued: 1967-
Price: $37 £15

NORTH AMERICAN INDIAN D6665
Designer: M. Henk
Size: Mini
Issued: 1967-
Price: $25 £10

OLD CHARLEY D5420
Designer: C. Noke
Size: Large
Issued: 1934-1983
Price: $52 £35

NEPTUNE   NIGHT WATCHMAN

NORTH AMERICAN INDIAN

OLD CHARLEY D5527
Designer: C. Noke
Size: Small
Issued: 1935-1983
Price: $33 £22

OLD CHARLEY D6046
Designer: C. Noke
Size: Mini
Issued: 1939-1982
Price: $27 £18

OLD CHARLEY D6144
Designer: C. Noke
Size: Tiny
Issued: 1940-1960
Price: $87 £58

OLD KING COLE D6036
Designer: H. Fenton
Size: Large
Issued: 1939-1960
Price: $165 £110

OLD KING COLE D6037
Designer: H. Fenton
Size: Small
Issued: 1939-1960
Price: $75 £50

OLD KING COLE (Yellow Crown) D6036
Designer: H. Fenton
Size: Large
Issued: 1939-1940
Price: $1200 £800

OLD KING COLE (Yellow Crown) D6037
Designer: H. Fenton
Size: Small
Issued: 1939-1940
Price: $2100 £1400

OLD SALT D6551
Designer: G. Sharpe
Size: Large
Issued: 1961-
Price: $69 £28

OLD SALT D6554
Designer: G. Sharpe
Size: Small
Issued: 1961-
Price: $37 £15

OLD SALT D6557
Designer: P. Gee
Size: Mini
Issued: 1984-
Price: $25 £10

OTHELLO D6673
Designer: M. Abberley
Size: Large
Issued: 1982-
Price: $87 £35

PADDY D5753
Designer: H. Fenton
Size: Large
Issued: 1937-1960
Price: $82 £55

OLD CHARLEY   OLD KING COLE

OLD KING COLE
(Yellow Crown)

OLD SALT   OTHELLO

PADDY D5768
Designer: H. Fenton
Size: Small
Issued: 1937-1960
Price: $52 £35

PADDY D6042
Designer: H. Fenton
Size: Mini
Issued: 1939-1960
Price: $42 £28

PADDY D6145
Designer: H. Fenton
Size: Tiny
Issued: 1940-1960
Price: $82 £55

PARSON BROWN D5486
Designer: C. Noke
Size: Large
Issued: 1935-1960
Price: $90 £60

PARSON BROWN D5529
Designer: C. Noke
Size: Small
Issued: 1935-1960
Price: $57 £38

PAUL McCARTNEY D6724
Designer: S. Taylor
Size: Medium
Issued: 1984-
Price: $50 £20

PEARLY BOY (Blue)
Designer: H. Fenton
Size: Large
Issued: 1947-
Price: $3375 £2250

PEARLY BOY (Blue)
Designer: H. Fenton
Size: Small
Issued: 1947-
Price: $1800 £1200

PEARLY BOY (Blue)
Designer: H. Fenton
Size: Mini
Issued: 1947-
Price: $1800 £1200

PEARLY BOY (Brown buttons)
An early version of 'ARRY'
Designer: H. Fenton
Size: Large
Issued: 1947-
Price: $975 £650

PEARLY BOY (Brown buttons)
An early version of 'ARRY'
Designer: H. Fenton
Size: Small
Issued: 1947-
Price: $675 £450

PEARLY BOY (Brown buttons)
An early version of 'ARRY'
Designer: H. Fenton
Size: Mini
Issued: 1947-
Price: $420 £280

PADDY

PARSON BROWN

BLUE PEARLY BOY

PEARLY GIRL (Blue)
A very rare version of 'ARRIET
Designer: H. Fenton
Size: Large
Issued: 1947-
Price: $6000 £4000

PEARLY GIRL (Blue)
A very rare version of 'ARRIET
Designer: H. Fenton
Size: Small
Issued: 1947-
Price: $6750 £4500

PIED PIPER D6403
Designer: G. Blower
Size: Large
Issued: 1954-1981
Price: $57 £38

PIED PIPER D6462
Designer: G. Blower
Size: Small
Issued: 1957-1981
Price: $42 £28

PIED PIPER D6514
Designer: G. Blower
Size: Mini
Issued: 1960-1981
Price: $30 £20

POACHER D6429
Designer: M. Henk
Size: Large
Issued: 1955-
Price: $69 £28

POACHER D6464
Designer: M. Henk
Size: Small
Issued: 1957-
Price: $37 £15

POACHER D6515
Designer: M. Henk
Size: Mini
Issued: 1960-
Price: $25 £10

PORTHOS D6440
Designer: M. Henk
Size: Large
Issued: 1956-
Price: $69 £28

PORTHOS D6453
Designer: M. Henk
Size: Small
Issued: 1956-
Price: $37 £15

PORTHOS D6516
Designer: M. Henk
Size: Mini
Issued: 1960-
Price: $25 £10

PUNCH AND JUDY MAN
D6590
Designer: D. Biggs
Size: Large
Issued: 1964-1969
Price: $435 £290

BLUE PEARLY GIRL

PIED PIPER

POACHER

PUNCH AND JUDY MAN
D6593
Designer: D. Biggs
Size: Small
Issued: 1964-1969
Price: $270 £180

PUNCH AND JUDY MAN
D6596
Designer: D. Biggs
Size: Mini
Issued: 1964-1969
Price: $270 £180

REGENCY BEAU D6559
Designer: D. Biggs
Size: Large
Issued: 1962-1967
Price: $675 £450

REGENCY BEAU D6562
Designer: D. Biggs
Size: Small
Issued: 1962-1967
Price: $630 £420

REGENCY BEAU D6565
Designer: D. Biggs
Size: Mini
Issued: 1962-1967
Price: $690 £460

RINGO STARR D6726
Designer: S. Taylor
Size: Medium
Issued: 1984-
Price: $50 £20

RIP VAN WINKLE D6438
Designer: G. Blower
Size: Large
Issued: 1955-
Price: $69 £28

RIP VAN WINKLE D6463
Designer: G. Blower
Size: Small
Issued: 1957-
Price: $37 £15

RIP VAN WINKLE D6517
Designer: G. Blower
Size: Mini
Issued: 1960-
Price: $25 £10

ROBIN HOOD (First version)
D6205
Designer: H. Fenton
Size: Large
Issued: 1947-1960
Price: $90 £60

ROBIN HOOD (First version)
D6234
Designer: H. Fenton
Size: Small
Issued: 1947-1960
Price: $52 £35

PUNCH AND JUDY MAN   RIP VAN WINKLE

REGENCY BEAU

87

ROBIN HOOD (First Version)
D6252
Designer: H. Fenton
Size: Mini
Issued: 1947-1960
Price: $52 £35

ROBIN HOOD (Second
version) D6527
Designer: M. Henk
Size: Large
Issued: 1960-
Price: $69 £28

ROBIN HOOD (Second
version) D6534
Designer: M. Henk
Size: Small
Issued: 1960-
Price: $37 £15

ROBIN HOOD (Second
version) D6541
Designer: M. Henk
Size: Mini
Issued: 1960-
Price: $25 £10

ROBINSON CRUSOE D6532
Designer: M. Henk
Size: Large
Issued: 1960-1983
Price: $45 £30

ROBINSON CRUSOE D6539
Designer: M. Henk
Size: Small
Issued: 1960-1983
Price: $37 £25

ROBINSON CRUSOE D6546
Designer: M. Henk
Size: Mini
Issued: 1960-1983
Price: $27 £18

ROMEO D6670
Designer: D. Biggs
Size: Large
Issued: 1983-
Price: $87 £35

RONALD REAGAN D6718
Designer: E. Griffiths
Size: Large
Issued: 1984
Price: $375 £250

ST. GEORGE D6618
Designer: M. Henk
Size: Large
Issued: 1968-1975
Price: $112 £75

ST. GEORGE D6621
Designer: M. Henk
Size: Small
Issued: 1968-1975
Price: $72 £48

SAIREY GAMP D5451
Designer: L. Harradine and
          H. Fenton
Size: Large
Issued: 1935-
Price: $69 £28

ROBIN HOOD (SECOND VERSION)   ROBINSON CRUSOE

ST. GEORGE

CHARACTER JUGS

SAIREY GAMP D5528
Designer: L. Harradine and
          H. Fenton
Size: Small
Issued: 1935-
Price: $37 £15

SAIREY GAMP D6045
Designer: L. Harradine and
          H. Fenton
Size: Mini
Issued: 1939-
Price: $25 £10

SAIREY GAMP D6146
Designer: L. Harradine and
          H. Fenton
Size: Tiny
Issued: 1940-1960
Price: $75 £50

SAM WELLER D6064
Designer: L. Harradine and
          H. Fenton
Size: Large
Issued: 1940-1960
Price: $112 £75

SAM WELLER D5841
Designer: L. Harradine and
          H. Fenton
Size: Intermediate
Issued: 1938-1948
Price: $120 £80

SAM WELLER D5841
Designer: L. Harradine and
          H. Fenton
Size: Small
Issued: 1948-1960
Price: $52 £35

SAM WELLER D6140
Designer: L. Harradine and
          H. Fenton
Size: Mini
Issued: 1940-1960
Price: $42 £28

SAM WELLER D6147
Designer: L. Harradine and
          H. Fenton
Size: Tiny
Issued: 1940-1960
Price: $97 £65

SAMUEL JOHNSON D6289
Designer: H. Fenton
Size: Large
Issued: 1950-1960
Price: $285 £190

SAMUEL JOHNSON D6296
Designer: H. Fenton
Size: Small
Issued: 1950-1960
Price: $135 £90

SANCHO PANZA D6456
Designer: G. Blower
Size: Large
Issued: 1957-1983
Price: $52 £35

SAIREY GAMP   SAM WELLER

SAMUEL JOHNSON

SANCHO PANZA D6461
Designer: G. Blower
Size: Small
Issued: 1957-1983
Price: $37 £25

SANCHO PANZA D6518
Designer: G. Blower
Size: Mini
Issued: 1960-1983
Price: $27 £18

SANTA ANNA/DAVY
CROCKET D6729
Designer: M. Abberley
Size: Large
Issued: 1985
Price: $120 £80

SANTA CLAUS D6668
Designer: M. Abberley
Size: Large with Peg
           Doll Handle
Issued: 1981
Price: $60 £40

SANTA CLAUS D6675
Designer: M. Abberley
Size: Large with Reindeer
           Handle
Issued: 1982
Price: $52 £35

SANTA CLAUS D6690
Designer: M. Abberley
Size: Large with Sack of
           Toys Handle
Issued: 1983
Price: $52 £35

SANTA CLAUS D6704
Designer: M. Abberley
Size: Large
Issued: 1984-
Price: $69 £28

SANTA CLAUS D6705
Designer: M. Abberley
Size: Small
Issued: 1984-
Price: $37 £15

SANTA CLAUS D6706
Designer: M. Abberley
Size: Mini
Issued: 1984-
Price: $25 £10

SCARAMOUCHE D6558
Designer: M. Henk
Size: Large
Issued: 1962-1967
Price: $630 £420

SCARAMOUCHE D6561
Designer: M. Henk
Size: Small
Issued: 1962-1967
Price: $315 £210

SCARAMOUCHE D6564
Designer: M. Henk
Size: Mini
Issued: 1962-1967
Price: $420 £280

SANCHO PANZA

SANTA CLAUS
(LARGE WITH SACK OF TOYS)

SCARAMOUCHE

**SIMON THE CELLARER
D5504**
Designer: C. Noke and
        H. Fenton
Size: Large
Issued: 1935-1960
Price: $90 £60

**SIMON THE CELLARER
D5616**
Designer: C. Noke and
        H. Fenton
Size: Small
Issued: 1936-1960
Price: $60 £40

SIMPLE SIMON D6374
Designer: G. Blower
Size: Large
Issued: 1953-1960
Price: $390 £260

SIR HENRY DOULTON D6703
Designer: E. Griffiths
Size: Small
Issued: 1984
Price: $45 £30

**SITTING BULL/GEORGE
ARMSTRONG CUSTER
D6712**
Designer: M. Abberley
Size: Large
Issued: 1984
Price: $112 £75

SLEUTH D6631
Designer: A. Moore
Size: Large
Issued: 1973-
Price: $69 £28

SLEUTH D6635
Designer: A. Moore
Size: Small
Issued: 1973-
Price: $37 £15

SLEUTH D6639
Designer: A. Moore
Size: Mini
Issued: 1973-
Price: $25 £10

SMUGGLER D6616
Designer: D. Biggs
Size: Large
Issued: 1968-1981
Price: $52 £35

SMUGGLER D6619
Designer: D. Biggs
Size: Small
Issued: 1968-1981
Price: $37 £25

SMUTS D6198
Designer: H. Fenton
Size: Large
Issued: 1946-c.1948
Price: $1200 £800

TAM O'SHANTER D6632
Designer: M. Henk
Size: Large
Issued: 1973-1980
Price: $52 £35

SIMON THE CELLARER   SIMPLE SIMON

SIR HENRY DOULTON   SLEUTH

SMUTS   TAM O'SHANTER

TAM O'SHANTER D6636
Designer: M. Henk
Size: Small
Issued: 1973-1980
Price: $37 £25

TAM O'SHANTER D6640
Designer: M. Henk
Size: Mini
Issued: 1973-1980
Price: $30 £20

TOBY GILLETTE D6717
Designer: E. Griffiths
Size: Large
Issued: 1984
Price: $18000 £12000

TOBY PHILPOTTS D5736
Designer: C. Noke
Size: Large
Issued: 1937-1969
Price: $90 £60

TOBY PHILPOTTS D5737
Designer: C. Noke
Size: Small
Issued: 1937-1969
Price: $52 £35

TOBY PHILPOTTS D6043
Designer: C. Noke
Size: Mini
Issued: 1939-1969
Price: $42 £28

TONY WELLER D5531
Designer: L. Harradine and
         H. Fenton
Size: Extra Large
Issued: c.1936
Price: $165 £110

TONY WELLER D5531
Designer: L. Harradine and
         H. Fenton
Size: Large
Issued: c.1936-1960
Price: $90 £60

TONY WELLER D5530
Designer: L. Harradine and
         H. Fenton
Size: Small
Issued: 1936-1960
Price: $57 £38

TONY WELLER D6044
Designer: L. Harradine and
         H. Fenton
Size: Mini
Issued: 1939-1960
Price: $45 £30

TOUCHSTONE D5613
Designer: C. Noke
Size: Large
Issued: 1936-1960
Price: $135 £90

TOWN CRIER D6530
Designer: D. Biggs
Size: Large
Issued: 1960-1973
Price: $150 £100

TONY WELLER

TOUCHSTONE

TOWN CRIER

TOWN CRIER D6537
Designer: D. Biggs
Size: Small
Issued: 1960-1973
Price: $90 £60

TOWN CRIER D6544
Designer: D. Biggs
Size: Mini
Issued: 1960-1973
Price: $112 £75

TRAPPER D6609
Designer: M. Henk and
          D. Biggs
Size: Large
Issued: 1967-1983
Price: $57 £38

TRAPPER D6612
Designer: M. Henk and
          D. Biggs
Size: Small
Issued: 1967-1983
Price: $30 £20

UGLY DUCHESS D6599
Designer: M. Henk
Size: Large
Issued: 1965-1973
Price: $345 £230

UGLY DUCHESS D6603
Designer: M. Henk
Size: Small
Issued: 1965-1973
Price: $300 £200

UGLY DUCHESS D6607
Designer: M. Henk
Size: Mini
Issued: 1965-1973
Price: $315 £210

**ULYSSES S. GRANT and
ROBERT E. LEE D6698**
Designer: M. Abberley
Size: Large
Issued: 1983-
Price: $120 £80

**UNCLE TOM COBBLEIGH
D6337**
Designer: M. Henk
Size: Large
Issued: 1952-1960
Price: $285 £190

VETERAN MOTORIST D6633
Designer: D. Biggs
Size: Large
Issued: 1973-1983
Price: $57 £38

VETERAN MOTORIST D6637
Designer: D. Biggs
Size: Small
Issued: 1973-1983
Price: $42 £28

VETERAN MOTORIST D6641
Designer: D. Biggs
Size: Mini
Issued: 1973-1983
Price: $30 £20

UGLY DUCHESS   VETERAN MOTORIST

UNCLE TOM COBBLEIGH

93

VICAR OF BRAY D5615
Designer: C. Noke and
           H. Fenton
Size: Large
Issued: 1936-1960
Price: $150 £100

VIKING D6496
Designer: M. Henk
Size: Large
Issued: 1959-1975
Price: $112 £75

VIKING D6502
Designer: M. Henk
Size: Small
Issued: 1959-1975
Price: $90 £60

VIKING D6526
Designer: M. Henk
Size: Mini
Issued: 1959-1975
Price: $90 £60

W.C. FIELDS D6674
Designer: D. Biggs
Size: Large
Issued: 1983-
Price: $57 £38

WALRUS AND CARPENTER D6600
Designer: M. Henk
Size: Large
Issued: 1965-1980
Price: $57 £38

WALRUS AND CARPENTER D6604
Designer: M. Henk
Size: Small
Issued: 1965-1980
Price: $37 £25

WALRUS AND CARPENTER D6608
Designer: M. Henk
Size: Mini
Issued: 1965-1980
Price: $27 £18

WILD BILL HICKOCK D6736
Designer: M. Abberley
Size: Medium
Issued: 1985
Price: $49 £20

WILLIAM SHAKESPEARE D6689
Designer: M. Abberley
Size: Large
Issued: 1983-
Price: $87 £35

WYATT EARP D6711
Designer: S. Taylor
Size: Medium
Issued: 1985
Price: $49 £20

YACHTSMAN D6622
Designer: D. Biggs
Size: Large
Issued: 1971-1980
Price: $57 £38

VIKING

WALRUS AND CARPENTER

WYATT EARP

FIGURES

A

A LA MODE HN2544
Designer: E. J. Griffiths
Height: 12¼in., 31.1cm.
Issued: 1974-1977
Price: $105 £70

ABDULLAH HN1410
Designer: L. Harradine
Height: 5¾in., 14.6cm.
Issued: 1930-1938
Price: $600 £400

ABDULLAH HN2104
Designer: L. Harradine
Height: 6in., 15.2cm.
Issued: 1953-1962
Colour variation
Price: $270 £180

A'COURTING HN2004
Designer: L. Harradine
Height: 7¼in., 18.4cm.
Issued: 1947-1953
Price: $225 £150

ADRIENNE HN2152
Designer: M. Davies
Height: 7½in., 19.1cm.
Issued: 1964-1976
Price: $75 £50

ADRIENNE HN2304
Designer: M. Davies
Height: 7½in., 19.1cm.
Issued: 1964-
Colour variation
Price: $157 £63

AFFECTION HN2236
Designer: M. Davies
Height: 4½in., 11.4cm.
Issued: 1962-
Price: $107 £43

AFTERNOON TEA HN1747
Designer: P. Railston
Height: 5¾in., 14.6cm.
Issued: 1935-1981
Price: $150 £100

AFTERNOON TEA HN1748
Designer: P. Railston
Height: 5¼in., 13.3cm.
Issued: 1935-1949
Colour variation
Price: $262 £175

AILEEN HN1645
Designer: L. Harradine
Height: 6in., 15.2cm.
Issued: 1934-1938
Price: $450 £300

AILEEN HN1664
Designer: L. Harradine
Height: 6in., 15.2cm.
Issued: 1934-1938
Colour variation
Price: $450 £300

A LA MODE HN 2544

ABDULLAH HN2104

A'COURTING HN2004

ADRIENNE HN2304

AFTERNOON TEA HN1747

AILEEN HN1664

AILEEN HN1803
Designer: L. Harradine
Height: 6in., 15.2cm.
Issued: 1937-1949
Colour variation
Price: $375 £250

AJAX HN2908
Designer: S. Keenan
Height: 9¾in., 24.8cm.
Issued: 1980 in a limited
edition of 950
Price: $240 £160

ALCHEMIST HN1259
Designer: L. Harradine
Height: 11½in., 29.2cm.
Issued: 1927-1938
Price: $900 £600

ALCHEMIST HN1282
Designer: L. Harradine
Height: 11¼in., 28.5cm.
Issued: 1928-1938
Colour variation
Price: $900 £600

ALEXANDRA HN2398
Designer: M. Davies
Height: 7¾in., 19.7cm.
Issued: 1970-1976
Price: $75 £50

ALFRED JINGLE HN541
Designer: L. Harradine
Height: 3¾in., 9.5cm.
Issued: 1922-1932
Price: $37 £25

ALFRED JINGLE M52
Designer: L. Harradine
Height: 3¾in., 9.5cm.
Issued: 1932-1982
Price: $30 £20

ALICE HN2158
Designer: M. Davies
Height: 5in., 12.7cm.
Issued: 1960-1980
Price: $57 £38

ALISON HN2336
Designer: M. Davies
Height: 7½in., 19.1cm.
Issued: 1966-
Price: $157 £63

ALL-A-BLOOMING HN1457
Designer: L. Harradine
Height: 6½in., 16.5cm.
Issued: 1931-not known
Price: $525 £350

ALL-A-BLOOMING HN1466
Designer: L. Harradine
Height: 6½in., 16.5cm.
Issued: 1931-1938
Price: $525 £350

ALL ABOARD HN2940
Designer: R. Tabbenor
Height: 9¼in., 23.5cm.
Issued: 1982-
Price: $237 £95

AJAX HN2908

ALCHEMIST HN1282

ALEXANDRA HN2398

ALFRED JINGLE HN541

ALICE HN2158

ALISON HN2336

FIGURES

AMY HN2958
Designer: Pauline Parsons
Height: 6in., 15cm.
Issued: 1982-
Price: $107 £43

AND ONE FOR YOU HN2970
Designer: A. Hughes
Height: 6½in., 16.5cm.
Issued: 1982-1985
Price: $61 £41

AND SO TO BED HN2966
Designer: P. Parsons
Height: 7½in., 19cm.
Issued: 1982-1985
Price: $61 £41

ANDREA HN3058
Designer: A. Hughes
Height: 5¼in., 13cm.
Issued: 1985-
Price: $65 £26

ANGELA (Style one) HN1204
Designer: L. Harradine
Height: 7¼in., 18.4cm.
Issued: 1926-1938
Price: $562 £375

ANGELA (Style one) HN1303
Designer: L. Harradine
Height: 7¼in., 18.4cm.
Issued: 1928-1938
        Colour variation
Price: $600 £400

ANGELA (Style two) HN2389
Designer: P. Davies
Height: 7½in., 19cm.
Issued: 1983-
Price: $117 £47

ANGELINA HN2013
Designer: L. Harradine
Height: 6¾in., 17.1cm.
Issued: 1948-1951
Price: $300 £200

ANN HN2739
Designer: D. Tootle
Height: 7¾in., 19.5cm.
Issued: 1983-
Price: $67 £45

ANNA HN2802
Designer: M. Davies
Height: 5¾in., 14.6cm.
Issued: 1976-1982
Price: $42 £28

ANNABELLA HN1871
Designer: L. Harradine
Height: 5¼in., 13.3cm.
Issued: 1938-1949
Price: $150 £100

ANNABELLA HN1872
Designer: L. Harradine
Height: 5¼in., 13.3cm.
Issued: 1938-1949
        Colour variation
Price: $150 £100

AMY HN2958

ANGELA (Style one) HN1204

ANGELINA HN2013

ANNA HN2802

ANNABELLA HN1871

ANNABELLA HN1872

ANNABELLA HN1875
Designer: L. Harradine
Height: 4¾in., 12.0cm.
Issued: 1938-1949
 Colour variation
Price: $150 £100

ANNETTE HN1471
Designer: L. Harradine
Height: 6¼in., 15.9cm.
Issued: 1931-1938
Price: $127 £85

ANNETTE HN1472
Designer: L. Harradine
Height: 6in., 15.2cm.
Issued: 1931-1949
 Colour variation
Price: $127 £85

ANNETTE HN1550
Designer: L. Harradine
Height: 6¼in., 15.9cm.
Issued: 1933-1949
Price: $127 £85

ANTHEA HN1526
Designer: L. Harradine
Height: 6½in., 16.5cm.
Issued: 1932-1938
Price: $375 £250

ANTHEA HN1527
Designer: L. Harradine
Height: 6½in., 16.5cm.
Issued: 1932-1949
 Colour variation
Price: $262 £175

ANTHEA HN1669
Designer: L. Harradine
Height: 6½in., 16.5cm.
Issued: 1934-1938
 Colour variation
Price: $375 £250

ANTOINETTE (Style one) HN1850
Designer: L. Harradine
Height: 8¼in., 21.0cm.
Issued: 1938-1949
Price: $450 £300

ANTOINETTE (Style one) HN1851
Designer: L. Harradine
Height: 8¼in., 21.0cm.
Issued: 1938-1949
 Colour variation
Price: $450 £300

ANTOINETTE (Style two) HN2326
Designer: M. Davies
Height: 6¼in., 15.9cm.
Issued: 1967-1978
Price: $75 £50

APPLE MAID HN2160
Designer: L. Harradine
Height: 6½in., 16.5cm.
Issued: 1957-1962
Price: $195 £130

ANNETTE HN1550

ANTHEA HN1526

ANTHEA HN1669

ANTOINETTE (Style one) HN1850

ANTOINETTE (Style one) HN1851

APPLE MAID HN2160

APRIL SHOWER HN3024
Designer: R. Jefferson
Height: 4¾in., 12cm.
Issued: 1983-
Price: $107 £43

ARAB HN33
Designer: C. J. Noke
Height: 15¾in., 40.0cm.
Issued: 1913-1938
Price: $600 £400

ARAB HN343
Designer: C. J. Noke
Height: 16½in., 41.9cm.
Issued: 1919-1938
        Colour variation
Price: $675 £450

ARAB HN378
Designer: C. J. Noke
Height: 16½in., 41.9cm.
Issued: 1920-1938
        Colour variation
Price: $600 £400

ARAGORN HN2916
Designer: H. Sales
Height: 6¼in., 15.9cm.
Issued: 1979-1984
Price: $30 £20

ARTFUL DODGER HN546
Designer: L. Harradine
Height: 3¾in., 9.5cm.
Issued: 1922-1932
Price: $42 £28

ARTFUL DODGER M55
Designer: L. Harradine
Height: 4¼in., 10.8cm.
Issued: 1932-1983
Price: $30 £20

AS GOOD AS NEW HN2971
Designer: A. Hughes
Height: 6½in., 16.5cm.
Issued: 1982-1985
Price: $61 £41

ASCOT HN2356
Designer: M. Davies
Height: 5¾in., 14.6cm.
Issued: 1968-
Price: $172 £69

AT EASE HN2473
Designer: M. Davies
Height: 6in., 15.2cm.
Issued: 1973-1978
Price: $105 £70

AUTUMN (Style one) HN314
Designer: Unknown
Height: 7¼in., 18.4cm.
Issued: 1918-1938
Price: $600 £400

AUTUMN (Style one) HN474
Designer: Unknown
Height: 7½in., 19.1cm.
Issued: 1921-1938
        Colour variation
Price: $675 £450

ARAB HN33

ARAGORN HN2916

ARTFUL DODGER HN546

ASCOT HN2356

AT EASE HN2473

AUTUMN (Style one) HN314

AUTUMN (Style two) HN2087
Designer: M. Davies
Height: 7¼in., 18.4cm.
Issued: 1952-1959
Price: $262 £175

AUTUMN BREEZES HN1911
Designer: L. Harradine
Height: 7½in., 19.1cm.
Issued: 1939-1976
Price: $105 £70

AUTUMN BREEZES HN1913
Designer: L. Harradine
Height: 7½in., 19.1cm.
Issued: 1939-1971
Colour variation
Price: $112 £75

AUTUMN BREEZES HN1934
Designer: L. Harradine
Height: 7½in., 19.1cm.
Issued: 1940-
Colour variation
Price: $172 £69

AUTUMN BREEZES HN2147
Designer: L. Harradine
Height: 7½in., 19.1cm.
Issued: 1955-1971
Colour variation
Price: $187 £125

AWAKENING HN1927
Designer: L. Harradine
Height: Unknown
Issued: 1940-1949
Price: $1050 £700

AWAKENING HN2837 (Black)
Designer: P. Davies
Height: 8½in., 22cm.
Issued: 1981
Price: $70 £28

AWAKENING HN2875 (White)
Designer: P. Davies
Height: 8½in., 22cm.
Issued: 1981-
Price: $70 £28

B

BABA HN1230
Designer: L. Harradine
Height: 3¼in., 8.3cm.
Issued: 1927-1938
Price: $300 £200

BABA HN1243
Designer: L. Harradine
Height: 3¼in., 8.3cm.
Issued: 1927-1938
Colour variation
Price: $300 £200

BABA HN1244
Designer: L. Harradine
Height: 3¼in., 8.3cm.
Issued: 1927-1938
Colour variation
Price: $300 £200

AUTUMN (Style two) HN2087   AUTUMN BREEZES HN1911

AUTUMN BREEZES HN1913   AUTUMN BREEZES HN1934

AWAKENING HN2837 (Black)   BABA HN1230

BABA HN1245
Designer: L. Harradine
Height: 3¼in., 8.3cm.
Issued: 1927-1938
Colour variation
Price: $300 £200

BABA HN1246
Designer: L. Harradine
Height: 3¼in., 8.3cm.
Issued: 1927-1938
Colour variation
Price: $300 £200

BABA HN1247
Designer: L. Harradine
Height: 3¼in., 8.3cm.
Issued: 1927-1938
Colour variation
Price: $300 £200

BABA HN1248
Designer: L. Harradine
Height: 3¼in., 8.3cm.
Issued: 1927-1938
Colour variation
Price: $300 £200

BABETTE HN1423
Designer: L. Harradine
Height: 5in., 12.7cm.
Issued: 1930-1938
Price: $300 £200

BABETTE HN1424
Designer: L. Harradine
Height: 5in., 12.7cm.
Issued: 1930-1938
Colour variation
Price: $375 £250

BABIE HN1679
Designer: L. Harradine
Height: 4¾in., 12.0cm.
Issued: 1935-
Price: $77 £31

BABIE HN1842
Designer: L. Harradine
Issued: 1938-1949
Height: 4¾in., 12.0cm.
Colour variation
Price: $97 £65

BABIE HN2121
Designer: L. Harradine
Height: 4¾in., 12.0cm.
Issued: 1983-
Price: $77 £31

BABY HN12
Designer: C. J. Noke
Height: Unknown
Issued: 1913-1938
Price: $1350 £900

BABY BUNTING HN2108
Designer: M. Davies
Height: 5¼in., 13.3cm.
Issued: 1953-1959
Price: $150 £100

BABA HN1247

BABETTE HN1423

BABETTE HN1424

BABIE HN1679

BABIE HN1842

BABY BUNTING HN2108

FIGURES

BACHELOR HN2319
Designer: M. Nicholl
Height: 7in., 17.8cm.
Issued: 1964-1975
Price: $180 £120

BALLAD SELLER HN2266
Designer: M. Davies
Height: 7½in., 19.1cm.
Issued: 1968-1973
Price: $180 £120

BALLERINA HN2116
Designer: M. Davies
Height: 7¼in., 18.4cm.
Issued: 1953-1973
Price: $180 £120

BALLOON BOY HN2934
Designer: P. Gee
Height: 7½in., 19cm.
Issued: 1984-
Price: $142 £57

BALLOON GIRL HN2818
Designer: W. K. Harper
Height: 6½in., 16.5cm.
Issued: 1982-
Price: $142 £57

BALLOON LADY HN2935
Designer: P. Gee
Height: 8¼in., 21cm.
Issued: 1984-
Price: $157 £63

BALLOON MAN HN1954
Designer: L. Harradine
Height: 7¼in., 18.4cm.
Issued: 1940-
Price: $172 £69

BALLOON SELLER HN479
Designer: L. Harradine
Height: 9in., 22.9cm.
Issued: 1921-1938
Price: $637 £425

BALLOON SELLER HN486
Designer: L. Harradine
Height: 9in., 22.9cm.
Issued: 1921-1938
Price: $487 £325

BALLOON SELLER HN548
Designer: L. Harradine
Height: 9in., 22.9cm.
Issued: 1922-1938
Colour variation
Price: $300 £200

BALLOON SELLER HN583
Designer: L. Harradine
Height: 9in., 22.9cm.
Issued: 1923-1949
Colour variation
Price: $187 £125

BACHELOR HN2319

BALLAD SELLER HN2266

BALLERINA HN2116

BALLOON GIRL HN2818

BALLOON MAN HN1954

BALLOON SELLER HN583

FIGURES

BALLOON SELLER
HN697
Designer: L. Harradine
Height: 9in., 22.9cm.
Issued: 1925-1938
        Colour variation
Price: $300 £200

BARBARA HN1421
Designer: L. Harradine
Height: 7¾in., 19.7cm.
Issued: 1930-1938
Price: $337 £225

BARBARA HN1432
Designer: L. Harradine
Height: 7¾in., 19.7cm.
Issued: 1930-1938
Price: $337 £225

BARBARA HN1461
Designer: L. Harradine
Height: 7¾in., 19.7cm.
Issued: 1931-1938
        Colour variation
Price: $337 £225

BARBARA HN2962
Designer: P. Parsons
Height: 8in., 20cm.
Issued: 1982-1984
Price: $45 £30

BARLIMAN BUTTERBUR
HN2923
Designer: D. Lyttleton
Height: 5¼in., 13cm.
Issued: 1982-1984
Price: $30 £20

BASKET WEAVER HN2245
Designer: M. Nicholl
Height: 5¾in., 14.6cm.
Issued: 1959-1962
Price: $300 £200

BATHER (Style one) HN597
Designer: L. Harradine
Height: 7¾in., 19.7cm.
Issued: 1924-1938
Price: $525 £350

BATHER (Style one) HN687
Designer: L. Harradine
Height: 7¾in., 19.7cm.
Issued: 1924-1949
        Colour variation
Price: $375 £250

BATHER (Style one) HN781
Designer: L. Harradine
Height: 7¾in., 19.7cm.
Issued: 1926-1938
        Colour variation
Price: $525 £350

BATHER (Style one) HN782
Designer: L. Harradine
Height: 7¾in., 19.7cm.
Issued: 1926-1938
        Colour variation
Price: $525 £350

BARBARA HN1432

BARBARA HN2962

BARLIMAN BUTTERBUR HN2923

BASKET WEAVER HN2245

BATHER (Style one) HN687

BATHER (Style one) HN782

103

FIGURES

BATHER (Style one) HN1238
Designer: L. Harradine
Height: 7¾in., 19.7cm.
Issued: 1927-1938
Colour variation
Price: $525 £350

BATHER (Style one) HN1708
Designer: L. Harradine
Height: 7¾in., 19.7cm.
Issued: 1935-1938
Colour variation
Price: $750 £500

BATHER (Style two) HN773
Designer: L. Harradine
Height: 7½in., 19.1cm.
Issued: 1925-1938
Price: $525 £350

BATHER (Style two) HN774
Designer: L. Harradine
Height: 7¾in., 19.7cm.
Issued: 1925-1938
Price: $525 £350

BATHER (Style two) HN1227
Designer: L. Harradine
Height: 7½in., 19.1cm.
Issued: 1927-1938
Colour variation
Price: $525 £350

BEACHCOMBER HN2487
Designer: M. Nicholl
Height: 6¼in., 15.9cm.
Issued: 1973-1976
Price: $105 £70

BEAT YOU TO IT HN2871
Designer: M. Davies
Height: 6½in., 16.5cm.
Issued: 1980-
Price: $337 £135

BEDTIME HN1978
Designer: L. Harradine
Height: 5¾in., 14.6cm.
Issued: 1945-
Price: $51 £21

BEDTIME STORY HN2059
Designer: L. Harradine
Height: 4¾in., 12.0cm.
Issued: 1950-
Price: $222 £89

BEETHOVEN HN1778
Designer: R. Garbe
Height: 22in., 55.8cm.
Issued: 1933 in a limited
edition of 25
Price: $3000 £2000

BEGGAR (Style one) HN526
Designer: L. Harradine
Height: 6½in., 16.5cm.
Issued: 1921-1949
Price: $300 £200

BEACHCOMBER HN2487

BATHER (Style two) HN774

BEDTIME STORY HN2059

BEAT YOU TO IT HN2871

BEETHOVEN HN1778

BEGGAR (Style one) HN526

BEGGAR (Style one) HN591
Designer: L. Harradine
Height: 6¾in., 17.2cm.
Issued: 1924-1949
Price: $300 £200

BEGGAR (Style two) HN2175
Designer: L. Harradine
Height: 6¾in., 17.2cm.
Issued: 1956-1972
Price: $270 £180

BELLE HN754
Designer: L. Harradine
Height: 6½in., 16.5cm.
Issued: 1925-1938
Price: $487 £325

BELLE HN776
Designer: L. Harradine
Height: 6½in., 16.5cm.
Issued: 1925-1938
Price: $487 £325

BELLE HN2340
Designer: M. Davies
Height: 4½in., 11.4cm.
Issued: 1968-
Price: $69 £28

BELLE 'O' THE BALL HN1997
Designer: L. Harradine
Height: 6in., 15.2cm.
Issued: 1947-1978
Price: $135 £90

BENMORE HN2909
Designer: S. Keenan
Height: 9¼in., 23.5cm.
Issued: 1980 in a limited
          edition of 950
Price: $240 £160

BERNICE HN2071
Designer: M. Davies
Height: 7¾in., 19.7cm.
Issued: 1951-1953
Price: $412 £275

BESS HN2002
Designer: L. Harradine
Height: 7¼in., 18.4cm.
Issued: 1947-1969
Price: $150 £100

BESS HN2003
Designer: L. Harradine
Height: 7¼in., 18.4cm.
Issued: 1947-1950
          Colour variation
Price: $225 £150

BETH HN2870
Designer: M. Davies
Height: 5¾in., 14.6cm.
Issued: 1980-1983
Price: $37 £25

BETSY HN2111
Designer: L. Harradine
Height: 7in., 17.8cm.
Issued: 1953-1959
Price: $180 £120

BEGGAR (Style two) HN2175

BELLE HN2340

BELLE O' THE BALL HN1997

BENMORE HN2909

BERNICE HN2071

BESS HN2002

BETTY (Style one) HN402
Designer: L. Harradine
Height: Unknown
Issued: 1920-1938
Price: $1200 £800

BETTY (Style one) HN403
Designer: L. Harradine
Height: Unknown
Issued: 1920-1938
　　　　　Colour variation
Price: $1200 £800

BETTY Style one) HN435
Designer: L. Harradine
Height: Unknown
Issued: 1921-1938
　　　　　Colour variation
Price: $1200 £800

BETTY (Style one) HN438
Designer: L. Harradine
Height: Unknown
Issued: 1921-1938
　　　　　Colour variation
Price: $1200 £800

BETTY (Style one) HN477
Designer: L. Harradine
Height: Unknown
Issued: 1921-1938
　　　　　Colour variation
Price: $1200 £800

BETTY (Style one) HN478
Designer: L. Harradine
Height: Unknown
Issued: 1921-1938
　　　　　Colour variation
Price: $1200 £800

BETTY (Style two) HN1404
Designer: L. Harradine
Height: 4½in., 11.4cm.
Issued: 1930-1938
Price: $300 £200

BETTY (Style two) HN1405
Designer: L. Harradine
Height: 4½in., 11.4cm.
Issued: 1930-1938
　　　　　Colour variation
Price: $300 £200

BETTY (Style two) HN1435
Designer: L. Harradine
Height: 4½in., 11.4cm.
Issued: 1930-1938
　　　　　Colour variation
Price: $300 £200

BETTY (Style two) HN1436
Designer: L. Harradine
Height: 4½in., 11.4cm.
Issued: 1930-1938
　　　　　Colour variation
Price: $300 £200

BIDDY HN1445
Designer: L. Harradine
Height: 5½in., 14.0cm.
Issued: 1931-1938
Price: $127 £85

BETTY (Style two) HN1404

106

FIGURES

BIDDY HN1500
Designer: L. Harradine
Height: 5½in., 14.0cm.
Issued: 1932-1938
Price: $127 £85

BIDDY HN1513
Designer: L. Harradine
Height: 5½in., 14.0cm.
Issued: 1932-1951
Colour variation
Price: $112 £75

BIDDY PENNY FARTHING HN1843
Designer: L. Harradine
Height: 9in., 22.9cm.
Issued: 1938-
Price: $172 £69

BILBO HN2914
Designer: Harry Sales
Height: 4½in., 11.4cm.
Issued: 1979-1984
Price: $30 £20

BILL SYKES HN537
Designer: L. Harradine
Height: 3¾in., 9.5cm.
Issued: 1922-1932
Price: $42 £28

BILL SYKES M54
Designer: L. Harradine
Height: 4¼in., 10.8cm.
Issued: 1932-1982
Price: $30 £20

BLACKSMITH OF WILLIAMSBURG HN2240
Designer: M. Davies
Height: 6¾in., 17.2cm.
Issued: 1960-1983
Price: $90 £60

BLIGHTY HN323
Designer: E. W. Light
Height: 11¼in., 28.5cm.
Issued: 1918-1938
Price: $420 £280

BLITHE MORNING HN2021
Designer: L. Harradine
Height: 7¼in., 18.4cm.
Issued: 1949-1971
Price: $135 £90

BLITHE MORNING HN2065
Designer: L. Harradine
Height: 7¼in., 18.4cm.
Issued: 1950-1973
Colour variation
Price: $135 £90

BLOSSOM HN1667
Designer: L. Harradine
Height: 6¾in., 17.2cm.
Issued: 1934-1949
Price: $600 £400

BIDDY HN1513

BIDDY PENNY FARTHING HN1843

BILBO HN2914

BILL SYKES HN537

BLIGHTY HN323

BLITHE MORNING HN2065

107

BLUE BEARD (Style one)
HN75
Designer: E. W. Light
Height: Unknown
Issued: 1917-1938
Price: $1500 £1000

BLUE BEARD (Style one)
HN410
Designer: E. W. Light
Height: Unknown
Issued: 1920-1938
Colour variation
Price: $1500 £1000

BLUEBEARD (Style two)
HN1528
Designer: L. Harradine
Height: 11½in., 29.2cm.
Issued: 1932-1949
Price: $300 £200

BLUEBEARD (Style two)
HN2105
Designer: L. Harradine
Height: 11in., 27.9cm.
Issued: 1953-
Colour variation
Price: $372 £149

BLUE BIRD HN1280
Designer: L. Harradine
Height: 4¾in., 12.0cm.
Issued: 1928-1938
Price: $262 £175

BOATMAN HN2417
Designer: M. Nicholl
Height: 6½in., 16.5cm.
Issued: 1971-
Price: $172 £69

BON APPETIT HN2444
Designer: M. Nicholl
Height: 6in., 15.2cm.
Issued: 1972-1976
Price: $90 £60

BONJOUR HN1879
Designer: L. Harradine
Height: 6¾in., 17.2cm.
Issued: 1938-1949
Price: $300 £200

BONJOUR HN1888
Designer: L. Harradine
Height: 6¾in., 17.2cm.
Issued: 1938-1949
Colour variation
Price: $300 £200

BONNIE LASSIE HN1626
Designer: L. Harradine
Height: 5¼in., 13.3cm.
Issued: 1934-1953
Price: $120 £80

BONNIE LASSIE HN1626A
Designer: L. Harradine
Height: 5¼in., 13.3cm.
Issued: Unknown
Colour variation
Price: $120 £80

BLUE BEARD (Style one) HN75

BLUE BEARD (Style one) HN410

BLUE BIRD HN1280

BOATMAN HN2417

BONJOUR HN1888

BONNIE LASSIE HN1626A

FIGURES

BO-PEEP (Style one) HN777
Designer: L. Harradine
Height: 6¾in., 17.2cm.
Issued: 1926-1938
Price: $750 £500

BO-PEEP (Style one) HN1202
Designer: L. Harradine
Height: 6¾in., 17.2cm.
Issued: 1926-1938
Colour variation
Price: $750 £500

BO-PEEP (Style one) HN1327
Designer: L. Harradine
Height: 6¾in., 17.2cm.
Issued: 1929-1938
Colour variation
Price: $750 £500

BO-PEEP (Style one) HN1328
Designer: L. Harradine
Height: 6¾in., 17.2cm.
Issued: 1929-1938
Colour variation
Price: $750 £500

BO-PEEP (Style two) HN1810
Designer: L. Harradine
Height: 5in., 12.7cm.
Issued: 1937-1949
Price: $120 £80

BO-PEEP (Style two) HN1811
Designer: L. Harradine
Height: 5in., 12.7cm.
Issued: 1937-
Colour variation
Price: $102 £41

BO-PEEP M82
Designer: L. Harradine
Height: 4in., 10.1cm.
Issued: 1939-1949
Price: $195 £130

BO-PEEP M83
Designer: L. Harradine
Height: 4in., 10.1cm.
Issued: 1939-1949
Colour variation
Price: $195 £130

BOROMIR HN2918
Designer: Harry Sales
Height: 6¾in., 17.2cm.
Issued: 1980-1984
Price: $31 £21

BOUDOIR HN2542
Designer: E. J. Griffiths
Height: 12¼in., 31.1cm.
Issued: 1974-1977
Price: $120 £80

BOUQUET HN406
Designer: G. Lambert
Height: 9in., 22.9cm.
Issued: 1920-1938
Price: $900 £600

BO-PEEP (Style one) HN1327

BO-PEEP (Style two) HN1810

BO-PEEP M82

BOROMIR HN2918

BOUDOIR HN2542

BOUQUET HN406

109

FIGURES

BOUQUET HN414
Designer: G. Lambert
Height: 9in., 22.9cm.
Issued: 1920-1938
Price: $900 £600

BOUQUET HN422
Designer: G. Lambert
Height: 9in., 22.9cm.
Issued: 1920-1938
  Colour variation
Price: $900 £600

BOUQUET HN428
Designer: G. Lambert
Height: 9in., 22.9cm.
Issued: 1921-1938
  Colour variation
Price: $900 £600

BOUQUET HN429
Designer: G. Lambert
Height: 9in., 22.9cm.
Issued: 1921-1938
  Colour variation
Price: $900 £600

BOUQUET HN567
Designer: G. Lambert
Height: 9½in., 24.1cm.
Issued: 1923-1938
  Colour variation
Price: $900 £600

BOUQUET HN794
Designer: G. Lambert
Height: 9in., 22.9cm.
Issued: 1926-1938
  Colour variation
Price: $975 £650

**BOY FROM
WILLIAMSBURG HN2183**
Designer: M. Davies
Height: 5½in., 14.0cm.
Issued: 1969-1983
Price: $52 £35

BOY ON CROCODILE HN373
Designer: C. J. Noke
Height: 5in., 12.7cm.
Length: 14½in., 36.8cm.
Issued: 1920-1938
Price: $2550 £1700

BOY ON PIG HN1369
Designer: C. J. Noke
Height: 4in., 10.1cm.
Issued: 1930-1938
Price: $1125 £750

BOY WITH TURBAN HN586
Designer: L.Harradine
Height: 3¾in., 9.5cm.
Issued: 1923-1938
Price: $412 £275

BOY WITH TURBAN HN587
Designer: L. Harradine
Height: 3¾in., 9.5cm.
Issued: 1923-1938
Price: $412 £275

BOUQUET HN422

BOY FROM WILLIAMSBURG HN2183

BOY ON CROCODILE HN373

BOY ON PIG HN1369

BOY WITH TURBAN HN587

FIGURES

BOY WITH TURBAN HN661
Designer: L. Harradine
Height: 3¾in., 9.5cm.
Issued: 1924-1938
Price: $412 £275

BOY WITH TURBAN HN662
Designer: L. Harradine
Height: 3¾in., 9.5cm.
Issued: 1924-1938
Colour variation
Price: $412 £275

BOY WITH TURBAN HN1210
Designer: L. Harradine
Height: 3¾in., 9.5cm.
Issued: 1926-1938
Colour variation
Price: $412 £275

BOY WITH TURBAN HN1212
Designer: L. Harradine
Height: 3¾in., 9.5cm.
Issued: 1926-1938
Price: $412 £275

BOY WITH TURBAN HN1213
Designer: L. Harradine
Height: 3¾in., 9.5cm.
Issued: 1926-1938
Colour variation
Price: $412 £275

BOY WITH TURBAN HN1214
Designer: L. Harradine
Height: 3½in., 8.9cm.
Issued: 1926-1938
Colour variation
Price: $412 £275

BOY WITH TURBAN HN1225
Designer: L. Harradine
Height: 3¾in., 9.5cm.
Issued: 1927-1938
Colour variation
Price: $412 £275

BRETON DANCER HN2383
Designer: P. Davies
Height: 8½in., 21.5cm.
Issued: 1981 in a limited
edition of 750
Price: $525 £350

BRIDE (Style one) HN1588
Designer: L. Harradine
Height: 8¾in., 22.2cm.
Issued: 1933-1938
Price: $412 £275

BRIDE (Style one) HN1600
Designer: L. Harradine
Height: 8¾in., 22.2cm.
Issued: 1933-1949
Colour variation
Price: $300 £200

BRIDE (Style one) HN1762
Designer: L. Harradine
Height: 8¾in., 22.2cm.
Issued: 1936-1949
Colour variation
Price: $375 £250

BOY WITH TURBAN HN1213

BOY WITH TURBAN HN1214

BRETON DANCER HN2383

BRIDE (Style one) HN1588

BRIDE (Style one) HN1600

BRIDE (Style one) HN1762

BRIDE (Style one) HN1841
Designer: L. Harradine
Height: 9½in., 24.1cm.
Issued: 1938-1949
Colour variation
Price: $375 £250

BRIDE (Style two) HN2166
Designer: M. Davies
Height: 8in., 20.3cm.
Issued: 1956-1976
Price: $112 £75

BRIDE (Style three) HN2873
Designer: M. Davies
Height: 8in., 20.3cm.
Issued: 1980-
Price: $172 £69

BRIDESMAID (Style one) HN1433
Designer: L. Harradine
Height: 5¼in., 13.3cm.
Issued: 1930-1951
Price: $90 £60

BRIDESMAID (Style one) HN1434
Designer: L. Harradine
Height: 5in., 12.7cm.
Issued: 1930-1949
Colour variation
Price: $90 £60

BRIDESMAID (Style one) HN1530
Designer: L. Harradine
Height: 5in., 12.7cm.
Issued: 1932-1938
Colour variation
Price: $90 £60

BRIDESMAID (Style two) HN2148
Designer: M. Davies
Height: 5½in., 14.0cm.
Issued: 1955-1959
Price: $97 £65

BRIDESMAID (Style three) HN2196
Designer: M. Davies
Height: 5¼in., 13.3cm.
Issued: 1960-1976
Price: $52 £35

BRIDESMAID (Style four) HN2874
Designer: M. Davies
Height: 5¼in., 13.3cm.
Issued: 1980-
Price: $102 £41

BRIDESMAID M11
Designer: L. Harradine
Height: 3¾in., 9.5cm.
Issued: 1932-1938
Price: $135 £90

BRIDESMAID M12
Designer: L. Harradine
Height: 3¾in., 9.5cm.
Issued: 1932-1945
Colour variation
Price: $135 £90

BRIDE (Style two) HN2166

BRIDE (Style three) HN2873

BRIDESMAID (Style one) HN1433

BRIDESMAID (Style two) HN2148

BRIDESMAID (Style three) HN2196

BRIDESMAID (Style four) HN2874

BRIDESMAID M30
Designer: L. Harradine
Height: 3¾in., 9.5cm.
Issued: 1932-1945
Colour variation
Price: $135 £90

BRIDGET HN2070
Designer: L. Harradine
Height: 7¾in., 19.7cm.
Issued: 1951-1973
Price: $165 £110

BRIGHT WATER HN3529
Designer: R. Jefferson
Height: 8½in., 21.5cm.
Issued: 1983-
Price: $64 £43

BROKEN LANCE HN2041
Designer: M. Davies
Height: 8¾in., 22.2cm.
Issued: 1949-1975
Price: $270 £180

BUDDIES HN2546
Designer: E. J. Griffiths
Height: 6in., 15.2cm.
Issued: 1973-1976
Price: $90 £60

BUMBLE M76
Designer: L. Harradine
Height: 4in., 10.1cm.
Issued: 1939-1982
Price: $30 £20

BUNNY HN2214
Designer: M. Davies
Height: 5in., 12.7cm.
Issued: 1960-1975
Price: $60 £40

BUTTERCUP HN2309
Designer: M. Davies
Height: 7in., 17.8cm.
Issued: 1964-
Price: $147 £59

BUTTERCUP HN2399
Designer: P. Davies
Height: 7½in., 19cm.
Issued: 1983-
Price: $147 £59

BUTTERFLY HN719
Designer: L. Harradine
Height: 6½in., 16.5cm.
Issued: 1925-1938
Price: $600 £400

BUTTERFLY HN720
Designer: L. Harradine
Height: 6½in., 16.5cm.
Issued: 1925-1938
Colour variation
Price: $600 £400

BUTTERFLY HN730
Designer: L. Harradine
Height: 6½in., 16.5cm.
Issued: 1925-1938
Colour variation
Price: $600 £400

BRIDGET HN2070

BROKEN LANCE HN2041

BUDDIES HN2546

BUNNY HN2214

BUTTERCUP HN2309

BUTTERFLY HN719

FIGURES

BUTTERFLY HN1203
Designer: L. Harradine
Height: 6½in., 16.5cm.
Issued: 1926-1938
Colour variation
Price: $600 £400

BUTTERFLY HN1456
Designer: L. Harradine
Height: 6½in., 16.5cm.
Issued: 1931-1938
Price: $600 £400

BUZ FUZ HN538
Designer: L. Harradine
Height: 3¾in., 9.5cm.
Issued: 1922-1932
Price: $45 £30

BUZ FUZ M53
Designer: L. Harradine
Height: 4in., 10.1cm.
Issued: 1932-1983
Price: $30 £20

C

CALLED LOVE, A LITTLE BOY HN1545
Designer: Unknown
Height: 3½in., 8.9cm.
Issued: 1933-1949
Price: $240 £160

CALUMET HN1428
Designer: C. J. Noke
Height: 6in., 15.2cm.
Issued: 1930-1949
Price: $375 £250

CALUMET HN1689
Designer: C. J. Noke
Height: 6½in., 16.5cm.
Issued: 1935-1949
Colour variation
Price: $375 £250

CALUMET HN2068
Designer: C. J. Noke
Height: 6¼in., 15.9cm.
Issued: 1950-1953
Colour variation
Price: $375 £250

CAMELLIA HN2222
Designer: M. Davies
Height: 7¾in., 19.7cm.
Issued: 1960-1971
Price: $112 £75

CAMILLA HN1710
Designer: L. Harradine
Height: 7in., 17.8cm.
Issued: 1935-1949
Price: $345 £230

CAMILLA HN1711
Designer: L. Harradine
Height: 7in., 17.8cm.
Issued: 1935-1949
Colour variation
Price: $345 £230

BUTTERFLY HN1456

BUZ FUZ HN538

CALLED LOVE, A LITTLE BOY HN1545

CALUMET HN1428

CAMELLIA HN2222

CAMILLA HN1710

114

FIGURES

CAMILLE HN1586
Designer: L. Harradine
Height: 6½in., 16.5cm.
Issued: 1933-1949
Price: $270 £180

CAMILLE HN1648
Designer: L. Harradine
Height: 6½in., 16.5cm.
Issued: 1934-1949
Colour variation
Price: $270 £180

CAMILLE HN1736
Designer: L. Harradine
Height: 6½in., 16.5cm.
Issued: 1935-1949
Colour variation
Price: $270 £180

CAPTAIN (Style one) HN778
Designer: L. Harradine
Height: 7in., 17.8cm.
Issued: 1926-1938
Price: $675 £450.

CAPTAIN (Style two) HN2260
Designer: M. Nicholl
Height: 9½in., 24.1cm.
Issued: 1965-1982
Price: $112 £75

CAPTAIN COOK HN2889
Designer: W. K. Harper
Height: 8in., 20.3cm.
Issued: 1980-1984
Price: $112 £75

CAPTAIN CUTTLE M77
Designer: L. Harradine
Height: 4in., 10.1cm.
Issued: 1939-1982
Price: $30 £20

CAPTAIN MacHEATH HN464
Designer: L. Harradine
Height: 7in., 17.8cm.
Issued: 1921-1949
Price: $560 £375

CAPTAIN MacHEATH HN590
Designer: L. Harradine
Height: 7in., 17.8cm.
Issued: 1924-1949
Price: $560 £375

CAPTAIN MacHEATH HN1256
Designer: L. Harradine
Height: 7in., 17.8cm.
Issued: 1927-1949
Price: $560 £375

CAPTAIN, 2ND NEW YORK REGIMENT 1755 HN2755
Designer: E. J. Griffiths
Height: 10in., 25.4cm.
Issued: 1976 in a limited edition of 350
Price: $150 £100

CAMILLE HN1586

CAMILLE HN1648

CAPTAIN (Style one) HN778

CAPTAIN (Style two) HN2260

CAPTAIN COOK HN2889

CAPTAIN CUTTLE M77

FIGURES

CARMEN (Style one) HN1267
Designer: L. Harradine
Height: 7in., 17.8cm.
Issued: 1928-1938
Price: $600 £400

CARMEN (Style one) HN1300
Designer: L. Harradine
Height: 7in., 17.8cm.
Issued: 1928-1938
Colour variation
Price: $600 £400

CARMEN (Style two) HN2545
Designer: E. J. Griffiths
Height: 11½in., 29.2cm.
Issued: 1974-1977
Price: $112 £75

CARNIVAL HN1260
Designer: L. Harradine
Height: 8¼in., 21.0cm.
Issued: 1927-1938
Price: $1200 £800

CARNIVAL HN1278
Designer: L. Harradine
Height: 8½in., 21.6cm.
Issued: 1928-1938
Colour variation
Price: $1200 £800

CAROL HN2961
Designer: P. Parsons
Height: 7½in., 19cm.
Issued: 1982-
Price: $117 £47

CAROLYN HN2112
Designer: L. Harradine
Height: 7in., 17.8cm.
Issued: 1953-1965
Price: $180 £120

CAROLYN HN2974
Designer: A. Hughes
Height: 5½in., 14cm.
Issued: 1983-
Price: $172 £69

CARPET SELLER (Style one)
HN1464
Designer: L. Harradine
Height: 9¼in., 23.5cm.
Issued: 1931-?
Price: $240 £160

CARPET SELLER (Style two)
HN1464A
Designer: L. Harradine
Height: 9in., 22.9cm.
Issued: 1924-1969
Price: $150 £100

CARPET VENDOR (Style one)
HN38
Designer: C. J. Noke
Height: Unknown
Issued: 1914-1938
Price: $1500 £1000

CARMEN (Style one) HN1267

CARMEN (Style two) HN2545

CARNIVAL HN1260

CAROL HN2961

CAROLYN HN2112

CARPET SELLER (Style two) HN1464A

FIGURES

CARPET VENDOR (Style one)
HN38A
Designer: C. J. Noke
Height: Unknown
Issued: 1914-1938
Price: $1500 £1000

CARPET VENDOR (Style one)
HN348
Designer: C. J. Noke
Height: Unknown
Issued: 1919-1938
Price: $1500 £1000

CARPET VENDOR (Style two)
HN76
Designer: C. J. Noke
Height: 5½in., 14.0cm.
Issued: 1917-1938
Price: $1800 £1200

CARPET VENDOR (Style two)
HN350
Designer: C. J. Noke
Height: 5½in., 14.0cm.
Issued: 1919-1938
Price: $1800 £1200

CARRIE HN2800
Designer: M. Davies
Height: 6in., 15.2cm.
Issued: 1976-1980
Price: $42 £28

CASSIM (Style one) HN1231
Designer: L. Harradine
Height: 3in., 7.6cm.
Issued: 1927-1938
Price: $375 £250

CASSIM (Style one) HN1232
Designer: L. Harradine
Height: 3in., 7.6cm.
Issued: 1927-1938
          Colour variation
Price: $375 £250

CASSIM (Style two) HN1311
Designer: L. Harradine
Height: 3¾in., 9.5cm.
Issued: 1929-1938
Price: $375 £250

CASSIM (Style two) HN1312
Designer: L. Harradine
Height: 3¾in., 9.5cm.
Issued: 1929-1938
Price: $375 £250

CATHERINE HN3044
Designer: P. Parsons
Height: 5in., 12.5cm.
Issued: 1985-
Price: $65 £26

CAVALIER (Style one) HN369
Designer: Unknown
Height: Unknown
Issued: 1920-1938
Price: $1350 £900

CARRIE HN2800

CARPET VENDOR (Style two) HN76

CASSIM (Style one) HN1231   CASSIM (Style one) HN1232

FIGURES

CAVALIER (Style two) HN2716
Designer: E. J. Griffiths
Height: 9¾in., 24.7cm.
Issued: 1976-1982
Price: $90 £60

CELESTE HN2237
Designer: M. Davies
Height: 6¾in., 17.2cm.
Issued: 1959-1971
Price: $112 £75

CELIA HN1726
Designer: L. Harradine
Height: 11½in., 29.2cm.
Issued: 1935-1949
Price: $600 £400

CELIA HN1727
Designer: L. Harradine
Height: 11½in., 29.2cm.
Issued: 1935-1949
Price: $600 £400

CELLIST HN2226
Designer: M. Davies
Height: 8in., 20.3cm.
Issued: 1960-1967
Price: $270 £180

CELLO HN2331
Designer: M. Davies
Height: 6in., 15.2cm.
Issued: 1970 in a limited
edition of 750
Price: $450 £300

CENTURION HN2726
Designer: W. K. Harper
Height: 9¼in., 23.5cm.
Issued: 1982-1984
Price: $97 £65

CERISE HN1607
Designer: L. Harradine
Height: 5¼in., 13.3cm.
Issued: 1933-1949
Price: $112 £75

CHARLEY'S AUNT (Style one)
HN35
Designer: A. Toft
Height: 6¾in., 17.2cm.
Issued: 1914-1938
Price: $300 £200

CHARLEY'S AUNT HN640
Designer: A. Toft
Height: 7in., 17.8cm.
Issued: 1924-1938
Colour variation
Price: $412 £275

CHARLEY'S AUNT (Style two)
HN1411
Designer: H. Fenton
Height: 8in., 20.3cm.
Issued: 1930-1938
Price: $600 £400

CAVALIER (Style two) HN2716

CELLO HN2331

CELIA HN1726

CENTURION HN2726

CERISE HN1607

CHARLEY'S AUNT (Style one) HN35

118

CHARLEY'S AUNT (Style two)
HN1554
Designer: H. Fenton
Height: 8in., 20.3cm.
Issued: 1933-1938
Price: $600 £400

CHARLEY'S AUNT (Style three) HN1703
Designer: A. Toft
Height: 6in., 15.2cm.
Issued: 1935-1938
Price: $525 £350

CHARLOTTE HN2421
Designer: J. Bromley
Height: 6½in., 16.5cm.
Issued: 1972-
Price: $182 £73

CHARMIAN HN1568
Designer: L. Harradine
Height: 6½in., 16.5cm.
Issued: 1933-1938
Price: $375 £250

CHARMIAN HN1569
Designer: L. Harradine
Height: 6½in., 16.5cm.
Issued: 1933-1938
             Colour variation
Price: $375 £250

CHARMIAN HN1651
Designer: L. Harradine
Height: 6½in., 16.5cm.
Issued: 1934-1938
             Cololur variation
Price: $375 £250

CHELSEA PAIR (Woman) HN577
Designer: L. Harradine
Height: 6in., 15.2cm.
Issued: 1923-1938
Price: $525 £350

CHELSEA PAIR (Woman) HN578
Designer: L. Harradine
Height: 6in., 15.2cm.
Issued: 1923-1938
             Colour variation
Price: $525 £350

CHELSEA PAIR (Man) HN579
Designer: L. Harradine
Height: 6in., 15.2cm.
Issued: 1923-1938
Price: $525 £350

CHELSEA PAIR (Man) HN580
Designer: L. Harradine
Height: 6in., 15.2cm.
Issued: 1923-1938
             Colour variation
Price: $525 £350

CHELSEA PENSIONER HN689
Designer: L. Harradine
Height: 5¾in., 14.6cm.
Issued: 1924-1938
Price: $750 £500

CHARLEY'S AUNT (Style two) HN1554

CHARLOTTE HN2421

CHARMIAN HN1568

CHELSEA PAIR (Woman) HN577

CHELSEA PAIR (Man) HN580

CHELSEA PENSIONER HN689

119

FIGURES

CHERIE HN2341
Designer: M. Davies
Height: 5½in., 14.0cm.
Issued: 1966-
Price: $102 £41

CHIEF HN2892
Designer: W. K. Harper
Height: 7in., 17.8cm.
Issued: 1979-
Price: $212 £85

CHIEFTAIN HN2929
Designer: S. Keenan
Height: 8¾in., 22.2cm.
Issued: 1982 in a limited
         edition of 950
Price: $150 £100

CHILD AND CRAB HN32
Designer: C. J. Noke
Height: 5¼in., 13.3cm.
Issued: 1913-1938
Price: $1125 £750

**CHILD FROM
WILLIAMSBURG HN2154**
Designer: M. Davies
Height: 5½in., 14.0cm.
Issued: 1964-1984
Price: $52 £35

**CHILD STUDY (Style one)
HN603A**
Designer: L. Harradine
Height: 4¾in., 12.0cm.
Issued: 1924-1938
Price: $187 £125

**CHILD STUDY (Style one)
HN603B**
Designer: L. Harradine
Height: 4¾in., 12.0cm.
Issued: 1924-1938
         Colour variation
Price: $187 £125

CHILD STUDY HN606A
Designer: L. Harradine
Height: 5in., 12.7cm.
Issued: 1924-1938
Price: $187 £125

CHILD STUDY HN1441
Designer: L. Harradine
Height: 5in., 12.7cm.
Issued: 1931-1938
Price: $255 £170

**CHILD STUDY (Style two)
HN604A**
Designer: L. Harradine
Height: 5½in., 14.0cm.
Issued: 1924-1938
Price: $225 £150

**CHILD STUDY (Style two)
HN604B**
Designer: L. Harradine
Height: 5½in., 14.0cm.
Issued: 1924-1938
         Colour variation
Price: $225 £150

CHERIE HN2341

CHIEF HN2892

CHIEFTAIN HN2929

CHILD AND CRAB HN32

CHILD FROM WILLIAMSBURG
HN2154

CHILD STUDY (Style one) HN603B

FIGURES

CHILD STUDY (Style two)
HN1442
Designer: L. Harradine
Height: 6¼in., 15.9cm.
Issued: 1931-1938
Price: $255 £170

CHILD STUDY (Style two)
HN1443
Designer: L. Harradine
Issued: 1931-1938
Height: 5in., 12.7cm.
Price: $225 £150

CHILD STUDY (Style three)
HN605A
Designer: L. Harradine
Height: Unknown
Issued: 1924-1938
Price: $187 £125

CHILD STUDY (Style three)
HN605B
Designer: L. Harradine
Height: Unknown
Issued: 1924-1938
Price: $187 £125

CHILD'S GRACE HN62
Designer: L. Perugini
Height: 6¾in., 17.2cm.
Issued: 1916-1938
Price: $1500 £1000

CHILD'S GRACE HN62A
Designer: L. Perugini
Height: 6¾in., 17.2cm.
Issued: 1916-1938
          Colour variation
Price: $1500 £1000

CHILD'S GRACE HN510
Designer: L. Perugini
Height: 6¾in., 17.1cm.
Issued: 1921-1938
Price: $1500 £1000

CHINA REPAIRER HN2943
Designer: R. Tabbenor
Height: 6¾in., 17cm.
Issued: 1983-
Price: $212 £85

CHINESE DANCER HN2840
Designer: M. Davies
Height: 9in., 22.9cm.
Issued: 1980 in a limited
          edition of 750
Price: $375 £250

CHITARRONE HN2700
Designer: M. Davies
Height: 7½in., 19.1cm.
Issued: 1974 in a limited
          edition of 750
Price: $450 £300

CHLOE HN1470
Designer: L. Harradine
Height: 5½in., 14.0cm.
Issued: 1931-1949
Price: $180 £120

CHILD'S GRACE HN62A

CHITARRONE HN2700

CHILD STUDY (Style two) HN1442

CHINESE DANCER HN2840

CHLOE HN1470

CHILD STUDY (Style two) HN1443

121

FIGURES

CHLOE HN1476
Designer: L. Harradine
Height: 5½in., 14.0cm.
Issued: 1931-1938
Colour variation
Price: $225 £150

CHLOE HN1479
Designer: L. Harradine
Height: 5½in., 14.0cm.
Issued: 1931-1949
Colour variation
Price: $180 £120

CHLOE HN1498
Designer: L. Harradine
Height: 6in., 15.2cm.
Issued: 1932-1938
Colour variation
Price: $225 £150

CHLOE HN1765
Designer: L. Harradine
Height: 6in., 15.2cm.
Issued: 1936-1950
Colour variation
Price: $150 £100

CHLOE HN1956
Designer: L. Harradine
Height: 6in., 15.2cm.
Issued: 1940-1949
Colour variation
Price: $180 £120

CHLOE M9
Designer: L. Harradine
Height: 2¾in., 7.0cm.
Issued: 1932-1945
Price: $150 £100

CHLOE M10
Designer: L. Harradine
Height: 2¾in., 7.0cm.
Issued: 1932-1945
Colour variation
Price: $150 £100

CHLOE M29
Designer: L. Harradine
Height: 2¾in., 7.0cm.
Issued: 1932-1945
Colour variation
Price: $150 £100

CHOICE HN1959
Designer: L. Harradine
Height: 7¼in., 18.4cm.
Issued: 1941-1949
Price: $375 £250

CHOICE HN1960
Designer: L. Harradine
Height: 7¼in., 18.4cm.
Issued: 1941-1949
Colour variation
Price: $375 £250

CHOIR BOY HN2141
Designer: M. Davies
Height: 4¾in., 12.0cm.
Issued: 1954-1975
Price: $67 £45

CHLOE HN1476

CHLOE HN1479

CHLOE M9

CHLOE M29

CHOICE HN1959

CHOIR BOY HN2141

CHORUS GIRL HN1401
Designer: Unknown
Height: Unknown
Issued: 1930-1938
Price: $675 £450

CHRISTINE (Style one) HN1839
Designer: L. Harradine
Height: 7¾in., 19.7cm.
Issued: 1938-1949
Price: $450 £300

CHRISTINE (Style one) HN1840
Designer: L. Harradine
Height: 7¾in., 19.7cm.
Issued: 1938-1949
          Colour variation
Price: $450 £300

CHRISTINE (Style two) HN2792
Designer: M. Davies
Height: 7½in., 19.1cm.
Issued: 1978-
Price: $247 £99

CHRISTMAS MORN HN1992
Designer: M. Davies
Height: 7in., 17.8cm.
Issued: 1947-
Price: $157 £63

CHRISTMAS PARCELS HN2851
Designer: W. K. Harper
Height: 8¾in., 22.2cm.
Issued: 1978-1982
Price: $90 £60

CHRISTMAS TIME HN2110
Designer: M. Davies
Height: 6½in., 16.5cm.
Issued: 1953-1967
Price: $195 £130

CICELY HN1516
Designer: L. Harradine
Height: 5¾in., 14.6cm.
Issued: 1932-1949
Price: $412 £275

CIRCE HN1249
Designer: L. Harradine
Height: 7¾in., 19.7cm.
Issued: 1927-1938
Price: $720 £480

CIRCE HN1250
Designer: L. Harradine
Height: 7½in., 19.1cm.
Issued: 1927-1938
Price: $720 £480

CIRCE HN1254
Designer: L. Harradine
Height: 7½in., 19.1cm.
Issued: 1927-1938
          Colour variation
Price: $720 £480

CHRISTINE (Style one) HN1839

CHRISTINE (Style two) HN2792

CHRISTMAS MORN HN1992

CHRISTMAS PARCELS HN2851

CHRISTMAS TIME HN2110

CIRCE HN1249

CIRCE HN1255
Designer: L. Harradine
Height: 7½in., 19.1cm.
Issued: 1927-1938
Colour variation
Price: $720 £480

CISSIE HN1808
Designer: L. Harradine
Height: 5in., 12.7cm.
Issued: 1937-1951
Price: $75 £50

CISSIE HN1809
Designer: L. Harradine
Height: 5in., 12.7cm.
Issued: 1937-
Colour variation
Price: $102 £41

CLARE HN2793
Designer: M. Davies
Height: 7½in., 19.1cm.
Issued: 1980-1984
Price: $82 £55

CLARIBEL HN1950
Designer: L. Harradine
Issued: 1940-1949
Height: 4¾in., 12.0cm.
Price: $127 £85

CLARIBEL HN1951
Designer: L. Harradine
Height: 4¾in., 12.0cm.
Issued: 1940-1949
Colour variation
Price: $127 £85

CLARINDA HN2724
Designer: W. K. Harper
Height: 8½in., 21.6cm.
Issued: 1975-1980
Price: $75 £50

CLARISSA (Style one) HN1525
Designer: L. Harradine
Height: 10in., 25.4cm.
Issued: 1932-1938
Price: $412 £275

CLARISSA (Style one) HN1687
Designer: L. Harradine
Height: 9¾in., 24.8cm.
Issued: 1935-1949
Colour variation
Price: $375 £250

CLARISSA (Style two) HN2345
Designer: M. Davies
Height: 7½in., 19.1cm.
Issued: 1968-1982
Price: $75 £50

CLEAR WATER HN3530
Designer: R. Jefferson
Height: 8¼in., 21cm.
Issued: 1983-
Price: $64 £43

CLEMENCY HN1633
Designer: L. Harradine
Height: 7in., 17.8cm.
Issued: 1934-1938
Price: $375 £250

CISSIE HN1808

CLARE HN2793

CLARIBEL HN1950

CLARINDA HN2724

CLARISSA (Style one) HN1525

CLARISSA (Style two) HN2345

CLEMENCY HN1634
Designer: L. Harradine
Height: 7in., 17.8cm.
Issued: 1934-1949
Colour variation
Price: $300 £200

CLEMENCY HN1643
Designer: L. Harradine
Height: 7in., 17.8cm.
Issued: 1934-1938
Colour variation
Price: $375 £250

CLEOPATRA HN2868
Designer: M. Davies
Height: 7¼in., 18.4cm.
Issued: 1980 in a limited
edition of 750
Price: $637 £425

CLOCKMAKER HN2279
Designer: M. Nicholl
Height: 7in., 17.8cm.
Issued: 1961-1975
Price: $142 £95

CLOTHILDE HN1598
Designer: L. Harradine
Height: 7¼in., 18.4cm.
Issued: 1933-1949
Price: $450 £300

CLOTHILDE HN1599
Designer: L. Harradine
Height: 7¼in., 18.4cm.
Issued: 1933-1949
Colour variation
Price: $450 £300

CLOUD HN1831
Designer: R. Garbe
Height: 23in., 58.4cm.
Issued: 1937-1949
Price: $1875 £1250

CLOWN HN2890
Designer: W. K. Harper
Height: 9in., 22.9cm.
Issued: 1979-
Price: $272 £109

COACHMAN HN2282
Designer: M. Nicholl
Height: 7¼in., 18.4cm.
Issued: 1963-1971
Price: $270 £180

COBBLER (Style one) HN542
Designer: C, J. Noke
Height: 7½in., 19.1cm.
Issued: 1922-1939
Price: $600 £400

COBBLER (Style one) HN543
Designer: C. J. Noke
Height: 7½in., 19.1cm.
Issued: 1922-1938
Colour variation
Price: $637 £425

CLEMENCY HN1634

CLEOPATRA HN2868

CLOCKMAKER HN2279

CLOTHILDE HN1598

CLOWN HN2890

COBBLER (Style one) HN542

125

FIGURES

COBBLER (Style one) HN682
Designer: C. J. Noke
Height: 7½in., 19.1cm.
Issued: 1924-1938
Colour variation
Price: $450 £300

COBBLER (Style two) HN681
Designer: C. J. Noke
Height: 8½in., 21.6cm.
Issued: 1924-1938
Price: $450 £300

COBBLER (Style two) HN1251
Designer: C. J. Noke
Height: 8½in., 21.6cm.
Issued: 1927-1938
Colour variation
Price: $450 £300

COBBLER (Style two) HN1283
Designer: C. J. Noke
Height: 8½in., 21.6cm.
Issued: 1928-1949
Colour variation
Price: $300 £200

COBBLER (Style three) HN1705
Designer: C. J. Noke
Height: 8in., 20.3cm.
Issued: 1935-1949
Price: $300 £200

COBBLER (Style three) HN1706
Designer: C. J. Noke
Height: 8½in., 21.0cm.
Issued: 1935-1969
Colour variation
Price: $150 £100

COLLINETTE HN1998
Designer: L. Harradine
Height: 7¼in., 18.4cm.
Issued: 1947-1949
Price: $412 £275

COLLINETTE HN1999
Designer: L. Harradine
Height: 7¼in., 18.4cm.
Issued: 1947-1949
Colour variation
Price: $300 £200

COLONEL FAIRFAX HN2903
Designer: W. K. Harper
Height: 11½in., 29cm.
Issued: 1982-
Price: $352 £235

COLUMBINE (Style one) HN1296
Designer: L. Harradine
Height: 6in., 15.2cm.
Issued: 1928-1938
Price: $412 £275

COLUMBINE (Style one) HN1297
Designer: L. Harradine
Height: 6in., 15.2cm.
Issued: 1928-1938
Colour variation
Price: $412 £275

COBBLER (Style two) HN1283

COBBLER (Style three) HN1705

COBBLER (Style three) HN1706

COLLINETTE HN1999

COLONEL FAIRFAX HN2903

COLUMBINE (Style one) HN1297

FIGURES

COLUMBINE (Style one)
HN1439
Designer: L. Harradine
Height: 6in., 15.2cm.
Issued: 1930-1938
         Colour variation
Price: $412 £275

COLUMBINE (Style two)
HN2185
Designer: M. Davies
Height: 7in., 17.8cm.
Issued: 1957-1969
Price: $135 £90

COLUMBINE HN2738
Designer: D. Tootle
Height: 12½in., 31cm.
Issued: 1982-
Price: $877 £355

COMING OF SPRING HN1722
Designer: L. Harradine
Height: 12½in., 31.7cm.
Issued: 1935-1949
Price: $1200 £800

COMING OF SPRING HN1723
Designer: L. Harradine
Height: 12½in., 31.7cm.
Issued: 1935-1949
         Colour variation
Price: $1200 £800

CONSTANCE HN1510
Designer: L. Harradine
Height: Unknown
Issued: 1932-1938
Price: $600 £400

CONSTANCE HN1511
Designer: L. Harradine
Height: Unknown
Issued: 1932-1938
         Colour variation
Price: $600 £400

CONTEMPLATION HN2213
Designer: P. Davies
Height: 12in., 30cm.
Issued: 1982-
Price: $107 £43

CONTEMPLATION HN2241
Designer: P. Davies
Height: 12in., 30cm.
Issued: 1982-
         Colour variation
Price: $107 £43

CONTENTMENT HN395
Designer: L. Harradine
Height: 7¼in., 18.4cm.
Issued: 1920-1938
Price: $750 £500

CONTENTMENT HN396
Designer: L. Harradine
Height: 7¼in., 18.4cm.
Issued: 1920-1938
         Colour variation
Price: $750 £500

COLUMBINE (Style one) HN1439

COLUMBINE (Style two) HN2185

COMING OF SPRING HN1722

CONSTANCE HN1511

CONTEMPLATION HN2213

CONTENTMENT HN395

CONTENTMENT HN421
Designer: L. Harradine
Height: 7¼in., 18.4cm.
Issued: 1920-1938
Colour variation
Price: $750 £500

CONTENTMENT HN468
Designer: L. Harradine
Height: 7¼in., 18.4cm.
Issued: 1921-1938
Colour variation
Price: $750 £500

CONTENTMENT HN572
Designer: L. Harradine
Height: 7¼in., 18.4cm.
Issued: 1923-1938
Colour variation
Price: $750 £500

CONTENTMENT HN685
Designer: L. Harradine
Height: 7¼in., 18.4cm.
Issued: 1923-1938
Colour variation
Price: $840 £560

CONTENTMENT HN686
Designer: L. Harradine
Height: 7¼in., 18.4cm.
Issued: 1924-1938
Colour variation
Price: $840 £560

CONTENTMENT HN1323
Designer: L. Harradine
Height: 7¼in., 18.4cm.
Issued: 1929-1938
Colour variation
Price: $750 £500

COOKIE HN2218
Designer: M. Davies
Height: 4¾in., 12.0cm.
Issued: 1958-1975
Price: $67 £45

COPPELIA HN2115
Designer: M. Davies
Height: 7¼in., 18.4cm.
Issued: 1953-1959
Price: $412 £275

COQUETTE HN37
Designer: W. White
Height: 9¼in., 23.5cm.
Issued: 1913-1938
Price: $1800 £1200

CORALIE HN2307
Designer: M. Davies
Height: 7¼in., 18.4cm.
Issued: 1964
Price: $157 £63

CORINTHIAN HN1973
Designer: H. Fenton
Height: 7¾in., 19.7cm.
Issued: 1941-1949
Price: $675 £450

CONTENTMENT HN1323

COOKIE HN2218

COPPELIA HN2115

COQUETTE HN37

CORALIE HN2307

CORINTHIAN HN1973

FIGURES

CORPORAL, 1st NEW HAMPSHIRE REGIMENT 1778 HN2780
Designer: E. J. Griffiths
Height: 13in., 33.0cm.
Issued: 1975 in a limited edition of 350
Price: $150 £100

COUNTRY LASS HN1991A
Designer: L. Harradine
Height: 7¼in., 18.4cm.
Issued: 1975-1981
Price: $82 £55
Also called MARKET DAY HN1991

COURT SHOEMAKER HN1755
Designer: L. Harradine
Height: 6¾in., 17.2cm.
Issued: 1936-1949
Price: $1050 £700

COURTIER HN1338
Designer: L. Harradine
Height: 4½in., 11.4cm.
Issued: 1929-1938
Price: $750 £500

COVENT GARDEN HN1339
Designer: L. Harradine
Height: 9in., 22.9cm.
Issued: 1929-1938
Price: $525 £350

CRADLE SONG HN2246
Designer: M. Davies
Height: 5½in., 14.0cm.
Issued: 1959-1962
Price: $330 £220

CRAFTSMAN HN2284
Designer: M. Nicholl
Height: 8¼in., 21.0cm.
Issued: 1961-1965
Price: $330 £220

CRINOLINE HN8
Designer: G. Lambert
Height: 6¼in., 15.8cm.
Issued: 1913-1938
Price: $750 £500

CRINOLINE HN9
Designer: G. Lambert
Height: 6¼in., 15.8cm.
Issued: 1913-1938
Colour variation
Price: $750 £500

CRINOLINE HN9A
Designer: G. Lambert
Height: 6¼in., 15.8cm.
Issued: 1913-1938
Colour variation
Price: $750 £500

CRINOLINE HN21
Designer: G. Lambert
Height: 6¼in., 15.8cm.
Issued: 1913-1938
Colour variation
Price: $750 £500

CORPORAL, 1st NEW HAMPSHIRE REGIMENT 1778 HN2780

COUNTRY LASS HN1991A

COURT SHOEMAKER HN1755

COVENT GARDEN HN1339

CRAFTSMAN HN2284

CRINOLINE HN8

129

CRINOLINE HN21A
Designer: G. Lambert
Height: 6¼in., 15.8cm.
Issued: 1913-1938
Colour variation
Price: $750 £500

CRINOLINE HN413
Designer: G. Lambert
Height: 6¼in., 15.9cm.
Issued: 1920-1938
Colour variation
Price: $750 £500

CRINOLINE HN566
Designer: G. Lambert
Height: 6¼in., 15.9cm.
Issued: 1923-1938
Colour variation
Price: $750 £500

CRINOLINE HN628
Designer: G. Lambert
Height: 6¼in., 15.9cm.
Issued: 1924-1938
Colour variation
Price: $750 £500

CRINOLINE LADY HN650
Designer: Unknown
Height: 3in., 7.6cm.
Issued: 1924-1938
Price: $750 £500

CRINOLINE LADY HN651
Designer: Unknown
Height: 3in., 7.6cm.
Issued: 1924-1938
Colour variation
Price: $750 £500

CRINOLINE LADY HN652
Designer: Unknown
Height: 3in., 7.6cm.
Issued: 1924-1938
Colour variation
Price: $750 £500

CRINOLINE LADY HN653
Designer: Unknown
Height: 3in., 7.6cm.
Issued: 1924-1938
Colour variation
Price: $750 £500

CRINOLINE LADY HN654
Designer: Unknown
Height: 3in., 7.6cm.
Issued: 1924-1938
Colour variation
Price: $750 £500

CRINOLINE LADY HN655
Designer: Unknown
Height: 3in., 7.6cm.
Issued: 1924-1938
Colour variation
Price: $750 £500

CROUCHING NUDE HN457
Designer: Unknown
Height: 5½in., 14.0cm.
Issued: 1921-1938
Price: $675 £450

CROUCHING NUDE HN457

130

FIGURES

CUP OF TEA HN2322
Designer: M. Nicholl
Height: 7in., 17.8cm.
Issued: 1964-1983
Price: $75 £50

CURLY KNOB HN1627
Designer: L. Harradine
Height: 6in., 15.2cm.
Issued: 1934-1949
Price: $277 £185

CURLY LOCKS HN2049
Designer: M. Davies
Height: 4½in., 11.4cm.
Issued: 1949-1953
Price: $240 £160

CURTSEY HN57
Designer: E. W. Light
Height: 11in., 27.9cm.
Issued: 1916-1938
Price: $675 £450

CURTSEY HN57B
Designer: E. W. Light
Height: 11in., 27.9cm.
Issued: 1916-1938
      Colour variation
Price: $675 £450

CURTSEY HN66A
Designer: E. W. Light
Height: 11in., 27.9cm.
Issued: 1916-1938
      Colour variation
Price: $675 £450

CURTSEY HN327
Designer: E. W. Light
Height: 11in., 27.9cm.
Issued: 1918-1938
      Colour variation
Price: $675 £450

CURTSEY HN334
Designer: E. W. Light
Height: 11in., 27.9cm.
Issued: 1918-1938
      Colour variation
Price: $675 £450

CURTSEY HN363
Designer: E. W. Light
Height: 11in., 27.9cm.
Issued: 1919-1938
      Colour variation
Price: $675 £450

CURTSEY HN371
Designer: E. W. Light
Height: 11in., 27.9cm.
Issued: 1920-1938
      Colour variation
Price: $675 £450

CURTSEY HN518
Designer: E. W. Light
Height: 11in., 27.9cm.
Issued: 1921-1938
      Colour variation
Price: $675 £450

CURLY KNOB HN1627

CUP OF TEA HN2322

CURTSEY HN57

CURLY LOCKS HN2049

CURTSEY HN547
Designer: E. W. Light
Height: 11in., 27.9cm.
Issued: 1922-1938
         Colour variation
Price: $675 £450

CURTSEY HN629
Designer: E. W. Light
Height: 11in., 27.9cm.
Issued: 1924-1938
         Colour variation
Price: $675 £450

CURTSEY HN670
Designer: E. W. Light
Height: 11in., 27.9cm.
Issued: 1924-1938
         Colour variation
Price: $675 £450

CYMBALS HN2699
Designer: M. Davies
Height: 7½in., 19.1cm.
Issued: 1974 in a limited
         edition of 750
Price: $450 £300

CYNTHIA HN1685
Designer: L. Harradine
Height: 5¾in., 14.6cm.
Issued: 1935-1949
Price: $345 £230

CYNTHIA HN1686
Designer: L. Harradine
Height: 5¾in., 14.6cm.
Issued: 1935-1949
         Colour variation
Price: $345 £230

CYNTHIA HN1686A
Designer: L. Harradine
Height: 5¾in., 14.6cm.
Issued: 1935-1949
         Colour variation
Price: $345 £230

CYNTHIA HN2440
Designer: P. Davies
Height: 7¼in., 18cm.
Issued: 1984-
Price: $142 £57

D

**DAFFY-DOWN-DILLY
HN1712**
Designer: L. Harradine
Height: 7¾in., 19.7cm.
Issued: 1935-1975
Price: $180 £120

**DAFFY-DOWN-DILLY
HN1713**
Designer: L. Harradine
Height: 8¼in., 21.0cm.
Issued: 1935-1949
         Colour variation
Price: $300 £200

DAINTY MAY HN1639
Designer: L. Harradine
Height: 6in., 15.2cm.
Issued: 1934-1949
Price: $180 £120

CURTSEY HN670

CYMBALS HN2699

CYNTHIA HN1685

CYNTHIA HN1686A

DAFFY-DOWN-DILLY HN1712

DAINTY MAY HN1639

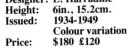

DAINTY MAY HN1656
Designer: L. Harradine
Height: 6in., 15.2cm.
Issued: 1934-1949
Colour variation
Price: $180 £120

DAINTY MAY M67
Designer: L. Harradine
Height: 4in., 10.1cm.
Issued: 1935-1949
Price: $180 £120

DAINTY MAY M73
Designer: L. Harradine
Height: 4in., 10.1cm.
Issued: 1936-1949
Colour variation
Price: $180 £120

DAISY HN1575
Designer: L. Harradine
Height: 3¾in., 9.5cm.
Issued: 1933-1949
Price: $150 £100

DAISY HN1961
Designer: L. Harradine
Height: 3½in., 8.9cm.
Issued: 1941-1949
Colour variation
Price: $150 £100

DAMARIS HN2079
Designer: M. Davies
Height: 7¼in., 18.4cm.
Issued: 1951-1952
Price: $450 £300

**"DANCING EYES AND
SUNNY HAIR" HN1543**
Designer: Unknown
Height: 5in., 12.7cm.
Issued: 1933-1949
Price: $180 £120

DANCING FIGURE HN311
Designer: Unknown
Height: 17¾in., 45.0cm.
Issued: 1918-1938
Price: $2250 £1500

DANCING YEARS HN2235
Designer: M. Davies
Height: 6¾in., 17.2cm.
Issued: 1965-1971
Price: $180 £120

DANDY HN753
Designer: L. Harradine
Height: 6¾in., 17.2cm.
Issued: 1925-1938
Price: $450 £300

DAPHNE HN2268
Designer: M. Davies
Height: 8¼in., 21.0cm.
Issued: 1963-1975
Price: $120 £80

DARBY HN1427
Designer: L. Harradine
Height: 5½in., 14.0cm.
Issued: 1930-1949
Price: $195 £130

DAINTY MAY M73

DAISY HN1575

DAMARIS HN2079

"DANCING EYES AND
SUNNY HAIR" HN1543

DANCING YEARS HN2235

DARBY HN1427

133

DARBY HN2024
Designer: L. Harradine
Height: 5¾in., 14.6cm.
Issued: 1949-1959
Price: $195 £130

DARLING (Style one) HN1
Designer: C. Vyse
Height: 7¾in., 19.5cm.
Issued: 1913-1928
Price: $450 £300

DARLING (Style one) HN1319
Designer: C. Vyse
Height: 7½in., 19.1cm.
Issued: 1929-1959
Colour variation
Price: $97 £65

DARLING (Style one) HN1371
Designer: C. Vyse
Height: 7½in., 19.1cm.
Issued: 1930-1938
Colour variation
Price: $255 £170

DARLING (Style one) HN1372
Designer: C. Vyse
Height: 7¾in., 19.7cm.
Issued: 1930-1938
Colour variation
Price: $225 £150

DARLING (Style two) HN1985
Designer: C. Vyse
Height: 5¼in., 13.3cm.
Issued: 1946-
Price: $51 £21

DAVID COPPERFIELD M88
Designer: L. Harradine
Height: 4¼in., 10.8cm.
Issued: 1949-1983
Price: $30 £20

DAWN HN1858
Designer: L. Harradine
Height: 10in., 25.4cm.
Issued: 1938-?
Price: $750 £500

DAWN HN1858A
Designer: L. Harradine
Height: 9¾in., 24.7cm.
Issued: ??-1949
Colour variation
Price: $750 £500

DAYDREAMS HN1731
Designer: L. Harradine
Height: 5¾in., 14.6cm.
Issued: 1935-
Price: $157 £63

DAYDREAMS HN1732
Designer: L. Harradine
Height: 5½in., 14.0cm.
Issued: 1935-1949
Colour variation
Price: $165 £110

DARLING (Style one) HN1

DARLING (Style one) HN1372

DARLING (Style two) HN1985

DAVID COPPERFIELD M88

DAWN HN1858

DAYDREAMS HN1731

134

FIGURES

DAYDREAMS HN1944
Designer: L. Harradine
Height: 5½in., 14.0cm.
Issued: 1940-1949
　　　　 Colour variation
Price: $165 £110

DEAUVILLE HN2344
Designer: P. Davies
Height: 8¼in., 20.9cm.
Issued: 1982 in a limited
　　　　 edition of 1500
Price: $225 £150

DEBBIE HN2385
Designer: M. Davies
Height: 5½in., 14.0cm.
Issued: 1969-1982
Price: $40 £27

DEBBIE HN2400
Designer: P. Davies
Height: 6in., 15cm.
Issued: 1983-
Price: $87 £35

DEBUTANTE HN2210
Designer: M. Davies
Height: 5in., 12.7cm.
Issued: 1963-1967
Price: $180 £120

DEIDRE HN2020
Designer: L. Harradine
Height: 7in., 17.8cm.
Issued: 1949-1955
Price: $217 £145

DELICIA HN1662
Designer: L. Harradine
Height: 5¾in., 14.6cm.
Issued: 1934-1938
Price: $390 £260

DELICIA HN1663
Designer: L. Harradine
Height: 5¾in., 14.6cm.
Issued: 1934-1938
　　　　 Colour variation
Price: $337 £225

DELICIA HN1681
Designer: L. Harradine
Height: 5¾in., 14.6cm.
Issued: 1935-1938
　　　　 Colour variation
Price: $337 £225

DELIGHT HN1772
Designer: L. Harradine
Height: 7in., 17.8cm.
Issued: 1936-1967
Price: $120 £80

DELIGHT HN1773
Designer: L. Harradine
Height: 6¾in., 17.2cm.
Issued: 1936-1949
　　　　 Colour variation
Price: $165 £110

DAYDREAMS HN1944

DEAUVILLE HN2344

DEBBIE HN2385

DEBUTANTE HN2210

DELICIA HN1662

DELIGHT HN1773

DELPHINE HN2136
Designer: M. Davies
Height: 7¼in., 18.4cm.
Issued: 1954-1967
Price: $127 £85

DENISE HN2273
Designer: M. Davies
Height: 7in., 17.8cm.
Issued: 1964-1971
Price: $165 £110

DENISE M34
Designer: Unknown
Height: 4½in., 11.4cm.
Issued: 1933-1945
Price: $240 £160

DENISE M35
Designer: Unknown
Height: 4½in., 11.4cm.
Issued: 1933-1945
Colour variation
Price: $240 £160

DELPHINE HN2136

DENISE HN2273

DERRICK HN1398
Designer: L. Harradine
Height: 8in., 20.3cm.
Issued: 1930-1938
Price: $375 £250

DESPAIR HN596
Designer: Unknown
Height: 4½in., 11.4cm.
Issued: 1924-1938
Price: $450 £300

DETECTIVE HN2359
Designer: E. J. Griffiths
Height: 9¼in., 23.5cm.
Issued: 1977-1983
Price: $75 £50

DIANA HN1716
Designer: L. Harradine
Height: 5¾in., 14.6cm.
Issued: 1935-1949
Price: $90 £60

DIANA HN1717
Designer: L. Harradine
Height: 5¾in., 14.6cm.
Issued: 1935-1949
Colour variation
Price: $90 £60

DIANA HN1986
Designer: L. Harradine
Height: 5¾in., 14.6cm.
Issued: 1946-1975
Colour variation
Price: $45 £30

DENISE M34

DERRICK HN1398

DICK SWIVELLER M90
Designer: L. Harradine
Height: 4¼in., 10.8cm.
Issued: 1949-1982
Price: $30 £20

DIGGER (Australian) HN322
Designer: E. W. Light
Height: 11¼in., 28.5cm.
Issued: 1918-1938
Price: $525 £350

DIANA HN1717

DICK SWIVELLER M90

DIGGER (Australian) HN353
Designer: E. W. Light
Height: 11¼in., 28.5cm.
Issued: 1919-1938
Price: $525 £350

DIGGER (New Zealand) HN321
Designer: E. W. Light
Height: 11¼in., 28.5cm.
Issued: 1918-1938
Price: $525 £350

DILIGENT SCHOLAR HN26
Designer: W. White
Height: 7in., 17.8cm.
Issued: 1913-1938
Price: $1200 £800

DIMITY HN2169
Designer: L. Harradine
Height: 5¾in., 14.6cm.
Issued: 1956-1959
Price: $195 £130

DINKY DO HN1678
Designer: L. Harradine
Height: 4¾in., 12.0cm.
Issued: 1934-
Colour variation
Price: $69 £28

DINKY DO HN2120
Designer: L. Harradine
Height: 4¾in., 12.0cm.
Issued: 1983
Price: $69 £28

"DO YOU WONDER ..."
HN1544
Designer: Unknown
Height: 5in., 12.7cm.
Issued: 1933-1949
Price: $180 £120

DOCTOR HN2858
Designer: W. K. Harper
Height: 7½in., 19.1cm.
Issued: 1979-
Price: $237 £95

DOLLY HN355
Designer: C. J. Noke
Height: 7¼in., 18.4cm.
Issued: 1919-1938
Price: $1050 £700

DOLLY VARDON HN1514
Designer: L. Harradine
Height: 8½in., 21.6cm.
Issued: 1932-1938
Price: $525 £350

DOLLY VARDON HN1515
Designer: L. Harradine
Height: 8½in., 21.6cm.
Issued: 1932-1949
Price: $412 £275

DORCAS HN1490
Designer: L. Harradine
Height: 7in., 17.8cm.
Issued: 1932-1938
Price: $225 £150

DIGGER (New Zealand) HN321

DILIGENT SCHOLAR HN26

DIMITY HN2169

DINKY DO HN1678

DOCTOR HN2858

DOLLY VARDON HN1514

FIGURES

DORCAS HN1491
Designer: L. Harradine
Height: 6¾in., 17.2cm.
Issued: 1932-1938
Price: $225 £150

DORCAS HN1558
Designer: L. Harradine
Height: 6¾in., 17.2cm.
Issued: 1933-1952
Colour variation
Price: $135 £90

DOREEN HN1363
Designer: L. Harradine
Height: 5¼in., 13.3cm.
Issued: 1929-1938
Price: $562 £375

DOREEN HN1389
Designer: L. Harradine
Height: 5¼in., 13.3cm.
Issued: 1930-1938
Colour variation
Price: $562 £375

DOREEN HN1390
Designer: L. Harradine
Height: 5¾in., 14.6cm.
Issued: 1929-1938
Colour variation
Price: $562 £375

DORIS KEENE as CAVALLINI
(Style one) HN90
Designer: C. J. Noke
Height: 11in., 27.9cm.
Issued: 1918-1936
Price: $1500 £1000

DORIS KEENE as CAVALLINI
(Style one) HN467
Designer: C. J. Noke
Height: 11in., 27.9cm.
Issued: 1921-1936
Colour variation
Price: $1500 £1000

DORIS KEENE as CAVALLINI
(Style two) HN96
Designer: C. J. Noke
Height: 10¾in., 27.8cm.
Issued: 1918-1938
Price: $1500 £1000

DORIS KEENE as CAVALLINI
(Style two) HN345
Designer: C. J. Noke
Height: 10½in., 26.6cm.
Issued: 1919-1949
Colour variation
Price: $1500 £1000

DOUBLE JESTER HN365
Designer: C. J. Noke
Height: Unknown
Issued: 1920-1938
Price: $2550 £1700

DREAMLAND HN1473
Designer: L. Harradine
Height: 4¾in., 12.0cm.
Issued: 1931-1938
Price: $1500 £1000

DORCAS HN1491

DORCAS HN1558

DOREEN HN1390

DORIS KEENE as CAVALLINI
(Style one) HN90

DORIS KEENE as CAVALLINI
(Style two) HN96

DREAMLAND HN1473

138

DREAMLAND HN1481
Designer: L. Harradine
Height: 4¾in., 12.0cm.
Issued: 1931-1938
Colour variation
Price: $1350 £900

DREAM WEAVER HN2283
Designer: M. Nicholl
Height: 8¼in., 21.0cm.
Issued: 1972-1976
Price: $97 £65

DRESSING UP HN2964
Designer: P. Parsons
Height: 7½in., 19cm.
Issued: 1982-
Price: $63 £42

DRUMMER BOY HN2679
Designer: M. Nicholl
Height: 8½in., 21.6cm.
Issued: 1976-1982
Price: $112 £75

DRYAD OF THE PINES HN1869
Designer: R. Garbe
Height: 23in., 58.4cm.
Issued: 1938-1949
Price: $1800 £1200

DULCIE HN2305
Designer: M. Davies
Height: 7¼in., 18.4cm.
Issued: 1981-1984
Price: $75 £50

DULCIMER HN2798
Designer: M. Davies
Height: 6½in., 16.5cm.
Issued: 1975 in a limited
edition of 750
Price: $300 £200

DULCINEA HN1343
Designer: L. Harradine
Height: 5½in., 14.0cm.
Issued: 1929-1938
Price: $1350 £900

DULCINEA HN1419
Designer: L. Harradine
Height: 5½in., 14.0cm.
Issued: 1930-1938
Colour variation
Price: $1350 £900

DUNCE HN6
Designer: C. J. Noke
Height: 10½in., 26.6cm.
Issued: 1913-1938
Price: $1350 £900

DUNCE HN310
Designer: C. J. Noke
Height: 10½in., 26.7cm.
Issued: 1918-1938
Colour variation
Price: $1350 £900

DREAMLAND HN1481

DREAM WEAVER HN2283

DULCIE HN2305

DRUMMER BOY HN2679

DULCIMER HN2798

DULCINEA HN1343

139

DUNCE HN357
Designer: C. J. Noke
Height: 10½in., 26.7cm.
Issued: 1919-1938
Colour variation
Price: $1350 £900

E

EASTER DAY HN1976
Designer: M. Davies
Height: 7¼in., 18.4cm.
Issued: 1945-1951
Price: $330 £220

EASTER DAY HN2039
Designer: M. Davies
Height: 7¼in., 18.4cm.
Issued: 1949-1969
Colour variation
Price: $210 £140

EDITH HN2957
Designer: P. Parsons
Height: 5¾in., 14.5cm.
Issued: 1982-1985
Price: $60 £40

ELAINE HN2791
Designer: M. Davies
Height: 7½in., 19.1cm.
Issued: 1980
Price: $182 £73

ELEANOR OF PROVINCE HN2009
Designer: M. Davies
Height: 9½in., 24.1cm.
Issued: 1948-1953
Price: $412 £275

ELEANORE HN1753
Designer: L. Harradine
Height: 7in., 17.8cm.
Issued: 1936-1949
Price: $525 £350

ELEANORE HN1754
Designer: L. Harradine
Height: 7in., 17.8cm.
Issued: 1936-1949
Colour variation
Price: $525 £350

ELEGANCE HN2264
Designer: M. Davies
Height: 7¼in., 18.4cm.
Issued: 1961-1985
Price: $90 £60

ELFREDA HN2078
Designer: L. Harradine
Height: 7¼in., 18.4cm.
Issued: 1951-1955
Price: $412 £275

ELIZA HN2543
Designer: E. J. Griffiths
Height: 11¼in., 28.6cm.
Issued: 1974-1975
Price: $135 £90

EASTER DAY HN2039

ELAINE HN2791

ELEANOR OF PROVINCE HN2009

ELEANORE HN1754

ELEGANCE HN2264

ELFREDA HN2078

ELIZA HN2543A
Designer: E. J. Griffiths
Height: 11¾in., 29.8cm.
Issued: 1975-1977
Colour variation
Price: $135 £90

ELIZABETH HN2946
Designer: B. Franks
Height: 8in., 20cm.
Issued: 1982-
Price: $262 £105

ELIZABETH FRY HN2
Designer: C. Vyse
Height: 17in., 43.2cm.
Issued: 1913-1938
Price: $2250 £1500

ELIZABETH FRY HN2A
Designer: C. Vyse
Height: 17in., 43.2cm.
Issued: 1913-1938
Price: $2250 £1500

ELLEN HN3020
Designer: P. Parsons
Height: 3½in., 9cm.
Issued: 1984
Price: $107 £43

ELLEN TERRY as QUEEN
CATHERINE HN379
Designer: C. J. Noke
Height: 12½in., 31.7cm.
Issued: 1920-1949
Price: $825 £550

ELSIE MAYNARD HN639
Designer: C. J. Noke
Height: 7in., 17.8cm.
Issued: 1924-1949
Price: $450 £300

ELSIE MAYNARD HN2902
Designer: W. K. Harper
Height: 11¼in., 28.5cm.
Issued: 1982-
Price: $352 £235

ELYSE HN2429
Designer: M. Davies
Height: 5¾in., 14.6cm.
Issued: 1972-
Price: $182 £73

EMBROIDERING HN2855
Designer: W. K. Harper
Height: 7¼in., 18.4cm.
Issued: 1980-
Price: $237 £95

EMIR HN1604
Designer: C. J. Noke
Height: 7½in., 19.1cm.
Issued: 1933-1949
Price: $375 £250

EMIR HN1605
Designer: C. J. Noke
Height: 7¼in., 18.4cm.
Issued: 1933-1949
Price: $375 £250
(Also called Ibrahim HN2095)

ELIZA HN2543A

ELIZABETH FRY HN2

EMBROIDERING HN2855

ELIZABETH HN2946

ELSIE MAYNARD HN639

EMIR HN1605

141

EMMA HN2834
Designer: M. Davies
Height: 5¾in., 14.6cm.
Issued: 1977-1982
Price: $42 £28

ENCHANTMENT HN2178
Designer: M. Davies
Height: 7½in., 19.1cm.
Issued: 1957-1982
Price: $75 £50

ERMINE COAT HN1981
Designer: L. Harradine
Height: 6¾in., 17.2cm.
Issued: 1945-1967
Price: $150 £100

ERMINE MUFF HN54
Designer: C. J. Noke
Height: 8½in., 21.6cm.
Issued: 1916-1938
Price: $675 £450

ERMINE MUFF HN332
Designer: C. J. Noke
Height: 8½in., 21.6cm.
Issued: 1918-1938
        Colour variation
Price: $675 £450

ERMINE MUFF HN671
Designer: C. J. Noke
Height: 8½in., 21.6cm.
Issued: 1924-1938
        Colour variation
Price: $675 £450

ERMINIE M40
Designer: Unknown
Height: 4in., 10.1cm.
Issued: 1933-1945
Price: $255 £170

ESMERALDA HN2168
Designer: M. Davies
Height: 5½in., 14.0cm.
Issued: 1956-1959
Price: $180 £120

ESTELLE HN1566
Designer: L. Harradine
Height: 8in., 20.3cm
Issued: 1933-1938
Price: $562 £375

ESTELLE HN1802
Designer: L. Harradine
Height: 8in., 20.3cm.
Issued: 1937-1949
        Colour variation
Price: $450 £300

EUGENE HN1520
Designer: L. Harradine
Height: 5¾in., 14.6cm.
Issued: 1932-1938
Price: $412 £275

EUGENE HN1521
Designer: L. Harradine
Height: 5in., 12.7cm.
Issued: 1932-1938
        Colour variation
Price: $412 £275

EMMA HN2834

ERMINE MUFF HN54

ERMINIE M40

ESMERALDA HN2168

ESTELLE HN1802

EUGENE HN1520

FIGURES

**EUROPA AND THE BULL
HN95**
Designer: H. Tittensor
Height: 9¾in., 24.7cm.
Issued: 1918-1938
Price: $3000 £2000

**EUROPA AND THE BULL
HN2828**
Designer: R. Jefferson
Height: 10½in., 26.5cm.
Issued: 1985-
Price: $2550 £1700

EVE HN2466
Designer: P. Davies
Height: 9¼in., 23.5cm.
Issued: 1984
Price: $675 £450

EVELYN HN1622
Designer: L. Harradine
Height: 6¼in., 15.9cm.
Issued: 1934-1949
Price: $450 £300

EVELYN HN1637
Designer: L. Harradine
Height: 6in., 15.2cm.
Issued: 1934-1938
Colour variation
Price: $450 £300

EVENTIDE HN2814
Designer: W. K. Harper
Height: 7¾in., 19.7cm.
Issued: 1977-
Price: $172 £69

F

FAGIN HN534
Designer: L. Harradine
Height: 4in., 10.1cm.
Issued: 1922-1932
Price: $45 £30

FAGIN M49
Designer: L. Harradine
Height: 4in., 10.1cm.
Issued: 1932-1983
Price: $30 £20

FAIR LADY HN2193
Designer: M. Davies
Height: 7¼in., 18.4cm.
Issued: 1963-
Price: $157 £63

FAIR LADY HN2832
Designer: M. Davies
Height: 7¼in., 18.4cm.
Issued: 1977-
Colour variation
Price: $157 £63

FAIR LADY HN2835
Designer: M. Davies
Height: 7¼in., 18.4cm.
Issued: 1977
Colour variation
Price: $157 £63

EUROPA AND THE BULL HN95

EVELYN HN1622

EVENTIDE HN2814

FAGIN HN534

FAIR LADY HN2193

FAIR LADY HN2832

FAIR MAIDEN HN2211
Designer: M. Davies
Height: 5¼in., 13.3cm.
Issued: 1967
Price: $102 £41

FAIR MAIDEN HN2434
Designer: P. Davies
Height: 5¼in., 13.3cm.
Issued: 1983-
Colour variation
Price: $102 £41

FAIRY (Style one) HN1324
Designer: L. Harradine
Height: Unknown
Issued: 1929-1938
Price: $375 £250

FAIRY (Style two) HN1374
Designer: L. Harradine
Height: 4in., 10.1cm.
Issued: 1930-1938
Price: $375 £250

FAIRY (Style two) HN1380
Designer: L. Harradine
Height: 4in., 10.1cm.
Issued: 1930-1938
Colour variation
Price: $375 £250

FAIRY (Style two) HN1532
Designer: L. Harradine
Height: 4in., 10.1cm.
Issued: 1932-1938
Price: $412 £275

FAIRY (Style three) HN1375
Designer: L. Harradine
Height: 3in., 7.6cm.
Issued: 1930-1938
Price: $375 £250

FAIRY (Style three) HN1395
Designer: L. Harradine
Height: 3in., 7.6cm.
Issued: 1930-1938
Colour variation
Price: $375 £250

FAIRY (Style three) HN1533
Designer: L. Harradine
Height: 3in., 7.6cm.
Issued: 1932-1938
Price: $412 £275

FAIRY (Style four) HN1376
Designer: L. Harradine
Height: 2½in., 6.3cm.
Issued: 1930-1938
Price: $375 £250

FAIRY (Style four) HN1536
Designer: L. Harradine
Height: 2½in., 6.3cm.
Issued: 1932-1938
Price: $412 £275

FAIRY (Style five) HN1378
Designer: L. Harradine
Height: 2½in., 6.3cm.
Issued: 1930-1938
Price: $375 £250

FAIR MAIDEN HN2211

FAIRY (Style one) HN1324

FAIRY (Style two) HN1380

FAIRY (Style three) HN1395

FAIRY (Style four) HN1376

FAIRY (Style five) HN1378

FAIRY (Style five) HN1396
Designer: L. Harradine
Height: 2½in., 6.3cm.
Issued: 1930-1938
Colour variation
Price: $375 £250

FAIRY (Style five) HN1535
Designer: L. Harradine
Height: 2½in., 6.3cm.
Issued: 1932-1938
Colour variation
Price: $412 £275

FAIRY (Style six) HN1379
Designer: L. Harradine
Height: 2½in., 6.3cm
Issued: 1930-1938
Price: $375 £250

FAIRY (Style six) HN1394
Designer: L. Harradine
Height: 2½in., 6.3cm.
Issued: 1930-1938
Colour variation
Price: $375 £250

FAIRY (Style six) HN1534
Designer: L. Harradine
Height: 2½in., 6.3cm.
Issued: 1932-1938
Price: $412 £275

FAIRY (Style seven) HN1393
Designer: L. Harradine
Height: 2½in., 6.3cm.
Issued: 1930-1938
Price: $375 £250

FAIRY SPELL HN2979
Designer: A. Hughes
Height: 5¼in., 13cm.
Issued: 1983-
Price: $92 £37

FALSTAFF (Style one) HN571
Designer: C. J. Noke
Height: 7in., 17.8cm.
Issued: 1923-1938
Price: $375 £250

FALSTAFF (Style one) HN575
Designer: C.J. Noke
Height: 7in., 17.8cm.
Issued: 1923-1938
Price: $375 £250

FALSTAFF (Style one) HN608
Designer: C.J. Noke
Height: 7in., 17.8cm.
Issued: 1924-1938
Colour variation
Price: $375 £250

FALSTAFF (Style one) HN609
Designer: C. J. Noke
Height: 7in., 17.8cm.
Issued: 1924-1938
Colour variation
Price: $375 £250

FALSTAFF (Style one) HN571

FALSTAFF (Style one) HN 619
Designer: C. J. Noke
Height: 7in., 17.8cm.
Issued: 1924-1938
Colour variation
Price: $375 £250

FALSTAFF (Style one) HN638
Designer: C. J. Noke
Height: 7in., 17.8cm.
Issued: 1924-1938
Colour variation
Price: $375 £250

FALSTAFF (Style one) HN1216
Designer: C. J. Noke
Height: 7in., 17.8cm.
Issued: 1926-1949
Colour variation
Price: $262 £175

FALSTAFF (Style one) HN1606
Designer: C. J. Noke
Height: 7in., 17.8cm.
Issued: 1933-1949
Colour variation
Price: $262 £175

FALSTAFF (Style two) HN618
Designer: C. J. Noke
Height: 7in., 17.8cm.
Issued: 1924-1938
Price: $262 £175

FALSTAFF (Style two) HN2054
Designer: C. J. Noke
Height: 7in., 17.8cm.
Issued: 1950-
Colour variation
Price: $157 £63

FAMILY HN2720 (White)
Designer: E. Griffiths
Height: 12in., 30.5cm.
Issued: 1981
Price: $150 £60

FAMILY HN2721 (Black)
Designer: E. Griffiths
Height: 12in., 30.5cm.
Issued: 1981
Price: $150 £60

FAMILY ALBUM HN2321
Designer: M. Nicholl
Height: 6¼in., 15.9cm.
Issued: 1966-1973
Price: $195 £130

FARAWAY HN2133
Designer: M. Davies
Height: 2½in., 6.3cm.
Issued: 1958-1962
Price: $240 £160

FARMER'S BOY HN2520
Designer: W. M. Chance
Height: 8½in., 21.6cm.
Issued: 1938-1960
Price: $900 £600

FARMER'S WIFE HN2069
Designer: L. Harradine
Height: 9in., 22.9cm.
Issued: 1951-1955
Price: $255 £170

FALSTAFF (Style one) HN1606

FALSTAFF (Style two) HN618

FAMILY HN2721 (Black)

FAMILY ALBUM HN2321

FARAWAY HN2133

FARMER'S BOY HN2520

FAT BOY (Style one) HN530
Designer: L. Harradine
Height: 3½in., 8.9cm.
Issued: 1922-1932
Price: $45 £30

FAT BOY (Style two) HN555
Designer: L. Harradine
Height: 7in., 17.8cm.
Issued: 1923-1939
Price: $330 £220

FAT BOY (Style two) HN1893
Designer: L. Harradine
Height: 7in., 17.8cm.
Issued: 1938-1952
          Colour variation
Price: $300 £200

FAT BOY (Style three) HN2096
Designer: L. Harradine
Height: 7¼in., 18.4cm.
Issued: 1952-1967
Price: $180 £120

FAT BOY M44
Designer: L. Harradine
Height: 4¼in., 10.8cm.
Issued: 1932-1982
Price: $30 £20

FAVOURITE HN2249
Designer: M. Nicholl
Height: 7¾in., 19.7cm.
Issued: 1960-
Price: $172 £69

FIDDLER HN2171
Designer: M. Nicholl
Height: 8¾in., 22.2cm.
Issued: 1956-1962
Price: $375 £250

FIONA (Style one) HN1924
Designer: L. Harradine
Height: 5¾in., 14.6cm.
Issued: 1940-1949
Price: $450 £300

FIONA (Style one) HN1925
Designer: L. Harradine
Height: 5¾in., 14.6cm.
Issued: 1940-1949
          Colour variation
Price: $450 £300

FIONA (Style one) HN1933
Designer: L. Harradine
Height: 5¾in., 14.6cm.
Issued: 1940-1949
          Colour variation
Price: $450 £300

FIONA (Style two) HN2694
Designer: M. Davies
Height: 7½in., 19.1cm.
Issued: 1974-1980
Price: $75 £50

FIRST DANCE HN2803
Designer: M. Davies
Height: 7¼in., 18.4cm.
Issued: 1977-
Price: $172 £69

FAT BOY (Style one) HN530

FAT BOY M44

FAVOURITE HN2249

FIDDLER HN2171

FIONA (Style one) HN1924

FIONA (Style two) HN2694

FIRST STEPS HN2242
Designer: M. Davies
Height: 6½in., 16.5cm.
Issued: 1959-1965
Price: $240 £160

FIRST WALTZ HN2862
Designer: M. Davies
Height: 7¼in., 18.4cm.
Issued: 1979-1983
Price: $82 £55

FISHERWOMEN HN80
Designer: Unknown
Height: Unknown
Issued: 1917-1938
Price: $1800 £1200

FISHERWOMEN HN349
Designer: Unknown
Height: Unknown
Issued: 1919-1938
Colour variation
Price: $1800 £1200

FISHERWOMEN HN359
Designer: Unknown
Height: Unknown
Issued: 1919-1938
Colour variation
Price: $1800 £1200

FISHERWOMEN HN631
Designer: Unknown
Height: Unknown
Issued: 1924-1938
Colour variation
Price: $1800 £1200

FITZHERBERT, MRS HN2007
Designer: M. Davies
Height: 9¼in., 23.5cm.
Issued: 1948-1953
Price: $525 £350

FLEUR HN2368
Designer: J. Bromley
Height: 7¼in., 18.4cm.
Issued: 1968-
Price: $172 £69

FLEUR (Red) HN2369
Designer: J. Bromley
Height: 7¾in., 19.5cm.
Issued: 1983-
Colour variation
Price: $172 £69

FLEURETTE HN1587
Designer: L. Harradine
Height: 6½in., 16.5cm.
Issued: 1933-1949
Price: $262 £175

FLORA HN2349
Designer: M. Nicholl
Height: 7¾in., 19.7cm.
Issued: 1966-1973
Price: $120 £80

FLOUNCED SKIRT HN57A
Designer: E. W. Light
Height: 9¾in., 24.7cm.
Issued: 1916-1938
Price: $675 £450

FIRST STEPS HN2242

FIRST WALTZ HN2862

FITZHERBERT, MRS HN2007

FLEUR HN2368

FLEURETTE HN1587

FLOUNCED SKIRT HN57A

148

FLOUNCED SKIRT HN66
Designer: E. W. Light
Height: 9¾in., 24.7cm.
Issued: 1916-1938
Colour variation
Price: $675 £450

FLOUNCED SKIRT HN77
Designer: E. W. Light
Height: 9¾in., 24.7cm.
Issued: 1917-1938
Colour variation
Price: $675 £450

FLOUNCED SKIRT HN78
Designer: E. W. Light
Height: 9¾in., 24.7cm.
Issued: 1917-1938
Colour variation
Price: $675 £450

FLOUNCED SKIRT HN333
Designer: E. W. Light
Height: 9¾in., 24.7cm.
Issued: 1918-1938
Colour variation
Price: $675 £450

FLOWER SELLER HN789
Designer: L. Harradine
Height: 8¾in., 22.2cm.
Issued: 1926-1938
Price: $675 £450

FLOWER SELLER'S CHILDREN HN525
Designer: L. Harradine
Height: 8¼in. 21.0cm.
Issued: 1921-1949
Price: $375 £250

FLOWER SELLER'S CHILDREN HN551
Designer: L. Harradine
Height: 8¼in. 21.0cm.
Issued: 1922-1949
Colour variation
Price: $375 £250

FLOWER SELLER'S CHILDREN HN1206
Designer: L. Harradine
Height: 8¼in. 21.0cm.
Issued: 1926-1949
Colour variation
Price: $375 £250

FLOWER SELLER'S CHILDREN HN1342
Designer: L. Harradine
Height: 8in., 20.3cm.
Issued: 1929-
Colour variation
Price: $397 £159

FLOWER SELLER'S CHILDREN HN1406
Designer: L. Harradine
Height: 8¼in., 21.0cm.
Issued: 1930-1938
Colour variation
Price: $525 £350

FLOUNCED SKIRT HN66

FLOUNCED SKIRT HN333

FLOWER SELLER HN789

FLOWER SELLER'S CHILDREN HN1206

FLOWER SELLER'S CHILDREN HN1342

FLOWER SELLER'S CHILDREN HN1406

FIGURES

FLUTE HN2483
Designer: M. Davies
Height: 6in., 15.2cm.
Issued: 1973 in a limited edition of 750
Price: $450 £300

FOAMING QUART HN2162
Designer: M. Davies
Height: 6in., 15.2cm.
Issued: 1955-
Price: $172 £69

FOLLY HN1335
Designer: L. Harradine
Height: 9in., 22.9cm.
Issued: 1929-1938
Price: $900 £600

FOLLY HN1750
Designer: L. Harradine
Height: 9½in., 24.1cm.
Issued: 1936-1949
Colour variation
Price: $675 £450

FORGET-ME-NOT HN1812
Designer: L. Harradine
Height: 6in., 15.2cm.
Issued: 1937-1949
Price: $195 £130

FORGET-ME-NOT HN1813
Designer: L. Harradine
Height: 6in., 15.2cm.
Issued: 1937-1949
Colour variation
Price: $195 £130

FORTUNE TELLER HN2159
Designer: L. Harradine
Height: 6½in., 16.5cm.
Issued: 1955-1967
Price: $262 £175

FORTY WINKS HN1974
Designer: H. Fenton
Height: 6¾in., 14.2cm.
Issued: 1945-1973
Price: $127 £85

FOUR O'CLOCK HN1760
Designer: L. Harradine
Height: 6in., 15.2cm.
Issued: 1936-1949
Price: $300 £200

FRAGRANCE HN2334
Designer: M. Davies
Height: 7¼in., 18.4cm.
Issued: 1966-
Price: $172 £69

FRANCINE HN2422
Designer: J. Bromley
Height: 5in., 12.7cm.
Issued: 1972-1980
Price: $52 £35

FRANGCON HN1720
Designer: L. Harradine
Height: 7½in., 19.1cm.
Issued: 1935-1949
Price: $375 £250

FLUTE HN2483

FOLLY HN1335

FOLLY HN1750

FORGET-ME-NOT HN1813

FOUR O'CLOCK HN1760

FRANCINE HN2422

FRANGÇON HN1721
Designer: L. Harradine
Height: 7¼in., 18.4cm.
Issued: 1935-1949
          Colour variation
Price: $375 £250

FRENCH HORN HN2795
Designer: M. Davies
Height: 6in., 15.2cm.
Issued: 1976 in a limited
          edition of 750
Price: $450 £300

FRENCH PEASANT HN2075
Designer: L. Harradine
Height: 9¼in., 23.5cm.
Issued: 1951-1955
Price: $300 £200

FRIAR TUCK HN2143
Designer: M. Davies
Height: 7½in., 19.1cm.
Issued: 1954-1965
Price: $300 £200

FRODO HN2912
Designer: H. Sales
Height: 4½in., 11.4cm.
Issued: 1979-1984
Price: $30 £20

FRUIT GATHERING HN449
Designer: L. Harradine
Height: 7¾in., 19.7cm.
Issued: 1921-1938
Price: $1125 £750

FRUIT GATHERING HN476
Designer: L. Harradine
Height: 7¾in., 19.7cm.
Issued: 1921-1938
          Colour variation
Price: $1125 £750

FRUIT GATHERING HN503
Designer: L. Harradine
Height: 7¾in., 19.7cm.
Issued: 1921-1938
          Colour variation
Price: $1125 £750

FRUIT GATHERING HN561
Designer: L. Harradine
Height: 7¾in., 19.7cm.
Issued: 1923-1938
          Colour variation
Price: $1125 £750

FRUIT GATHERING HN562
Designer: L. Harradine
Height: 7¾in., 19.7cm.
Issued: 1923-1938
          Colour variation
Price: $1125 £750

FRUIT GATHERING HN706
Designer: L. Harradine
Height: 7¼in., 18.4cm.
Issued: 1925-1938
          Colour variation
Price: $1125 £750

FRANGÇON HN1721

FRENCH HORN HN2795

FRENCH PEASANT HN2075

FRIAR TUCK HN2143

FRODO HN2912

FRUIT GATHERING HN562

151

FRUIT GATHERING HN707
Designer: L. Harradine
Height: 7¼in., 18.4cm.
Issued: 1925-1938
Colour variation
Price: $1125 £750

G

GAFFER HN2053
Designer: L. Harradine
Height: 7¾in., 19.7cm.
Issued: 1950-1959
Price: $195 £130

GAINSBOROUGH HAT HN46
Designer: H. Tittensor
Height: 8¾in., 22.2cm.
Issued: 1915-1938
Price: $525 £350

GAINSBOROUGH HAT HN46A
Designer: H. Tittensor
Height: 8¾in., 22.2cm
Issued: 1915-1938
Colour variation
Price: $525 £350

GAINSBOROUGH HAT HN47
Designer: H. Tittensor
Height: 8¾in., 22.2cm.
Issued: 1915-1938
Colour variation
Price: $525 £350

GAINSBOROUGH HAT HN329
Designer: H. Tittensor
Height: 8¾in., 22.2cm.
Issued: 1918-1938
Colour variation
Price: $525 £350

GAINSBOROUGH HAT HN352
Designer: H. Tittensor
Height: 8¾in., 22.2cm.
Issued: 1919-1938
Colour variation
Price: $525 £350

GAINSBOROUGH HAT HN383
Designer: H. Tittensor
Height: 8¾in., 22.2cm.
Issued: 1920-1938
Colour variation
Price: $525 £350

GAINSBOROUGH HAT HN453
Designer: H. Tittensor
Height: 8¾in., 22.2cm.
Issued: 1921-1938
Colour variation
Price: $525 £350

GAINSBOROUGH HAT HN675
Designer: H. Tittensor
Height: 8¾in., 22.2cm.
Issued: 1924-1938
Colour variation
Price: $525 £350

FRUIT GATHERING HN707

GAFFER HN2053

GAINSBOROUGH HAT HN47

GAINSBOROUGH HAT HN352

GAINSBOROUGH HAT HN453

GAINSBOROUGH HAT HN675

GAINSBOROUGH HAT
HN705
Designer: H. Tittensor
Height: 9in., 22.9cm.
Issued: 1925-1938
Colour variation
Price: $525 £350

GALADRIEL HN2915
Designer: H. Sales
Height: 5½in., 14.0cm.
Issued: 1979-1984
Price: $30 £20

GAMEKEEPER HN2879
Designer: E. Griffiths
Height: 7in., 17.8cm.
Issued: 1984-
Price: $142 £57

GANDALF HN2911
Designer: H. Sales
Height: 7in., 17.8cm.
Issued: 1979-1984
Price: $30 £20

GAY MORNING HN2135
Designer: M. Davies
Height: 7in., 17.8cm.
Issued: 1954-1967
Price: $150 £100

GEISHA (Style one) HN354
Designer: H. Tittensor
Height: 10¾in., 27.3cm.
Issued: 1919-1938
Price: $862 £575

GEISHA (Style one) HN376
Designer: H. Tittensor
Height: 10¾in., 27.3cm.
Issued: 1920-1938
Colour variation
Price: $862 £575

GEISHA (Style one) HN387
Designer: H. Tittensor
Height: 10¾in., 27.3cm.
Issued: 1920-1938
Colour variation
Price: $862 £575

GIESHA (Style one) HN634
Designer: H. Tittensor
Height: 10¾in., 27.3cm.
Issued: 1924-1938
Colour variation
Price: $862 £575

GEISHA (Style one) HN741
Designer: H. Tittensor
Height: 10¾in., 27.3cm.
Issued: 1925-1938
Colour variation
Price: $862 £575

GEISHA (Style one) HN779
Designer: H. Tittensor
Height: 10¾in., 27.3cm.
Issued: 1926-1938
Colour variation
Price: $862 £575

GALADRIEL HN2915

GANDALF HN2911

GAY MORNING HN2135

GEISHA (Style one) HN354

GEISHA (Style one) HN634

GEISHA (Style one) HN779

GEISHA (Style one) HN1321
Designer: H. Tittensor
Height: 10¾in., 27.3cm.
Issued: 1929-1938
Colour variation
Price: $862 £575

GEISHA (Style one) HN1322
Designer: H. Tittensor
Height: 10¾in., 27.3cm.
Issued: 1929-1938
Colour variation
Price: $862 £575

GEISHA (Style two) HN1223
Designer: C. J. Noke
Height: 6¾in., 17.2cm.
Issued: 1927-1938
Price: $600 £400

GEISHA (Style two) HN1234
Designer: C. J. Noke
Height: 6¾in., 17.2cm.
Issued: 1927-1938
Colur variation
Price: $600 £400

GEISHA (Style two) HN1292
Designer: C. J. Noke
Height: 6¾in., 17.2cm.
Issued: 1928-1938
Colour variation
Price: $600 £400

GEISHA (Style two) HN1310
Designer: C. J. Noke
Height: 6¾in., 17.2cm.
Issued: 1929-1938
Colour variation
Price: $600 £400

GENEVIEVE HN1962
Designer: L. Harradine
Height: 7in., 17.8cm.
Issued: 1941-1975
Price: $120 £80

GENIE HN2989
Designer: R. Tabbenor
Height: 9¾in., 24.5cm.
Issued: 1983-
Price: $147 £59

**GENTLEMAN FROM
WILLIAMSBURG HN2227**
Designer: M. Davies
Height: 6¼in., 15.9cm.
Issued: 1960-
Price: $90 £60

GENTLEWOMAN HN1632
Designer: L. Harradine
Height: 7½in., 19.1cm.
Issued: 1934-1949
Price: $275 £190

**GEORGE WASHINGTON
AT PRAYER HN2861**
Designer: L. Ispanky
Height: 12½in., 31.7cm.
Issued: 1977 in a limited
edition of 750
Price: $375 £250

GEISHA (Style two) HN1223

GEISHA (Style two) HN1292

GENEVIEVE HN1962

GENTLEMAN FROM
WILLIAMSBURG HN2227

GENTLEWOMAN HN1632

GEORGE WASHINGTON
AT PRAYER HN2861

FIGURES

GEORGIANA HN2093
Designer: M. Davies
Height: 8¼in., 21.0cm.
Issued: 1952-1955
Price: $375 £250

GEORGINA HN2377
Designer: M. Davies
Height: 5¾in., 14.6cm.
Issued: 1981-
Price: $107 £43

GERALDINE HN2348
Designer: M. Davies
Height: 7¼in., 18.4cm.
Issued: 1972-1976
Price: $75 £50

GILLIAN HN1670
Designer: L. Harradine
Height: 7¾in., 19.7cm.
Issued: 1934-1949
Price: $225 £150

GILLIAN HN1670A
Designer: L. Harradine
Height: 7¾in., 19.7cm.
Issued: Unknown
Colour variation
Price: $262 £175

GILLIAN HN3042
Designer: P. Parsons
Height: 8¼in., 21.0cm.
Issued: 1985-
Price: $147 £59

GIMLI HN2922
Designer: H. Sales
Height: 5½in., 14.0cm.
Issued: 1980-1984
Price: $30 £20

GIRL WITH YELLOW FROCK HN588
Designer: Unknown
Height: 6¼in., 15.9cm.
Issued: 1923-1938
Price: $1125 £750

GISELLE HN2139
Designer: M. Davies
Height: 6in., 15.2cm.
Issued: 1954-1969
Price: $180 £120

GISELLE, THE FOREST GLADE HN2140
Designer: M. Davies
Height: 7in., 17.8cm.
Issued: 1954-1965
Price: $180 £120

GLADYS HN1740
Designer: L. Harradine
Height: 5¼in., 13.3cm.
Issued: 1935-1949
Price: $450 £300

GLADYS HN1741
Designer: L. Harradine
Height: 5in., 12.7cm.
Issued: 1935-1938
Colour variation
Price: $450 £300

GEORGIANA HN2093

GEORGINA HN2377

GERALDINE HN2348

GILLIAN HN1670

GIRL WITH YELLOW FROCK HN588

GISELLE, THE FOREST GLADE HN2140

155

GLORIA HN1488
Designer: L. Harradine
Height: 7¼in., 18.4cm.
Issued: 1932-1938
Price: $412 £275

GLORIA HN1700
Designer: L. Harradine
Height: 7in., 17.8cm.
Issued: 1935-1938
        Colour variation
Price: $412 £275

GNOME HN319
Designer: H. Tittensor
Height: 6¼in., 15.9cm.
Issued: 1918-1938
Price: $375 £250

GNOME HN380
Designer: H. Tittensor
Height: 6¼in., 15.9cm.
Issued: 1920-1938
        Colour variation
Price: $375 £250

GNOME HN381
Designer: H. Tittensor
Height: 6¼in., 15.9cm.
Issued: 1920-1938
        Colour variation
Price: $375 £250

GOLDEN DAYS HN2274
Designer: M. Davies
Height: 3¾in., 9.5cm.
Issued: 1964-1973
Price: $67 £45

GOLLUM HN2913
Designer: H. Sales
Height: 3¼in., 8.3cm.
Issued: 1979-1984
Price: $30 £20

GOLLYWOG HN1979
Designer: L. Harradine
Height: 5¼in., 13.3cm.
Issued: 1945-1959
Price: $210 £140

GOLLYWOG HN2040
Designer: L. Harradine
Height: 5¼in., 13.3cm.
Issued: 1949-1959
        Colour variation
Price: $210 £140

GOOD CATCH HN2258
Designer: M. Nicholl
Height: 7¼in., 18.4cm.
Issued: 1966-
Price: $172 £69

GOOD FRIENDS HN2783
Designer: W. K. Harper
Height: 9in., 23cm.
Issued: 1985-
Price: $157 £63

GLORIA HN1488

GLORIA HN1700

GOLDEN DAYS HN2274

GOLLUM HN2913

GOLLYWOG HN1979

GOOD CATCH HN2258

GOOD KING WENCESLAS
HN2118
Designer: M. Davies
Height: 8½in., 21.6cm.
Issued: 1953-1976
Price: $187 £125

GOOD MORNING HN2671
Designer: M. Nicholl
Height: 8in., 20.3cm.
Issued: 1974-1976
Price: $82 £55

GOODY TWO SHOES
HN1889
Designer: L. Harradine
Height: 4¾in., 12.0cm.
Issued: 1938-1949
Price: $127 £85

GOODY TWO SHOES
HN1905
Designer: L. Harradine
Height: 4¾in., 12.0cm.
Issued: 1939-1949
           Colour variation
Price: $127 £85

GOODY TWO SHOES
HN2037
Designer: L. Harradine
Height: 5in., 12.7cm.
Issued: 1949-
           Colour variation
Price: $102 £41

GOODY TWO SHOES M80
Designer: L. Harradine
Height: 4in., 10.1cm.
Issued: 1939-1949
Price: $180 £120

GOODY TWO SHOES M81
Designer: L. Harradine
Height: 4in., 10.1cm.
Issued: 1939-1949
           Colour variation
Price: $180 £120

GOOSEGIRL HN425
Designer: L. Harradine
Height: Unknown
Issued: 1921-1938
Price: $1200 £800

GOOSEGIRL HN436
Designer: L. Harradine
Height: Unknown
Issued: 1921-1938
           Colour variation
Price: $1200 £800

GOOSEGIRL HN437
Designer: L. Harradine
Height: Unknown
Issued: 1921-1938
           Colour variation
Price: $1200 £800

GOOD KING WENCESLAS HN2118

FIGURES

GOOSEGIRL HN448
Designer: L. Harradine
Height: Unknown
Issued: 1921-1938
           Colour variation
Price: $1200 £800

GOOSEGIRL HN559
Designer: L. Harradine
Height: Unknown
Issued: 1923-1938
           Colour variation
Price: $1200 £800

GOOSEGIRL HN560
Designer; L. Harradine
Height: Unknown
Issued: 1923-1938
           Colour variation
Price: $1200 £800

GOSSIPS HN1426
Designer: L. Harradine
Height: 5¾in., 14.6cm.
Issued: 1930-1949
Price: $300 £200

GOSSIPS HN1429
Designer: L. Harradine
Height: 5¾in., 14.6cm.
Issued: 1930-1949
           Colour variation
Price: $300 £200

GOSSIPS HN2025
Designer: L. Harradine
Height: 5½in., 14.0cm.
Issued: 1949-1967
           Colour variation
Price: $195 £130

GRACE HN2318
Designer: M. Nicholl
Height: 7¾in., 19.7cm.
Issued: 1966-1980
Price: $82 £55

GRADUATE (The Female) HN3016
Designer: P. Parsons
Height: 8¾in., 22.0cm.
Issued: 1984
Price: $142 £57

GRADUATE (The Male) HN3017
Designer: P. Parsons
Height: 9¼in., 23.5cm.
Issued: 1984-
Price: $142 £57

GRAND MANNER HN2723
Designer: W. K. Harper
Height: 7¾in., 19.7cm.
Issued: 1975-1982
Price: $127 £85

GRANDMA HN2052
Designer: L. Harradine
Height: 6¾in., 17.2cm.
Issued: 1950-1959
Price: $187 £125

GOSSIPS HN1426

GOSSIPS HN1429

GOSSIPS HN2025

GRACE HN2318

GRAND MANNER HN2723

GRANDMA HN2052

FIGURES

GRANDMA HN2052A
Designer: L. Harradine
Height: 6¾in., 17.2cm.
Issued: Unknown
Colour variation
Price: $187 £125

GRANNY HN1804
Designer: L. Harradine
Height: 7in., 17.8cm.
Issued: 1937-1949
Price: $337 £225

GRANNY HN1832
Designer: L. Harradine
Height: 6¾in., 17.1cm.
Issued: 1937-1949
Colour variation
Price: $337 £225

GRANNY'S HERITAGE HN1873
Designer: L. Harradine
Height: 6¾in., 17.1cm.
Issued: 1938-1949
Price: $525 £350

GRANNY'S HERITAGE HN1874
Designer: L. Harradine
Height: 6¼in., 15.9cm.
Issued: 1938-1949
Colour variation
Price: $525 £350

GRANNY'S HERITAGE HN2031
Designer: L. Harradine
Height: 6¾in., 17.2cm.
Issued: 1949-1969
Colour variation
Price: $180 £120

GRANNY'S SHAWL HN1642
Designer: L. Harradine
Height: 5¾in., 14.6cm.
Issued: 1934-1949
Price: $150 £100

GRANNY'S SHAWL HN1647
Designer: L. Harradine
Height: 5¾in., 14.6cm.
Issued: 1934-1949
Colour variation
Price: $150 £100

GRETA HN1485
Designer: L. Harradine
Height: 5½in., 14.0cm.
Issued: 1931-1953
Price: $112 £75

GRETCHEN HN1397
Designer: L. Harradine
Height: 7¾in., 19.7cm.
Issued: 1930-1938
Price: $525 £350

GRETCHEN HN1562
Designer: L. Harradine
Height: 7¾in., 19.7cm.
Issued: 1933-1938
Colour variation
Price: $525 £350

GRANDMA HN2052A

GRANNY HN1804

GRANNY'S HERITAGE HN2031

GRANNY'S SHAWL HN1642

GRETA HN1485

GRETCHEN HN1397

159

FIGURES

GRIEF HN595
Designer: Unknown
Height: 2in., 5.1cm.
Issued: 1924-1938
Price: $562 £375

GRISELDA HN1993
Designer: L. Harradine
Height: 5¾in., 14.6cm.
Issued: 1947-1953
Price: $300 £200

GRIZEL HN1629
Designer: L. Harradine
Height: 6¾in., 17.2cm.
Issued: 1934-1938
Price: $412 £275

GROSSMITH'S TSANG IHANG HN582
Designer: Unknown
Height: 11½in., 29.2cm.
Issued: 1923-?
Price: $1125 £750

GUY FAWKES HN98
Designer: C. J. Noke
Height: 10½in., 26.7cm.
Issued: 1918-1949
Price: $975 £650

GUY FAWKES HN347
Designer: C. J. Noke
Height: 10½in., 26.7cm.
Issued: 1919-1938
Colour variation
Price: $975 £650

GUY FAWKES HN445
Designer: C. J. Nokes
Height: 10½in., 26.7cm.
Issued: 1921-1938
Colour variation
Price: $975 £650

GWENDOLEN HN1494
Designer: L. Harradine
Height: 6in., 15.2cm.
Issued: 1932-1938
Price: $330 £220

GWENDOLEN HN1503
Designer: L. Harradine
Height: 6in., 15.2cm.
Issued: 1932-1949
Colour variation
Price: $330 £220

GWENDOLEN HN1570
Designer: L. Harradine
Height: 6in., 15.2cm.
Issued: 1933-1949
Colour variation
Price: $330 £220

GWYNNETH HN1980
Designer: L. Harradine
Height: 7in., 17.8cm.
Issued: 1934-1952
Price: $262 £175

GRISELDA HN1993

GRIZEL HN1629

GROSSMITH'S TSANG IHANG HN582

GUY FAWKES HN347

GWENDOLEN HN1503

GWYNNETH HN1980

160

GYPSY DANCE (Style one)
HN2157
Designer: M. Davies
Height: 7in., 17.8cm.
Issued: 1955-1957
Price: $195 £130

GYPSY DANCE (Style two)
HN2230
Designer: M. Davies
Height: 7in., 17.8cm.
Issued: 1959-1971
Price: $165 £110

GYPSY GIRL WITH
FLOWERS HN1302
Designer: Unknown
Height: Unknown
Issued: 1928-1938
Price: $1275 £850

GYPSY WOMAN WITH
CHILD HN1301
Designer: Unknown
Height: Unknown
Issued: 1928-1938
Price: $1275 £850

H

"HAPPY JOY BABY BOY . . ."
HN1541
Designer: Unknown
Height: 6¼in., 15.9cm.
Issued: 1933-1949
Price: $210 £140

HARLEQUIN HN2186
Designer: M. Davies
Height: 7¼in., 18.4cm.
Issued: 1957-1969
Price: $150 £100

HARLEQUIN HN2737
Designer: D. Tootle
Height: 12½in., 31.0cm.
Issued: 1982-
Price: $877 £355

HARLEQUINADE HN585
Designer: L. Harradine
Height: 6½in., 16.5cm.
Issued: 1923-1938
Price: $750 £500

HARLEQUINADE HN635
Designer: L. Harradine
Height: 6½in., 16.5cm.
Issued: 1924-1938
    Colour variation
Price: $840 £560

HARLEQUINADE HN711
Designer: L. Harradine
Height: 6½in., 16.5cm.
Issued: 1925-1938
    Colour variation
Price: $750 £500

HARLEQUINADE HN780
Designer: L. Harradine
Height: 6½in., 16.5cm.
Issued: 1926-1939
    Colour variation
Price: $750 £500

GYPSY DANCE (Style one) HN2157

GYPSY DANCE (Style two) HN2230

"HAPPY JOY BABY BOY . . ."
HN1541

HARLEQUIN HN2186

HARLEQUINADE HN635

HARLEQUINADE HN780

161

HARLEQUINADE MASKED
HN768
Designer: L. Harradine
Height: 6½in., 16.5cm.
Issued: 1925-1938
Price: $1125 £750

HARLEQUINADE MASKED
HN769
Designer: L. Harradine
Height: 6½in., 16.5cm.
Issued: 1925-1938
      Colour variation
Price: $1125 £750

HARLEQUINADE MASKED
HN1274
Designer: L. Harradine
Height: 6½in., 16.5cm.
Issued: 1928-1938
      Colour variation
Price: $1125 £750

HARLEQUINADE MASKED
HN1304
Designer: L. Harradine
Height: 6½in., 16.5cm.
Issued: 1928-1938
      Colour variation
Price: $1125 £750

HARMONY HN2824
Designer: R. Jefferson
Height: 8in., 20.3cm.
Issued: 1978-1984
Price: $82 £55

HARP HN2482
Designer: M. Davies
Height: 8¾in., 22.2cm.
Issued: 1973 in a limited
      edition of 750
Price: $450 £300

HAZEL HN1796
Designer: M. Davies
Height: 5¼in., 13.3cm.
Issued: 1936-1949
Price: $180 £120

HAZEL HN1797
Designer: L. Harradine
Height: 5¼in., 13.3cm.
Issued: 1936-1949
      Colour variation
Price: $180 £120

HE LOVES ME HN2046
Designer: L. Harradine
Height: 5½in., 14.0cm.
Issued: 1949-1962
Price: $112 £75

HEART TO HEART HN2276
Designer: M. Davies
Height: 5½in., 14.0cm.
Issued: 1961-1971
Price: $195 £130

HEATHER HN2956
Designer: P. Parsons
Height: 6in., 15.0cm.
Issued: 1982-
Price: $117 £47

HARLEQUINADE MASKED HN1274

HARMONY HN2824

HARP HN2482

HAZEL HN1796

HE LOVES ME HN2046

HEART TO HEART HN2276

FIGURES

HEIDI HN2975
Designer: A. Hughes
Height: 4½in., 11.5cm.
Issued: 1983-
Price: $39 £26

HELEN HN1508
Designer: L. Harradine
Height: 8in., 20.3cm.
Issued: 1932-1938
Price: $442 £295

HELEN HN1509
Designer: L. Harradine
Height: 8in., 20.3cm.
Issued: 1932-1938
        Colour variation
Price: $442 £295

HELEN HN1572
Designer: L. Harradine
Height: 8in., 20.3cm.
Issued: 1933-1938
        Colour variation
Price: $442 £295

HELEN HN2994
Designer: R. Tabbenor
Height: 5in., 12.5cm.
Issued: 1985-
Price: $65 £26

HELEN OF TROY HN2387
Designer: P. Davies
Height: 9¼in., 23.4cm.
Issued: 1981 in a limited
        edition of 750
Price: $750 £500

HELMSMAN HN2499
Designer: M. Nicholl
Height: 9in., 22.9cm.
Issued: 1974-
Price: $222 £89

HENRIETTA MARIA HN2005
Designer: M. Davies
Height: 9½in., 24.1cm.
Issued: 1948-1953
Price: $525 £350

HENRY VIII (Style one) HN370
Designer: C. J. Noke
Height: Unknown
Issued: 1920-1938
Price: $1500 £1000

HENRY VIII (Style one) HN673
Designer: C. J. Noke
Height: Unknown
Issued: 1924-1938
        Colour variation
Price: $1500 £1000

HENRY VIII (Style two) HN1792
Designer: C. J. Noke
Height: 11½in., 29.2cm.
Issued: 1933 in a limited
        edition of 200
Price: $1312 £875

HELEN HN1508

HELEN HN1509

HELEN OF TROY HN2387

HELMSMAN HN2499

HENRIETTA MARIA HN2005

HENRY VIII (Style two) HN1792

FIGURES

HENRY IRVING AS CARDINAL WOLSEY HN344
Designer: C. J. Noke
Height: 13¼in., 33.7cm.
Issued: 1919-1949
Price: $900 £600

HENRY LYTTON AS JACK POINT HN610
Designer: C. J. Noke
Height: 6½in., 16.5cm.
Issued: 1924-1949
Price: $600 £400

HER LADYSHIP HN1977
Designer: L. Harradine
Height: 7¼in., 18.4cm.
Issued: 1945-1959
Price: $240 £160

HER MAJESTY QUEEN ELIZABETH II HN2878
Designer: E. Griffiths
Height: 10½in., 27.0cm.
Issued: 1983-
Price: $562 £225

HER MAJESTY QUEEN ELIZABETH, THE QUEEN MOTHER HN2882
Designer: Unknown
Height: 11¾in., 29.8cm.
Issued: 1980 in a limited edition of 1500
Price: $525 £350

"HERE A LITTLE CHILD I STAND" HN1546
Designer: Unknown
Height: 6¼in., 15.9cm.
Issued: 1933-1949
Price: $180 £120

HERMINIA HN1644
Designer: L. Harradine
Height; 6½in., 16.5cm.
Issued: 1934-1938
Price: $525 £350

HERMINIA HN1646
Designer: L. Harradine
Height: 6½in., 16.5cm.
Issued: 1934-1938
Colour variation
Price: $570 £380

HERMINIA HN1704
Designer: L. Harradine
Height: 6¾in., 17.2cm.
Issued: 1935-1938
Colour variation
Price: $525 £350

HERMIONE HN2058
Designer: M. Davies
Height: 7¾in., 19.7cm.
Issued: 1950-1952
Price: $450 £300

HENRY IRVING AS CARDINAL WOLSEY HN344

HENRY LYTTON AS JACK POINT HN610

HER MAJESTY QUEEN ELIZABETH II HN2878

HER MAJESTY QUEEN ELIZABETH THE QUEEN MOTHER HN2882

"HERE A LITTLE CHILD I STAND" HN1546

HERMINIA HN1644

FIGURES

HIBERNIA HN2932
Designer: S. Keenan
Height: 9in., 23cm.
Issued: 1983 in a limited
        edition of 950
Price: $180 £120

HIGHWAYMAN HN527
Designer: L. Harradine
Height: 6½in., 16.5cm.
Issued: 1921-1949
Price: $450 £300

HIGHWAYMAN HN592
Designer: L. Harradine
Height: 6½in., 16.5cm.
Issued: 1924-1949
Price: $450 £300

HIGHWAYMAN HN1257
Designer: L. Harradine
Height: 6½in., 16.5cm.
Issued: 1927-1949
Price: $450 £300

HILARY HN2335
Designer: M. Davies
Height: 7¼in., 18.4cm.
Issued: 1967-1980
Price: $75 £50

HINGED PARASOL HN1578
Designer: L. Harradine
Height: 6½in., 16.5cm.
Issued: 1933-1949
Price: $375 £250

HINGED PARASOL HN1579
Designer: L. Harradine
Height: 6½in., 16.5cm.
Issued: 1933-1949
        Colour variation
Price: $375 £250

**HIS ROYAL HIGHNESS
PRINCE PHILIP DUKE OF
EDINBURGH HN2386**
Designer: Unknown
Height: 8¼in., 21.0cm.
Issued: 1981 in a limited
        edition of 1500
Price: $240 £160

HOME AGAIN HN2167
Designer: M. Davies
Height: 3¼in., 8.3cm.
Issued: 1956-
Price: $117 £47

HONEY HN1909
Designer: L. Harradine
Height: 7in., 17.8cm.
Issued: 1939-1949
Price: $262 £175

HONEY HN1910
Designer: L. Harradine
Height: 6¾in., 17.2cm.
Issued: 1939-1949
        Colour variation
Price: $262 £175

HIGHWAYMAN HN527

HINGED PARASOL HN1578

HINGED PARASOL HN1579

**HIS ROYAL HIGHNESS PRINCE PHILIP
DUKE OF EDINBURGH HN2386**

HOME AGAIN HN2167

HONEY HN1909

HONEY HN1963
Designer: L. Harradine
Height: 6¾in., 17.2cm.
Issued: 1941-1949
Colour variation
Price: $262 £175

HORNPIPE HN2161
Designer: M. Nicholl
Height: 9¼in., 23.5cm.
Issued: 1955-1962
Price: $480 £320

HOSTESS OF WILLIAMSBURG HN2209
Designer: M. Davies
Height: 7¼in., 18.4cm.
Issued: 1960-1983
Price: $82 £55

HUCKLEBERRY FINN HN2927
Designer: D. Lyttleton
Height: 7in., 17.5cm.
Issued: 1982-1985
Price: $30 £20

HUNTING SQUIRE HN1409
Designer: Unknown
Height: 9¾in., 24.7cm.
Issued: 1930-1938
Price: $1500 £1000

HUNTS LADY HN1201
Designer: L Harradine
Height: 8¼in., 21.0cm.
Issued: 1926-1938
Price: $1350 £900

HUNTSMAN (Style one) HN1226
Designer: L. Harradine
Height: 8¾in., 22.2cm.
Issued: 1927-1938
Price: $1350 £900

HUNTSMAN (Style two) HN1815
Designer: Unknown
Height: 9½in., 24.1cm.
Issued: 1937-1949
Price: $1500 £1000
Also called John Peel

HUNTSMAN (Style three) HN2492
Designer: M. Nicholl
Height: 7½in., 19.1cm.
Issued: 1974-1978
Price: $75 £50

HURDY GURDY HN2796
Designer: M. Davies
Height: 6in., 15.2cm.
Issued: 1975 in a limited
edition of 750
Price: $487 £325

I

IBRAHIM HN2095
Designer: C. J. Noke
Height: 7¾in., 19.7cm.
Issued: 1952-1955
Price: $375 £250
Also called Emir

HORNPIPE HN2161

HOSTESS OF WILLIAMSBURG HN2209

HUNTS LADY HN1201

HUNTSMAN (Style one) HN1226

HURDY GURDY HN2796

IBRAHIM HN2095

FIGURES

I'M NEARLY READY HN2976
Designer: A. Hughes
Height: 7½in., 19.0cm.
Issued: 1984-
Price: $61 £41

IN GRANDMA'S DAYS HN339
Designer: C. J. Noke
Height: 8¾in., 22.2cm.
Issued: 1919-1938
Price: $600 £400

IN GRANDMA'S DAYS HN340
Designer: C. J. Noke
Height: 8¾in., 22.2cm.
Issued: 1919-1938
Colour variation
Price: $600 £400

IN GRANDMA'S DAYS HN388
Designer: C. J. Noke
Height: 8¾in., 22.2cm.
Issued: 1920-1938
Colour variation
Price: $600 £400

IN GRANDMA'S DAYS HN339

IN GRANDMA'S DAYS HN442

IN GRANDMA'S DAYS HN442
Designer: C. J. Noke
Height: 8¾in., 22.2cm.
Issued: 1921-1938
Colour variation
Price: $600 £400
Also called Lilac Shawl and
Poke Bonnet

IN THE STOCKS (Style one)
HN1474
Designer: L. Harradine
Height: 5in., 12.7cm.
Issued: 1931-1938
Price: $1200 £800

IN THE STOCKS (Style one)
HN1475
Designer: L. Harradine
Height: 5¼in., 13.3cm.
Issued: 1931-1938
Colour variation
Price: $1200 £800

IN THE STOCKS (Style one) HN1475

IN THE STOCKS (Style two) HN2163

IN THE STOCKS (Style two)
HN2163
Designer: M. Nicholl
Height: 5¾in., 14.6cm.
Issued: 1955-1959
Price: $450 £300

INDIAN BRAVE HN2376
Designer: M. Davies
Height: 16in., 40.6cm.
Issued: 1967 in a limited
edition of 500
Price: $5250 £3500

INDIAN TEMPLE DANCER
HN2830
Designer: M. Davies
Height: 9¼in., 23.5cm.
Issued: 1977 in a limited
edition of 750
Price: $450 £300

INDIAN BRAVE HN2376

INDIAN TEMPLE DANCER HN2830

INNOCENCE HN2842
Designer: E. J. Griffiths
Height: 7½in., 19.1cm.
Issued: 1979-
Price: $82 £55

INVITATION HN2170
Designer: M. Davies
Height: 5½in., 14.0cm.
Issued: 1956-1975
Price: $90 £60

IONA HN1346
Designer: L. Harradine
Height: 7½in., 19.1cm.
Issued: 1929-1938
Price: $1500 £1000

IRENE HN1621
Designer: L. Harradine
Height: 6½in., 16.5cm.
Issued: 1934-1951
Price: $240 £160

IRENE HN1697
Designer: L. Harradine
Height: 7in., 17.8cm.
Issued: 1935-1949
Colour variation
Price: $270 £180

IRENE HN1952
Designer: L. Harradine
Height: 6¾in., 17.2cm.
Issued: 1940-1950
Colour variation
Price: $270 £180

IRISH COLLEEN HN766
Designer: L. Harradine
Height: 6½in., 16.5cm.
Issued: 1925-1938
Price: $975 £650

IRISH COLLEEN HN767
Designer: L. Harradine
Height: 6½in., 16.5cm.
Issued: 1925-1938
Price: $975 £650

IRISHMAN HN1307
Designer: H. Fenton
Height: 6¾in., 17.2cm.
Issued: 1928-1938
Price: $600 £400

IT WON'T HURT HN2963
Designer: P. Parsons
Height: 7½in., 19.0cm.
Issued: 1982-
Price: $61 £41

IVY HN1768
Designer: L. Harradine
Height: 4¾in., 12.0cm.
Issued: 1936-1979
Price: $60 £40

IVY HN1769
Designer: L. Harradine
Height: 4¾in., 12.0cm.
Issued: 1936-1979
Colour variation
Price: $60 £40

INNOCENCE HN2842

INVITATION HN2170

IONA HN1346

IRENE HN1621

IRISH COLLEEN HN766

IVY HN1769

J

JACK HN2060
Designer: L. Harradine
Height: 5½in., 14.0cm.
Issued: 1950-1971
Price: $82 £55

JACK POINT HN85
Designer: C. J. Noke
Height: 16¼in., 41.2cm.
Issued: 1918-1938
Price: $1200 £800

JACK POINT HN91
Designer: C. J. Noke
Height: 16¼in., 41.2cm.
Issued: 1918-1938
Colour variation
Price: $1200 £800

JACK POINT HN99
Designer: C. J. Noke
Height: 16¼in., 41.2cm.
Issued: 1918-1938
Colour variation
Price: $1200 £800

JACK POINT HN2080
Designer: C. J. Noke
Height: 16in., 40.6cm.
Issued: 1952-
Colour variation
Price: $1625 £650

JACQUELINE HN2000
Designer: L. Harradine
Height: 7¼in., 18.4cm.
Issued: 1947-1951
Price: $262 £175

JACQUELINE HN2333
Designer: P. Davies
Height: 7½in., 19.0cm.
Issued: 1983-
Price: $172 £69

JACQUELINE HN2001
Designer: L. Harradine
Height: 7¼in., 18.4cm.
Issued: 1947-1951
Colour variation
Price: $262 £175

JAMES HN3013
Designer: P. Parsons
Height: 6in., 15cm.
Issued: 1983-
Price: $107 £43

JANE HN2014
Designer: L. Harradine
Height: 6¼in., 15.9cm.
Issued: 1948-1951
Price: $210 £140

JANE HN2806
Designer: P. Davies
Height: 8in., 20.0cm.
Issued: 1983-
Price: $172 £69

JACK HN2060

JACK POINT HN91

JACK POINT HN99

JACK POINT HN2080

JACQUELINE HN2000

JANE HN2014

FIGURES

JANET (Style one) HN1537
Designer: Unknown
Height: 6¼in., 15.9cm.
Issued: 1932-
Price: $117 £47

JANET (Style one) HN1538
Designer: Unknown
Height: 6¼in., 15.9cm.
Issued: 1932-1949
Colour variation
Price: $127 £85

JANET (Style one) HN1652
Designer: L. Harradine
Height: 6½in., 16.5cm.
Issued: 1934-1949
Colour variation
Price: $127 £85

JANET (Style one) HN1737
Designer: L. Harradine
Height: 6¼in., 15.9cm.
Issued: 1935-1949
Colour variation
Price: $127 £85

JANET (Style two) HN1916
Designer: L. Harradine
Height: 5¼in., 13.3cm.
Issued: 1939-1949
Price: $120 £80

JANET (Style two) HN1964
Designer: L. Harradine
Height: 5in., 12.7cm.
Issued: 1941-1949
Colour variation
Price: $120 £80

JANET M69
Designer: L. Harradine
Height: 4in., 10.1cm.
Issued: 1936-1949
Price: $150 £100

JANET M75
Designer: L. Harradine
Height: 4in., 10.1cm.
Issued: 1936-1949
Colour variation
Price: $150 £100

JANICE HN2022
Designer: M. Davies
Height: 7¼in., 18.4cm.
Issued: 1949-1955
Price: $240 £160

JANICE HN2165
Designer: M. Davies
Height: 7¼in., 18.4cm.
Issued: 1955-1965
Colour variation
Price: $240 £160

JANINE HN2461
Designer: J. Bromley
Height: 7½in., 19.1cm.
Issued: 1971-
Price: $172 £69

JANET (Style one) HN1537

JANET (Style one) HN1538

JANET (Style two) HN1916

JANICE HN2022

JANICE HN2165

JANINE HN2461

170

JAPANESE FAN HN399
Designer: H. Tittensor
Height: 4¾in., 12.1cm.
Issued: 1920-1938
Price: $675 £450

JAPANESE·FAN HN405
Designer: H. Tittensor
Height: 4¾in., 12.1cm.
Issued: 1920-1938
         Colour variation
Price: $675 £450

JAPANESE FAN HN439
Designer: H. Tittensor
Height: 4½in., 12.1cm.
Issued: 1921-1938
         Colour variation
Price: $675 £450

JAPANESE FAN HN440
Designer: H. Tittensor
Height: 4¾in., 12.1cm.
Issued: 1921-1938
         Colour variation
Price: $675 £450

JASMINE HN1862
Designer: L. Harradine
Height: 7¼in., 18.4cm.
Issued: 1938-1949
Price: $292 £195

JASMINE HN1863
Designer: L. Harradine
Height: 7½in., 19.1cm.
Issued: 1938-1949
         Colour variation
Price: $292 £195

JASMINE HN1876
Designer: L. Harradine
Height: 7½in., 19.1cm.
Issued: 1938-1949
         Colour variation
Price: $292 £195

JEAN HN1877
Designer: L. Harradine
Height: 7½in., 19.1cm.
Issued: 1938-1949
Price: $202 £135

JEAN HN1878
Designer: L. Harradine
Height: 7½in., 19.1cm.
Issued: 1938-1949
         Colour variation
Price: $202 £135

JEAN HN2032
Designer: L. Harradine
Height: 7½in., 19.1cm.
Issued: 1949-1959
         Colour variation
Price: $210 £140

JEAN HN2710
Designer: P. Davies
Height: 5¾in., 14.5cm.
Issued: 1983-
Price: $117 £47

JAPANESE FAN HN399

JASMINE HN1862

JASMINE HN1863

JASMINE HN1876

JEAN HN1877

JEAN HN2032

171

FIGURES

JENNIFER HN1484
Designer: L. Harradine
Height: 6½in., 16.5cm.
Issued: 1931-1949
Price: $270 £180

JENNIFER HN2392
Designer: P. Davies
Height: 7in., 17.5cm.
Issued: 1982-
Price: $182 £73

JERSEY MILKMAID HN2057
Designer: L. Harradine
Height: 6½in., 16.5cm
Issued: 1950-1959
Price: $90 £60
Also called The Milkmaid

JESTER (Style one) HN45
Designer: C. J. Noke
Height: 9½in., 24.1cm.
Issued: 1915-1938
Price: $750 £500

JESTER (Style one) HN71
Designer: C. J. Noke
Height: 9½in., 24.1cm.
Issued: 1917-1938
Colour variation
Price: $750 £500

JESTER (Style one) HN71A
Designer: C. J. Noke
Height: 9½in., 24.1cm.
Issued: 1917-1938
Colour variation
Price: $750 £500

JESTER (Style one) HN320
Designer: C. J. Noke
Height: 10in., 25.4cm.
Issued: 1918-1938
Colour variation
Price: $750 £500

JESTER (Style one) HN367
Designer: C. J. Noke
Height: 10in., 25.4cm.
Issued: 1920-1938
Colour variation
Price: $750 £500

JESTER (Style one) HN412
Designer: C. J. Noke
Height: 10in., 25.4cm.
Issued: 1920-1938
Colour variation
Price: $750 £500

JESTER (Style one) HN426
Designer: C. J. Noke
Height: 10in., 25.4cm.
Issued: 1921-1938
Colour variation
Price: $750 £500

JESTER (Style one) HN446
Designer: C. J. Noke
Height: 10in., 25.4cm.
Issued: 1921-1938
Colour variation
Price: $750 £500

JENNIFER HN1484

MILKMAID HN2057A

JENNIFER HN2392

JERSEY MILKMAID HN2057

JESTER (Style one) HN552
Designer: C. J. Noke
Height:　10in., 25.4cm.
Issued:　1922-1938
　　　　　Colour variation
Price:　　$750　£500

JESTER (Style one) HN616
Designer: C. J. Noke
Height:　10in., 25.4cm.
Issued:　1924-1938
　　　　　Colour variation
Price:　　$750　£500

JESTER (Style one) HN627
Designer: C. J. Noke
Height:　10in., 25.4cm.
Issued:　1924-1938
　　　　　Colour variation
Price:　　$750　£500

JESTER (Style one) HN1295
Designer: C. J. Noke
Height:　10in., 25.4cm.
Issued:　1928-1949
　　　　　Colour variation
Price:　　$600　£400

JESTER (Style one) HN1702
Designer: C. J. Noke
Height:　10in., 25.4cm.
Issued:　1935-1949
　　　　　Colour variation
Price:　　$525　£350

JESTER (Style one) HN2016
Designer: C. J. Noke
Height:　10in., 25.4cm.
Issued:　1949-
　　　　　Colour variation
Price:　　$222　£89

JESTER (Style two) HN45A
Designer: C. J. Noke
Height:　10¼in., 26.0cm.
Issued:　1915-1938
Price:　　$750　£500

JESTER (Style two) HN45B
Designer: C. J. Noke
Height:　10¼in., 26.0cm.
Issued:　1915-1938
　　　　　Colour variation
Price:　　$750　£500

JESTER (Style two) HN55
Designer: C. J. Noke
Height:　10¼in., 26.0cm.
Issued:　1916-1938
　　　　　Colour variation
Price:　　$750　£500

JESTER (Style two) HN308
Designer: C. J. Noke
Height:　10¼in., 26.0cm.
Issued:　1918-1938
　　　　　Colour variation
Price:　　$750　£500

JESTER (Style two) HN630
Designer: C. J. Noke
Height:　10¼in., 26.0cm.
Issued:　1924-1938
　　　　　Colour variation
Price:　　$750　£500

JESTER (Style one) HN45

JESTER (Style one) HN2016

JESTER (Style one) HN367

JESTER (Style two) HN45B

FIGURES

JESTER (Style two) HN1333
Designer: C. J. Noke
Height: 10¼in., 26.0cm.
Issued: 1929-1949
Colour variation
Price: $750 £500

JILL HN2061
Designer: L. Harradine
Height: 5½in., 14.0cm.
Issued: 1950-1971
Price: $75 £50

JOAN HN1422
Designer: L. Harradine
Height: 5½in., 14.0cm.
Issued: 1930-1949
Price: $180 £120

JOAN HN2023
Designer: L. Harradine
Height: 5¾in., 14.6cm.
Issued 1949-1959
Colour variation
Price: $187 £125

JOANNE HN2373
Designer: J. Bromley
Height: 5¼in., 13.0cm.
Issued: 1982-
Price: $117 £47

JOHN PEEL HN1408
Designer: Unknown
Height: 9½in., 24.1cm.
Issued: 1930-1937
Price: $1500 £1000
Also called Huntsman

JOLLY SAILOR HN2172
Designer: M. Nicholl
Height: 6½in., 16.5cm.
Issued: 1956-1965
Price: $337 £225

JOVIAL MONK HN2144
Designer: M. Davies
Height: 7¾in., 19.7cm.
Issued: 1954-1976
Price: $165 £110

JUDGE HN2443
Designer: M. Nicholl
Height: 6½in., 16.5cm.
Issued: 1972-1976
Matte
Price: $182 £73

JUDGE HN2443A
Designer: M. Nicholl
Height: 6½in., 16.5cm.
Issued: 1976
Gloss
Price: $140 £70

JUDGE AND JURY HN1264
Designer: J. G. Hughes
Height: 6in., 15.2cm.
Issued: 1927-1938
Price: $1800 £1200

JILL HN2061

JOAN HN1422

JOHN PEEL HN1408

JOLLY SAILOR HN2172

JOVIAL MONK HN2144

JUDGE HN2443

JUDITH HN2089
Designer: L. Harradine
Height: 7in., 17.8cm.
Issued: 1952-1959
Price: $185 £125

JULIA HN2705
Designer: M. Davies
Height: 7½in., 19.1cm.
Issued: 1975-
Price: $157 £63

JULIA HN2706
Designer: P. Davies
Height: 7½in., 19.1cm.
Issued: 1985-
Colour variation
Price: $127 £51

JULIE HN2995
Designer: R. Tabbenor
Height: 5in., 12.5cm.
Issued: 1985-
Price: $65 £26

JUNE HN1690
Designer: L. Harradine
Height: 7¼in., 18.4cm.
Issued: 1935-1949
Price: $292 £195

JUNE HN1691
Designer: L. Harradine
Height: 7¼in., 18.4cm.
Issued: 1935-1949
Colour variation
Price: $240 £160

JUNE HN1947
Designer: L. Harradine
Height: 7¼in., 18.4cm.
Issued: 1940-1949
Colour variation
Price: $292 £195

JUNE HN2027
Designer: L. Harradine
Height: 7¼in., 18.4cm.
Issued: 1949-1952
Colour variation
Price: $240 £160

JUNE M65
Designer: L. Harradine
Height: 4¼in., 10.8cm.
Issued: 1935-1949
Price: $180 £120

JUNE M71
Designer: L. Harradine
Height: 4¼in., 10.8cm.
Issued: 1936-1949
Colour variation
Price: $180 £120

JUNO AND THE PEACOCK
HN2827
Designer: R. Jefferson
Height: 11in., 27.9cm.
Issued: 1984 in a limited
edition of 300
Price $1425 £950

JUDITH HN2089

JULIA HN2705

JUNE HN1690

JUNE HN1691

JUNE HN2027

JUNE M65

JUST ONE MORE HN2980
Designer: A. Hughes
Height: 7in., 17.5cm.
Issued: 1984-
Price: $61 £41

K

KAREN HN1994
Designer: L. Harradine
Height: 8in., 20.3cm.
Issued: 1947-1955
Price: $255 £170

KAREN HN2388
Designer: P. Davies
Height: 8in., 20.0cm.
Issued: 1982-
Price: $247 £99

KATE HN2789
Designer: M. Davies
Height: 7½in., 19.1cm.
Issued: 1978-
Price: $157 £63

KATE HARDCASTLE HN1718
Designer: L. Harradine
Height: 8in., 20.3cm.
Issued: 1935-1949
Price: $277 £185

KATE HARDCASTLE HN1719
Designer: L. Harradine
Height: 8in., 20.3cm.
Issued: 1935-1949
Colour variation
Price: $277 £185

KATE HARDCASTLE HN1734
Designer: L. Harradine
Height: 8¼in., 21.0cm.
Issued: 1935-1949
Colour variation
Price: $375 £250

KATE HARDCASTLE HN1861
Designer: L. Harradine
Height: 8in., 20.3cm.
Issued: 1938-1949
Colour variation
Price: $450 £300

KATE HARDCASTLE HN1919
Designer: L. Harradine
Height: 8¼in., 21.0cm.
Issued: 1939-1949
Colour variation
Price: $450 £300

KATE HARDCASTLE HN2028
Designer: L. Harradine
Height: 7¾in., 19.7cm.
Issued: 1949-1952
Colour variation
Price: $277 £185

KATHARINE HN61
Designer: C. J. Noke
Height: 5¾in., 14.6cm.
Issued: 1916-1938
Price: $825 £550

KAREN HN1994

KAREN HN2388

KATE HN2789

KATE HARDCASTLE HN1718

KATE HARDCASTLE HN1719

KATHARINE HN61

KATHARINE HN74
Designer: C. J. Noke
Height: 5¾in., 14.6cm.
Issued: 1917-1938
Colour variation
Price: $825 £550

KATHARINE HN341
Designer: C. J. Noke
Height: 5¾in., 14.6cm.
Issued: 1919-1938
Colour variation
Price: $870 £580

KATHARINE HN471
Designer: C. J. Noke
Height: 5¾in., 14.6cm.
Issued: 1921-1938
Colour variation
Price: $825 £550

KATHARINE HN615
Designer: C. J. Noke
Height: 5¾in., 14.6cm.
Issued: 1924-1938
Colour variation
Price: $825 £550

KATHARINE HN793
Designer: C. J. Noke
Height: 5¾in., 14.6cm.
Issued: 1926-1938
Colour variation
Price: $825 £550

KATHLEEN HN1252
Designer: L. Harradine
Height: 7¾in., 19.7cm.
Issued: 1927-1938
Price: $405 £270

KATHLEEN HN1253
Designer: L. Harradine
Height: 7½in., 19.1cm.
Issued: 1927-1938
Colour variation
Price: $405 £270

KATHLEEN HN1275
Designer: L. Harradine
Height: 7½in., 19.1cm.
Issued: 1928-1939
Colour variation
Price: $405 £270

KATHLEEN HN1279
Designer: L. Harradine
Height: 7¾in., 19.7cm.
Issued: 1928-1938
Colour variation
Price: $375 £250

KATHLEEN HN1291
Designer: L. Harradine
Height: 7½in., 19.1cm.
Issued: 1928-1938
Colour variation
Price: $435 £290

KATHLEEN HN1357
Designer: L. Harradine
Height: 7½in., 19.1cm.
Issued: 1929-1938
Colour variation
Price: $375 £250

KATHLEEN HN1252

KATHLEEN HN1512
Designer: L. Harradine
Height: 7½in., 19.1cm.
Issued: 1932-1938
Colour variation
Price: $375 £250

KATHLEEN HN2933
Designer: S. Keenan
Height: 6½in., 16.5cm.
Issued: 1984-
Price: $237 $95

KATHY HN2346
Designer: M. Davies
Height: 4¾in., 12.0cm.
Issued: 1981-
Price: $107 £43

KATRINA HN2327
Designer: M. Davies
Height: 7½in., 19.1cm.
Issued: 1965-1969
Price: $150 £100

KELLY HN2478
Designer: P. Davies
Height: 7½in., 19.0cm.
Issued: 1985-
Price: $127 £51

KING CHARLES HN404
Designer: C. J. Noke and
H. Tittensor
Height: 16¾in., 42.5cm.
Issued: 1920-1951
Price: $2025 £1350

KING CHARLES HN2084
Designer: C. J. Noke
Height: 16in., 40.6cm.
Issued: 1952-
Price: $1437 £575

KIRSTY HN2381
Designer: M. Davies
Height: 7½in., 19.1cm.
Issued: 1971-
Price: $182 £73

KITTY HN1367
Designer: Unknown
Height: 4in., 10.1cm.
Issued: 1930-1938
Price: $675 £450

KO-KO (Style one) HN1266
Designer: L. Harradine
Height: 5in., 12.7cm.
Issued: 1928-1949
Price: $375 £250

KO-KO (Style one) HN1286
Designer: L. Harradine
Height: 5in., 12.7cm.
Issued: 1938-1949
Colour variation
Price: $375 £250

KO-KO (Style two) HN2898
Designer: W. K. Harper
Height: 11½in., 29.2cm.
Issued: 1980-
Price: $352 £235

KATHY HN2346

KATRINA HN2327

KING CHARLES HN404

KIRSTY HN2381

KO-KO (Style one) HN1266

KO-KO (Style two) HN2898

KURDISH DANCER HN2867
Designer: M. Davies
Height: 8¼in., 21.0cm.
Issued: 1979 in a limited
          edition of 750
Price: $450 £300

L

LA SYLPHIDE HN2138
Designer: M. Davies
Height: 7in., 17.8cm.
Issued: 1956-1965
Price: $187 £125

LADY AND BLACKAMOOR
(Style one) HN374
Designer: H. Tittensor
Height: Unknown
Issued: 1920-1938
Price: $1800 £1200

LADY AND BLACKAMOOR
(Style two) HN375
Designer: H. Tittensor
Height: Unknown
Issued: 1920-1938
Price: $1800 £1200

LADY AND BLACKAMOOR
(Style two) HN377
Designer: H. Tittensor
Height: Unknown
Issued: 1920-1938
          Colour variation
Price: $1800 £1200

LADY AND BLACKAMOOR
(Style two) HN470
Designer: H. Tittensor
Height: Unknown
Issued: 1921-1938
          Colour variation
Price: $1800 £1200

LADY AND THE UNICORN
HN2825
Designer: R. Jefferson
Height: 8¾in., 22.2cm.
Issued: 1982 in a limited
          edition of 300
Price: $1425 £950

LADY ANNE HN83
Designer: E. W. Light
Height: Unknown
Issued: 1918-1938
Price: $1500 £1000

LADY ANNE HN87
Designer: E. W. Light
Height: Unknown
Issued: 1918-1938
          Colour variation
Price: $1500 £1000

LADY ANNE HN93
Designer: E. W. Light
Height: Unknown
Issued: 1918-1938
          Colour variation
Price: $1500 £1000

KURDISH DANCER HN2867   LA SYLPHIDE HN2138

LADY AND THE UNICORN HN2825

LADY ANNE NEVILL HN2006
Designer: M. Davies
Height: 9¾in., 24.7cm.
Issued: 1948-1953
Price: $600 £400

LADY APRIL HN1958
Designer: L. Harradine
Height: 7in., 17.8cm.
Issued: 1940-1959
Price: $210 £140

LADY APRIL HN1965
Designer: L. Harradine
Height: 7in., 17.8cm.
Issued: 1941-1949
        Colour variation
Price: $210 £140

LADY BETTY HN1967
Designer: L. Harradine
Height: 6½in., 16.5cm.
Issued: 1941-1951
Price: $210 £140

LADY CHARMIAN HN1948
Designer: L. Harradine
Height: 8in., 20.3cm.
Issued: 1940-1973
Price: $150 £100

LADY CHARMIAN HN1949
Designer: L. Harradine
Height: 8in., 20.3cm.
Issued: 1940-1975
        Colour variation
Price: £150 £100

LADY CLARE HN1465
Designer: L. Harradine
Height: 7¾in., 19.7cm.
Issued: 1931-1938
Price: $420 £280

LADY CLOWN HN717
Designer: L. Harradine
Height: 7½in., 19.1cm.
Issued: 1925-1938
Price: $1125 £750

LADY CLOWN HN718
Designer: L. Harradine
Height: 7½in., 19.1cm.
Issued: 1925-1938
        Colour variation
Price: $1125 £750

LADY CLOWN HN738
Designer: L. Harradine
Height: 7½in., 19.1cm.
Issued: 1925-1938
        Colour variation
Price: $1125 £750

LADY CLOWN HN770
Designer: L. Harradine
Height: 7½in., 19.1cm.
Issued: 1925-1938
        Colour variation
Price: $1125 £750

LADY ANNE NEVILL HN2006

LADY APRIL HN1958

LADY BETTY HN1967

LADY CHARMIAN HN1948

LADY CLARE HN1465

LADY CLOWN HN738

LADY CLOWN HN1263
Designer: L. Harradine
Height: 7¼in., 18.4cm.
Issued: 1927-1938
Colour variation
Price: $1125 £750
Also called CLOWNETTE

**LADY DIANA SPENCER
HN2885**
Designer: E. Griffiths
Height: 7¾in., 19.6cm.
Issued: 1982 in a limited
edition of 1500
Price: $225 £150

LADY FAYRE HN1265
Designer: L. Harradine
Height; 5¼in., 13.3cm.
Issued: 1928-1938
Price: $337 £225

LADY FAYRE HN1557
Designer: L. Harradine
Height: 5¾in., 14.6cm.
Issued: 1933-1938
Colour variation
Price: $375 £250

LADY FROM WILLIAMSBURG HN2228
Height: 6in., 15.2cm.
Designer: M. Davies
Issued: 1960
Price: $75 £50

**LADY JESTER (Style one)
HN1221**
Designer: L. Harradine
Height: 7in., 17.8cm.
Issued: 1927-1938
Price: $1125 £750

**LADY JESTER (Style one)
HN1222**
Designer: L. Harradine
Height: 7in., 17.8cm.
Issued: 1927-1938
Colour variation
Price: $1125 £750

**LADY JESTER (Style one)
HN1332**
Designer: L. Harradine
Height: 7in., 17.8cm.
Issued: 1929-1938
Colour variation
Price: $1125 £750

**LADY JESTER (Style two)
HN1284**
Designer: L. Harradine
Height: 4¼in., 10.8cm.
Issued: 1928-1938
Price: $1125 £750

**LADY JESTER (Style two)
HN1285**
Designer: L. Harradine
Height: 4¼in., 10.8cm.
Issued: 1928-1938
Colour variation
Price: $1125 £750

LADY FAYRE HN1265   **LADY FROM WILLIAMSBURG HN2228**

LADY JESTER (Style one) HN1222   **LADY JESTER (Style one) HN1332**

LADY JESTER (Style two) HN1284   **LADY JESTER (Style two) HN1285**

**LADY OF THE ELIZABETHAN
PERIOD (Style one) HN40**
Designer: E. W. Light
Height;   9½in., 24.1cm.
Issued: 1914-1938
Price: $1200 £800

**LADY OF THE ELIZABETHAN
PERIOD (Style one) HN40A**
Designer: E. W. Light
Height: 9½in., 24.1cm.
Issued: 1914-1938
Price: $1200 £800

**LADY OF THE ELIZABETHAN
PERIOD (Style one) HN73**
Designer: E. W. Light
Height: 9½in., 24.1cm.
Issued: 1917-1938
           Colour variation
Price: $1200 £800

**LADY OF THE ELIZABETHAN
PERIOD (Style one) HN411**
Designer: E. W. Light
Height: 9¾in., 24.7cm.
Issued   1920-1938
           Colour variation
Price: $1200 £800

**LADY OF THE ELIZABETHAN
PERIOD (Style two) HN309**
Designer: E. W. Light
Height: 9½in., 24.1cm.
Issued: 1918-1938
Price: $1200 £800

LADY OF THE FAN HN48
Designer: E. W. Light
Height: 9½in., 24.1cm.
Issued: 1916-1938
Price: $1050 £700

LADY OF THE FAN HN52
Designer: E. W. Light
Height: 9½in., 24.1cm.
Issued: 1916-1938
           Colour variation
Price: $1050 £700

LADY OF THE FAN HN335
Designer: E. W. Light
Height: 9½in., 24.1cm
Issued: 1919-1938
           Colour variation
Price: $1050 £700

LADY OF THE FAN HN509
Designer: E. W. Light
Height: 9½in., 24.1cm.
Issued: 1921-1938
           Colour variation
Price: $1050 £700

LADY OF THE FAN HN53A
Designer: E. W. Light
Height: 9in., 22.9cm.
Issued: 1916-1938
           Colour variation
Price: $1050 £700

LADY OF THE ELIZABETHAN PERIOD (Style two) HN309

LADY OF THE FAN HN53
Designer: E. W. Light
Height: 9½in., 24.1cm.
Issued: 1916-1938
Colour variation
Price: $1050 £700

LADY OF THE GEORGIAN PERIOD HN41
Designer: E. W. Light
Height; 10¼in., 26.0cm.
Issued: 1914-1938
Price: $1200 £800

LADY OF THE GEORGIAN PERIOD HN331
Designer: E. W. Light
Height: 10¼in., 26.0cm.
Issued: 1918-1938
Colour variation
Price: $1200 £800

LADY OF THE GEORGIAN PERIOD HN444
Designer: E. W. Light
Height: 10¼in., 26.0cm.
Issued: 1921-1938
Colour variation
Price: $1200 £800

LADY OF THE GEORGIAN PERIOD HN690
Designer: E. W. Light
Height: 10¼in., 26.0cm.
Issued: 1925-1938
Price: $1200 £800

LADY OF THE GEORGIAN PERIOD HN702
Designer: E. W. Light
Height: 10¼in., 26.0cm.
Issued: 1925-1938
Colour variation
Price: $1200 £800

LADY OF THE SNOWS HN1780
Designer: R. Garbe
Height: Unknown
Issued: 1933-?
Price: $1800 £1200

LADY OF THE SNOWS HN1830
Designer: R. Garbe
Height: Unknown
Issued: 1937-1949
Price: $1800 £1200

LADY OF THE TIME OF HENRY VI HN43
Designer: E. W. Light
Height: 9¼in., 23.5cm.
Issued: 1914-1938
Price: $1500 £1000

LADY PAMELA HN2718
Designer: D. V. Tootle
Height: 8in., 23.0cm.
Issued: 1974-1980
Price: $82 £55

LADY OF THE FAN HN53

LADY OF THE GEORGIAN PERIOD HN690

LADY OF THE SNOWS HN1780

LADY PAMELA HN2718

**LADY WITH ERMINE MUFF
HN82**
Designer: E. W. Light
Height: 6¾in., 17.2cm.
Issued: 1918-1938
Price: $1500 £1000
Also known as 'The Afternoon
Call'

LADY WITH ROSE HN48A
Designer: E. W. Light
Height: 9½in., 24.1cm.
Issued: 1916-1938
Price: $1200 £800

LADY WITH ROSE HN52A
Designer: E. W. Light
Height: 9½in., 24.1cm.
Issued: 1916-1938
Colour variation
Price: $1200 £800

LADY WITH ROSE HN68
Designer: E. W. Light
Height: 9½in., 24.1cm.
Issued: 1916-1938
Colour variation
Price: $1200 £800

LADY WITH ROSE HN304
Designer: E. W. Light
Height: 9½in., 24.1cm.
Issued: 1918-1938
Colour variation
Price: $1200 £800

LADY WITH ROSE HN336
Designer: E. W. Light
Height: 9½in., 24.1cm.
Issued: 1919-1938
Colour variation
Price: $1200 £800.

LADY WITH ROSE HN515
Designer: E. W. Light
Height: 9½in., 24.1cm.
Issued: 1921-1938
Colour variation
Price: $1275 £850

LADY WITH ROSE HN517
Designer: E. W. Light
Height: 9½in., 24.1cm.
Issued: 1921-1938
Colour variation
Price: $1275 £850

LADY WITH ROSE HN584
Designer: E. W. Light
Height: 9½in., 24.1cm.
Issued: 1923-1938
Colour variation
Price: $1275 £850

LADY WITH ROSE HN624
Designer: E. W. Light
Height: 9½in., 24.1cm.
Issued: 1924-1938
Colour variation
Price: $1275 £850

LADY WITH SHAWL HN447
Designer: L. Harradine
Height: 13¼in., 33.7cm.
Issued: 1921-1938
Price: $1800 £1200

LADY WITH ERMINE MUFF HN82

LADY WITH ROSE HN48A   LADY WITH SHAWL HN447

FIGURES

LADY WITH SHAWL HN458
Designer: L. Harradine
Height: 13¼in., 33.7cm.
Issued: 1921-1938
Colour variation
Price: $1800 £1200

LADY WITH SHAWL HN626
Designer: L. Harradine
Height: 13¼in., 33.7cm.
Issued: 1924-1938
Colour variation
Price: $1800 £1200

LADY WITH SHAWL HN678
Designer: L. Harradine
Height: 13¼in., 33.7cm.
Issued: 1924-1938
Colour variation
Price: $1800 £1200

LADY WITH SHAWL HN679
Designer: L. Harradine
Height: 13¼in., 33.7cm.
Issued: 1924-1938
Colour variation
Price: $1800 £1200

LADY WITHOUT BOUQUET HN393
Designer: G. Lambert
Height: 9in., 22.9cm.
Issued: 1920-1938
Price: $1500 £1000

LADY WITHOUT BOUQUET HN394
Designer: G. Lambert
Height: 9in., 22.9cm.
Issued: 1920-1938
Colour variation
Price: $1500 £1000

LADYBIRD HN1638
Designer: L. Harradine
Height: 7¾in., 19.7cm.
Issued: 1934-1949
Price: $675 £450

LADYBIRD HN1640
Designer: L. Harradine
Height: 7¾in., 19.7cm.
Issued: 1934-1938
Colour variation
Price: $825 £550

LAIRD HN2361
Designer: M. Nicholl
Height: 8in., 20.3cm.
Issued: 1969-
Price: $182 £73

LALLA ROOKH HN2910
Designer: S. Keenan
Height: 9in., 22.8cm.
Issued: 1981 in a limited edition of 950
Price: $150 £100

LAMBETH WALK HN1880
Designer: L. Harradine
Height: 10in., 25.4cm.
Issued: 1938-1949
Price: $1125 £750

LADYBIRD HN1640   LAIRD HN2361

LALLA ROOKH HN2910   LAMBETH WALK HN1880

185

FIGURES

LAMBETH WALK HN1881
Designer: L. Harradine
Height: 10in., 25.4cm.
Issued: 1938-1949
Colour variation
Price: $1125 £750

LAMBING TIME HN1890
Designer: L. Harradine
Height: 9¼in., 23.5cm.
Issued: 1938-1980
Price: $112 £75

LAND OF NOD HN56
Designer: H. Tittensor
Height: 9½in., 24.1cm.
Issued: 1916-1938
Price: $1200 £800

LAND OF NOD HN56A
Designer: H. Tittensor
Height: 9½in., 24.1cm.
Issued: 1916-1938
Price: $1200 £800

LAND OF NOD HN56B
Designer: H. Tittensor
Height: 9½in., 24.1cm.
Issued: 1916-1938
Colour variation
Price: $1200 £800

LAST WALTZ HN2315
Designer: M. Davies
Height: 7¾in., 19.7cm.
Issued: 1967-
Price: $182 £73

LAURA HN2960
Designer: P. Parsons
Height: 7¼in., 18.0cm
Issued: 1983-
Price: $172 £69

LAURIANNE HN2719
Designer: D. V. Tootle
Height: 6¼in., 15.9cm.
Issued: 1974-1978
Price: $90 £60

LAVENDER WOMAN HN22
Designer: P. Stabler
Height: 8¼in., 21.0cm.
Issued: 1913-1938
Price: $1275 £850

LAVENDER WOMAN HN23
Designer: P. Stabler
Height: 8¼in., 21.0cm.
Issued: 1913-1938
Colour variation
Price: $1275 £850

LAVENDER WOMAN HN23A
Designer: P. Stabler
Height: 8¼in., 21.0cm.
Issued: 1913-1938
Colour variation
Price: $1275 £850

LAVENDER WOMAN HN342
Designer: P. Stabler
Height: 8¼in., 21.0cm.
Issued: 1919-1938
Colour variation
Price: $1275 £850

LAMBETH WALK HN1881

LAMBING TIME HN1890

LAND OF NOD HN56

LAST WALTZ HN2315

LAURIANNE HN2719

LAVENDER WOMAN HN23A

186

LAVENDER WOMAN HN569
Designer: P. Stabler
Height: 8¼in., 21.0cm.
Issued: 1924-1938
Colour variation
Price: $1275 £850

LAVENDER WOMAN HN744
Designer: P. Stadler
Height: 8¼in., 21.0cm.
Issued: 1925-1938
Colour variation
Price: $1275 £850

LAVINIA HN1955
Designer: L. Harradine
Height: 5in., 12.7cm.
Issued: 1940-1978
Price: $52 £35

LAWYER HN3041
Designer: P. Parsons
Height: 9in., 23.0cm.
Issued: 1985-
Price: $147 £59

LEADING LADY HN2269
Designer: M. Davies
Height: 7¾in., 19.7cm.
Issued: 1965-1976
Price: $82 £55

LEDA AND THE SWAN HN2826
Designer: R. Jefferson
Height: 9¾in., 25.0cm.
Issued: 1983 — in a limited edition of 300
Price: $900 £600

LEGOLAS HN2917
Designer: H. Sales
Height: 6¼in., 15.9cm.
Issued: 1980-1984
Price: $30 £20

LEISURE HOUR HN2055
Designer: M. Davies
Height: 7in., 17.8cm.
Issued: 1950-1965
Price: $262 £175

LIDO LADY HN1220
Designer: L. Harradine
Height: 6¾in., 17.2cm.
Issued: 1927-1938
Price: $675 £450

LIDO LADY HN1229
Designer: L. Harradine
Height: 6¾in., 17.2cm.
Issued: 1927-1938
Colour variation
Price: $675 £450

LIGHTS OUT HN2262
Designer: M. Davies
Height: 5in., 12.7cm.
Issued: 1965-1969
Price: $210 £140

LILAC SHAWL HN44
Designer: C. J. Noke
Height: 8¾in., 22.2cm.
Issued: 1915-1938
Price: $600 £400

LAVINIA HN1955

LEADING LADY HN2269

LEGOLAS HN2917

LIDO LADY HN1220

LIGHTS OUT HN2262

LILAC SHAWL HN44

FIGURES

LILAC SHAWL HN44A
Designer: C. J. Noke
Height: 8¾in., 22.2cm.
Issued: 1915-1938
Colour variation
Price: $600 £400
**Also called In Grandma's Days
and Poke Bonnet**

LILAC TIME HN2137
Designer: M. Davies
Height: 7¼in., 18.4cm.
Issued: 1954-1969
Price: $210 £140

LILY HN1798
Designer: L. Harradine
Height: 5in., 12.7cm.
Issued: 1936-1949
Price: $90 £60

LILY HN1799
Designer: L. Harradine
Height: 5in., 12.7cm.
Issued: 1936-1949
Colour variation
Price: $97 £65

LINDA HN2106
Designer: L. Harradine
Height: 4¾in., 12.0cm.
Issued: 1953-1976
Price: $82 £55

LINDA HN2758
Designer: E. Griffiths
Height: 7¾in., 19.5cm.
Issued: 1984-
Price: $117 £47

LISA HN2310
Designer: M. Davies
Height: 7¼in., 18.4cm.
Issued: 1969-1982
Price: $75 £50

LISA HN2394
Designer: P. Davies
Height: 7¾in., 19.5cm.
Issued: 1983-
Price: $147 £59

LISETTE HN1523
Designer: L. Harradine
Height: 5¼in., 13.3cm.
Issued: 1932-1938
Price: $337 £225

LISETTE HN1524
Designer: L. Harradine
Height: 5¼in., 13.3cm.
Issued: 1932-1938
Colour variation
Price: $337 £225

LISETTE HN1684
Designer: L. Harradine
Height: 6½in., 16.5cm.
Issued: 1935-1938
Colour variation
Price: $337 £225

LILAC SHAWL HN44A

LILAC TIME HN2137

LILY HN1798

LINDA HN2106

LISA HN2310

LISETTE HN1524

188

FIGURES

LITTLE BO-PEEP HN3030
Designer: A. Hughes
Height: 8in., 20.0cm.
Issued: 1984-
Price: $107 £43

LITTLE BOY BLUE HN2062
Designer: L. Harradine
Height: 5½in., 14.0cm.
Issued: 1950-1973
Price: $97 £65

LITTLE BOY BLUE HN3035
Designer: A. Hughes
Height: 7¾in., 19.5cm.
Issued: 1984-
Price: $107 £43

**"LITTLE CHILD SO RARE
AND SWEET" (Style One)
HN1540**
Designer: Unknown
Height: 5in., 12.7cm.
Issued: 1933-1949
Price: $195 £130

**"LITTLE CHILD SO RARE
AND SWEET" (Style two)
HN1542**
Designer: Unknown
Height: 5in., 12.7cm.
Issued: 1933-1949
Price: $195 £130

**LITTLE JACK HORNER
HN2063**
Designer: L. Harradine
Height: 4½in., 11.4cm.
Issued: 1950-1953
Price: $195 £130

**LITTLE JACK HORNER
HN3034**
Designer: A. Hughes
Height: 7in., 17.5cm.
Issued: 1984-
Price: $107 £43

**LITTLE LADY MAKE
BELIEVE HN1870**
Designer: L. Harradine
Height: 6¼in., 15.9cm.
Issued: 1938-1949
Price: $210 £140

LITTLE LAND HN63
Designer: H. TIttensor
Height: 7½in., 19.1cm.
Issued: 1916-1938
Price: $1350 £900

LITTLE LAND HN67
Designer: H. Tittensor
Height: 7½in., 19cm.
Issued: 1916-1938
Price: $1350 £900

**LITTLE LORD
FAUNTLEROY HN2972**
Designer: A. Hughes
Height: 6¼in., 16.0cm
Issued: 1982-
Price: $39 £26

LITTLE BOY BLUE HN2062

"LITTLE CHILD SO RARE
AND SWEET" (Style one) HN1540

LITTLE JACK HORNER HN2063

LITTLE LADY MAKE BELIEVE HN1870

LITTLE LAND HN63

LITTLE LAND HN67

LITTLE MISS MUFFET
HN2727
Designer: W. K. Harper
Height: 6¼in., 16.0cm.
Issued: 1984-
Price: $107 £43

LITTLE MISTRESS HN1449
Designer; L. Harradine
Height: 5¾in., 14.6cm.
Issued: 1931-1949
Price: $210 £140

LITTLE MOTHER (Style one)
HN389
Designer: H. Tittensor
Height: Unknown
Issued: 1920-1938
Price: $1875 £1250

LITTLE MOTHER (Style one)
HN390
Designer: H. Tittensor
Height: Unknown
Issued: 1920-1938
Colour variation
Price: $1875 £1250

LITTLE MOTHER (Style one)
HN469
Designer: H. Tittensor
Height: Unknown
Issued: 1921-1938
Colour variation
Price: $1500 £1000

LITTLE MOTHER (Style two)
HN1418
Designer: L. Harradine
Height: 8in., 20.3cm.
Issued: 1930-1938
Price: $1200 £800

LITTLE MOTHER (Style two)
HN1641
Designer: L. Harradine
Height: 8in., 20.3cm.
Issued: 1934-1949
Price: $900 £600
Also called Young Widow

LITTLE NELL HN540
Designer: L. Harradine
Height: 4in., 10.1cm.
Issued: 1922-1932
Price: $45 £30

LITTLE NELL M51
Designer: L. Harradine
Height: 4¼in., 10.8cm.
Issued: 1932-1982
Price: $33 £22

LIZANA HN1756
Designer: L. Harradine
Height: 8½in., 21.6cm
Issued: 1936-1949
Price: $270 £180

LIZANA HN1761
Designer: L. Harradine
Height: 8½in., 21.6cm.
Issued: 1936-1938
Price: $270 £180

LIZANA HN1756

LOBSTER MAN HN2317
Designer: M. Nicholl
Height: 7¼in., 18.4cm.
Issued: 1964-
Price: $172 £69

LONDON CRY,
STRAWBERRIES HN749
Designer: L. Harradine
Height: 6¾in., 17.2cm.
Issued: 1925-1938
Price: $600 £400

LONDON CRY,
STRAWBERRIES HN772
Designer: L. Harradine
Height: 6¾in., 17.2cm.
Issued: 1925-1938
        Colour variation
Price: $600 £400

LONDON CRY, TURNIPS
AND CARROTS HN752
Designer: L. Harradine
Height: 6¾in., 17.2cm.
Issued: 1925-1938
Price: $600 £400

LONDON CRY, TURNIPS
AND CARROTS HN771
Designer: L. Harradine
Height: 6¾in., 17.2cm.
Issued: 1925-1938
Price: $600 £400

LONG JOHN SILVER HN2204
Designer: M. Nicholl
Height: 9in., 22.9cm.
Issued: 1957-1965
Price: $270 £180

LORD OLIVIER AS
RICHARD III HN2881
Designer: E. Griffiths
Height: 11¼in., 28.5cm
Issued: 1985 in a limited
        edition of 750
Price: $625 £250

LORETTA HN2337
Designer: M. Davies
Height: 7¾in., 19.7cm.
Issued: 1966-1980
Price: $82 £55

LORI HN2801
Designer: M. Davies
Height: 5¾in., 14.6cm.
Issued: 1976-
Price: $107 £43

LORNA HN2311
Designer: M. Davies
Height: 8¼in., 21.0cm.
Issued: 1965-1985
Price: $67 £45

LOUISE HN2869
Designer: M. Davies
Height: 6in., 15.2cm.
Issued: 1980-
Price: $107 £43

LOBSTER MAN HN2317

LONDON CRY, STRAWBERRIES
HN749

LONDON CRY, TURNIPS AND
CARROTS HN752

LONG JOHN SILVER HN2204

LORI HN2801

LOUISE HN2869

FIGURES

LOVE LETTER HN2149
Designer: M. Davies
Height: 5½in., 14.0cm.
Issued: 1958-1976
Price: $225 £150

LOVERS HN2762 (White)
Designer: D. Tootle
Height: 12in., 30.5cm.
Issued: 1981
Price: $150 £60

LOVERS HN2763 (Black)
Designer: D. Tootle
Height: 12in., 30.5cm.
Issued: 1981
Price: $150 £60

LUCREZIA BORGIA HN2342
Designer: P. Davies
Height: 8in., 20.0cm.
Issued: 1985 in a limited
edition of 750
Price: $662 £435

LUCY HN2863
Designer: M. Davies
Height: 6in., 15.2cm.
Issued: 1980-1984
Price: $52 £35

LUCY ANN HN1502
Designer: L. Harradine
Height: 5¼in., 13.3cm.
Issued: 1932-1951
Price: $105 £70

LUCY ANN HN1565
Designer: L. Harradine
Height: 5¼in., 13.3cm.
Issued: 1933-1938
Colour variation
Price: $135 £90

**LUCY LOCKETT (Style one)
HN485**
Designer: L. Harradine
Height: 6in., 15.2cm.
Issued: 1921-1949
Price: $450 £300

**LUCY LOCKETT (Style one)
HN524**
Designer: L. Harradine
Height: 6in., 15.2cm.
Issued: 1921-1949
Colour variation
Price: $450 £300

**LUCY LOCKETT (Style two)
HN695**
Designer: L. Harradine
Height: 6in., 15.2cm.
Issued: 1925-1949
Price: $300 £200

**LUCY LOCKETT (Style two)
HN696**
Designer: L. Harradine
Height: 6in., 15.2cm.
Issued: 1925-1949
Colour variation
Price: $300 £200

LOVE LETTER HN2149

LOVERS HN2762 (White)

LUCY HN2863

LUCY ANN HN1502

LUCY LOCKETT (Style one) HN524

LUCY LOCKETT (Style two) HN695

192

FIGURES

LUNCHTIME HN2485
Designer: M. Nicholl
Height: 8in., 20.3cm.
Issued: 1973-1980
Price: $90 £60

LUTE HN2431
Designer: M. Davies
Height: 6¼in., 15.9cm.
Issued: 1972 in a limited
          edition of 750
Price: $450 £300

LYDIA HN1906
Designer: L. Harradine
Height: 4¼in., 10.8cm.
Issued: 1939-1949
Price: $112 £75

LYDIA HN1907
Designer: L. Harradine
Height: 4¾in., 12.0cm.
Issued: 1939-1949
          Colour variation
Price: $112 £75

LYDIA HN1908
Designer: L. Harradine
Height: 4¾in., 12.0cm.
Issued: 1939-
          Colour variation
Price: $117 £47

LYNNE HN2329
Designer: M. Davies
Height: 7in., 17.8cm.
Issued: 1971-
Price: $172 £69

LYNSEY HN3043
Designer: P. Parsons
Height: 4¾in., 12.0cm.
Issued: 1985-
Price: $65 £26

LYRIC HN2757
Designer: E. Griffiths
Height: 6¼in., 16.0cm.
Issued: 1983-
Price: $75 £50

M

MADONNA OF THE SQUARE HN10
Designer: P. Stabler
Height: 7in., 17.8cm.
Issued: 1913-1938
Price: $750 £500

MADONNA OF THE SQUARE HN10A
Designer: P. Stabler
Height: 7in., 17.8cm.
Issued: 1913-1938
          Colour variation
Price: $750 £500

LUNCHTIME HN2485

LUTE HN2431

LYDIA HN1907

LYDIA HN1908

LYNNE HN2329

MADONNA OF THE SQUARE HN10A

MADONNA OF THE SQUARE HN326

MADONNA OF THE SQUARE HN11
Designer: P. Stabler
Height: 7in., 17.8cm.
Issued: 1913-1938
Colour variation
Price: $750 £500

MADONNA OF THE SQUARE HN14
Designer: P. Stabler
Height: 7in., 17.8cm.
Issued: 1913-1938
Colour variation
Price: $750 £500

MADONNA OF THE SQUARE HN27
Designer: P. Stabler
Height: 7in., 17.8cm.
Issued: 1913-1938
Colour variation
Price: $750 £500

MADONNA OF THE SQUARE HN326
Designer: P. Stabler
Height: 7in., 17.8cm.
Issued: 1918-1938
Colour variation
Price: $750 £500

MADONNA OF THE SQUARE HN573
Designer: P. Stabler
Height: 7in., 17.8cm.
Issued: 1913-1938
Colour variation
Price: $750 £500

MADONNA OF THE SQUARE HN576
Designer: P. Stabler
Height: 7in., 17.8cm.
Issued: 1923-1938
Colour variation
Price: $750 £500

MADONNA OF THE SQUARE HN594
Designer: P. Stabler
Height: 7in., 17.8cm.
Issued: 1924-1938
Colour variation
Price: $750 £500

MADONNA OF THE SQUARE HN613
Designer: P. Stabler
Height: 7in., 17.8cm.
Issued: 1924-1938
Colour variation
Price: $750 £500

MADONNA OF THE SQUARE HN764
Designer: P. Stabler
Height: 7in., 17.8cm.
Issued: 1925-1938
Colour variation
Price: $750 £500

MADONNA OF THE SQUARE
HN1968
Designer: P. Stabler
Height: 7in., 17.8cm.
Issued: 1941-1949
          Colour variation
Price: $675 £450

MADONNA OF THE SQUARE
HN1969
Designer: P. Stabler
Height: 7in., 17.8cm.
Issued: 1941-1949
          Colour variation
Price: $675 £450

MADONNA OF THE SQUARE
HN2034
Designer: P. Stabler
Height: 7in., 17.8cm.
Issued: 1949-1951
          Colour variation
Price: $675 £450

MAGIC DRAGON HN2977
Designer: A. Hughes
Height: 4¾in., 12.0cm.
Issued: 1983-
Price: $107 £43

MAGPIE RING HN2978
Designer: A. Hughes
Height: 8in., 20.0cm.
Issued: 1983-
Price: $132 £53

MAISIE HN1618
Designer: L. Harradine
Height: 6¼in., 15.9cm.
Issued: 1934-1949
Price: $187 £125

MAISIE HN1619
Designer: L. Harradine
Height: 6¼in., 15.9cm.
Issued: 1934-1949
          Colour variation
Price: $187 £125

MAJOR, 3rd NEW JERSEY
REGIMENT 1776 HN2752
Designer: E. J. Griffiths
Height: 10in., 25.4cm.
Issued: 1975 in a limited
          edition of 350
Price: $375 £250

MAKE BELIEVE HN2225
Designer: M. Nicholl
Height: 5¾in., 14.6cm.
Issued: 1962-
Price: $107 £43

MAKE BELIEVE (white)
HN2224
Designer: M. Nicholl
Height: 5¾in., 14.6cm.
Issued: 1984-
          Colour variation
Price: $65 £26

MADONNA OF THE SQUARE HN2034

MAJOR, 3rd NEW JERSEY REGIMENT 1776 HN2752   **MAKE BELIEVE HN2225**

MAM'SELLE HN658
Designer: L. Harradine
Height: 7in., 17.8cm.
Issued: 1924-1938
Price: $750 £500

MAM'SELLE HN659
Designer: L. Harradine
Height: 7in., 17.8cm.
Issued: 1924-1938
Colour variation
Price: $750 £500

MAM'SELLE HN724
Designer: L. Harradine
Height: 7in., 17.8cm.
Issued: 1925-1938
Colour variation
Price: $750 £500

MAM'SELLE HN786
Designer: L. Harradine
Height: 7in., 17.8cm.
Issued: 1926-1938
Colour variation
Price: $750 £500

MAN IN TUDOR COSTUME HN563
Designer: Unknown
Height: 3¾in., 9.5cm.
Issued: 1923-1938
Price: $925 £650

MANDARIN (Style one) HN84
Designer: C. J. Noke
Height: 10¼in., 26.0cm.
Issued: 1918-1938
Price: $1650 £1100

MANDARIN (Style one) HN316
Designer: C. J. Noke
Height: 10¼in., 26.0cm.
Issued: 1918-1938
Colour variation
Price: $1650 £1100

MANDARIN (Style one) HN318
Designer: C. J. Noke
Height: 10¾in., 26.0cm.
Issued: 1918-1938
Colour variation
Price: $1650 £1100

MANDARIN (Style one) HN382
Designer: C. J. Noke
Height: 10¼in., 26.0cm.
Issued: 1920-1938
Colour variation
Price: $1650 £1100

MANDARIN (Style one) HN611
Designer: C. J. Noke
Height: 10¼in., 26.0cm.
Issued: 1924-1938
Colour variation
Price: $1500 £1000

MANDARIN (Style one) HN746
Designer: C. J. Noke
Height: 10¼in., 26.0cm.
Issued: 1925-1938
Colour variation
Price: $1500 £1000

MAM'SELLE HN659

MAM'SELLE HN724

MAN IN TUDOR COSTUME HN563

MANDARIN (Style three) HN450

MANDARIN (Style one) HN787
Designer: C. J. Noke
Height: 10¼in., 26.0cm.
Issued: 1926-1938
Colour variation
Price: $1500 £1000

MANDARIN (Style one) HN791
Designer: C.J. Noke
Height: 10¼in., 26.0cm.
Issued: 1926-1938
Colour variation
Price: $1500 £1000

MANDARIN (Style two) HN366
Designer: C. J. Noke
Height: 8¼in., 21.0cm.
Issued: 1920-1938
Price: $1500 £1000

MANDARIN (Style two) HN455
Designer: C. J. Noke
Height: Unknown
Issued: 1921-1938
Price: $1500 £1000

MANDARIN (Style two) HN641
Designer: C. J. Noke
Height: 8¼in., 21.0cm.
Issued: 1924-1938
Colour variation
Price: $1500 £1000

MANDARIN (Style three) HN450
Designer: C. J. Noke
Height: Unknown
Issued: 1921-1938
Price: $1500 £1000

MANDARIN (Style three) HN460
Designer: C. J. Noke
Height: Unknown
Issued: 1921-1938
Colour variation
Price: $1500 £1000

MANDARIN (Style three) HN461
Designer: C. J. Noke
Height: Unknown
Issued: 1921-1938
Colour variation
Price: $1500 £1000

MANDARIN (Style three) HN601
Designer: C. J. Noke
Height: Unknown
Issued: 1924-1938
Colour variation
Price: $1500 £1000

MANDY HN2476
Designer: P. Davies
Height: 4½in., 11.5cm.
Issued: 1982-
Price: $77 £31

MANTILLA HN2712
Designer: E. J. Griffiths
Height: 11½in., 29.2cm.
Issued: 1974-1977
Price: $217 £145

MANTILLA HN2712

MARGARET HN1989
Designer: L. Harradine
Height: 7¼in., 18.4cm.
Issued: 1947-1959
Price: $195 £130

MARGARET HN2397
Designer: P. Davies
Height: 7½in., 19.0cm.
Issued: 1982-
Price: $117 £47

MARGARET OF ANJOU
HN2012
Designer: M. Davies
Height: 9¼in., 23.5cm.
Issued: 1949-1953
Price: $525 £350

MARGERY HN1413
Designer: L. Harradine
Height: 11in., 27.9cm.
Issued: 1930-1949
Price: $262 £175

MARGOT HN1628
Designer: L. Harradine
Height: 5½in., 14.0cm.
Issued: 1934-1938
Price: $412 £275

MARGOT HN1636
Designer: L. Harradine
Height: 5¾in., 14.6cm.
Issued: 1934-1938
        Colour variation
Price: $412 £275

MARGOT HN1653
Designer: L. Harrradine
Height: 5¾in., 14.6cm.
Issued: 1934-1938
        Colour variation
Price: $412 £275

MARGUERITE HN1928
Designer: L. Harradine
Height: 8in., 20.3cm.
Issued: 1940-1959
Price: $195 £130

MARGUERITE HN1929
Designer: L. Harradine
Height: 8in., 20.3cm.
Issued: 1940-1949
        Colour variation
Price: $262 £175

MARGUERITE HN1930
Designer: L. Harradine
Height: 8in., 20.3cm.
Issued: 1940-1949
        Colour variation
Price: $262 £175

MARGUERITE HN1946
Designer: L. Harradine
Height: 8in., 20.3 cm.
Issued: 1940-1949
        Colour variation
Price: $225 £150

MARGARET HN1989

MARGARET HN2397

MARGARET OF ANJOU HN2012

MARGERY HN1413

MARGOT HN1628

MARGUERITE HN1946

MARIANNE HN2074
Designer: L. Harradine
Height: 7¼in., 18.4cm.
Issued: 1951-1953
Price: $330 £220

MARIE (Style one) HN401
Designer: L. Harradine
Height: Unknown
Issued: 1920-1938
Price: $1125 £750

MARIE (Style one) HN434
Designer: L. Harradine
Height: Unknown
Issued: 1921-1938
          Colour variation
Price: $1125 £750

MARIE (Style one) HN502
Designer: L. Harradine
Height: Unknown
Issued: 1921-1938
          Colour variation
Price: $1125 £750

MARIE (Style one) HN504
Designer: L. Harradine
Height: Unknown
Issued: 1921-1938
          Colour variation
Price: $1125 £750

MARIE (Style one) HN505
Designer: L. Harradine
Height: Unknown
Issued: 1921-1938
          Colour variation
Price: $1125 £750

MARIE (Style one) HN506
Designer: L. Harradine
Height: Unknown
Issued: 1921-1938
          Colour variation
Price: $1125 £750

MARIE (Style two) HN1370
Designer: L. Harradine
Height: 4¾in., 12.0cm.
Issued: 1930-
Price: $69 £28

MARIE (Style two) HN1388
Designer: L. Harradine
Height: 4½in., 11.4cm.
Issued: 1930-1938
          Colour variation
Price: $112 £75

MARIE (Style two) HN1417
Designer: L. Harradine
Height: 4¾in., 12.0cm.
Issued: 1930-1949
          Colour variation
Price: $82 £55

MARIE (Style two) HN1489
Designer: L. Harradine
Height: 4½in., 11.4cm.
Issued: 1932-1949
          Colour variation
Price: $82 £55

MARIANNE HN2074

MARIE (Style two) HN1531
Designer: L. Harradine
Height: 4½in., 11.4cm.
Issued: 1932-1938
　　　　Colour variation
Price: $112 £75

MARIE (Style two) HN1635
Designer: L. Harradine
Height: 4¾in., 12.0cm.
Issued: 1934-1949
　　　　Colour variation
Price: $82 £55

MARIE (Style two) HN1655
Designer: L. Harradine
Height: 4½in., 11.4cm.
Issued: 1934-1938
　　　　Colour variation
Price: $112 £75

MARIETTA HN1341
Designer: L. Harradine
Height: 8in., 20.3cm.
Issued: 1929-1949
Price: $450 £300

MARIETTA HN1446
Designer: L. Harradine
Height: 8in., 20.3cm.
Issued: 1931-1949
　　　　Colour variation
Price: $450 £300

MARIETTA HN1699
Designer: L. Harradine
Height: 8in., 20.3cm.
Issued: 1935-1949
Price: $450 £300

MARIGOLD HN1447
Designer: L. Harradine
Height: 6in., 15.2cm.
Issued: 1931-1949
Price: $210 £140

MARIGOLD HN1451
Designer: L. Harradine
Height: 6in., 15.2cm.
Issued: 1931-1938
Price: $210 £140

MARIGOLD HN1555
Designer: L. Harradine
Height: 6in., 15.2cm.
Issued: 1933-1949
　　　　Colour variation
Price: $210 £140

MARION HN1582
Designer: L. Harradine
Height: 6½in., 16.5cm.
Issued: 1933-1938
Price: $375 £250

MARION HN1583
Designer: L. Harradine
Height: 6½in., 16.5cm.
Issued: 1933-1938
　　　　Colour variation
Price: $375 £250

MARIETTA HN1341

MARIQUITA HN1837
Designer: L. Harradine
Height: 8in., 20.3cm.
Issued: 1938-1949
Price: $750 £500

MARJORIE HN2788
Designer: M. Davies
Height: 5¼in., 13.3cm.
Issued: 1980-1984
Price: $82 £55

MARKET DAY HN1991
Designer: L. Harradine
Height: 7¼in., 18.4cm.
Issued: 1975-1981
Price: $180 £120
Also called Country Lass

MARRIAGE OF ART AND INDUSTRY HN2261
Designer: M. Davies
Height: 19in., 48.3cm.
Issued: 1958 in a limited
           edition of 12
Price: $3750 £2500

MARY HN2374
Designer: J. Bromley
Height: 7¾in., 19.5cm.
Issued: 1984
Price: $117 £47

MARY HAD A LITTLE LAMB HN2048
Designer: M. Davies
Height: 3½in., 8.9cm.
Issued: 1949-
Price: $102 £41

MARY JANE HN1990
Designer: L. Harradine
Height: 7½in., 19.1cm.
Issued: 1947-1959
Price: $187 £125

MARY, MARY HN2044
Designer: L. Harradine
Height: 5in., 12.7cm.
Issued: 1949-1973
Price: $90 £60

MARY QUEEN OF SCOTS HN2931
Designer: S. Keenan
Height: 9½in., 24.0cm.
Issued: 1983 in a limited
           edition of 300
Price: $300 £200

MASK HN656
Designer: L. Harradine
Height: 6¾in., 17.2cm.
Issued: 1924-1938
Price: $900 £600

MASK HN657
Designer: L. Harradine
Height: 6¾in., 17.2cm.
Issued: 1924-1938
           Colour variation
Price: $900 £600

MARIQUITA HN1837

MARJORIE HN 2788

MARKET DAY HN1991

MARRIAGE OF ART AND INDUSTRY HN2261

MARY, MARY HN2044

MASK HN656

MASK HN729
Designer: L. Harradine
Height: 6¾in., 17.2cm.
Issued: 1925-1938
            Colour variation
Price: $900 £600

MASK HN733
Designer: L. Harradine
Height: 6¾in., 17.2cm.
Issued: 1925-1938
            Colour variation
Price: $900 £600

MASK HN785
Designer: L. Harradine
Height   6¾in., 17.2cm.
Issued: ·   1926-1938
            Colour variation
Price: $900 £600

MASK HN1271
Designer: L. Harradine
Height: 6¾in., 17.2cm.
Issued: 1928-1938
            Colour variation
Price: $900 £600

MASK SELLER HN1361
Designer: L. Harradine
Height: 8½in., 21.6cm.
Issued: 1929-1938
Price: $525 £350

MASK SELLER HN2103
Designer: L. Harradine
Height: 8½in., 21.6cm.
Issued: 1953-
            Colour variation
Price: **$182 £73**

MASQUE HN2554
Designer: D. V. Tootle
Height: 8½in., 21.6cm.
Issued: 1973-1982
Price: $82 £55

MASQUE HN2554A
Designer: D. V. Tootle
Height: 8½in., 21.6cm.
Issued: 1973-1982
            Colour variation
Price: £82 £55

MASQUERADE (Style one, man) HN599
Designer; L. Harradine
Height: 6¾in., 17.2cm.
Issued: 1924-1949
Price: $525 £350

MASQUERADE (Style one, man) HN636
Designer: L. Harradine
Height: 6¾in., 17.2cm.
Issued: 1924-1938
            Colour variation
Price: $675 £450

MASQUERADE (Style one, man) HN683
Designer: L. Harradine
Height: 7¼in., 18.4cm.
Issued: 1924-1938
            Colour variation
Price: $675 £450

MASK SELLER HN1361

202

MASQUERADE (Style one,
woman) HN600
Designer: L. Harradine
Height: 6¾in., 17.2cm.
Issued: 1924-1949
Price: $525 £350

MASQUERADE (Style one,
woman) HN600A
Designer: L. Harradine
Height: 6in., 15.2cm.
Issued: 1924-1949
           Colour variation
Price: $525 £350

MASQUERADE (Style one,
woman) HN637
Designer: L. Harradine
Height: 6¾in., 17.2cm.
Issued: 1924-1938
           Colour variation
Price: $675 £450

MASQUERADE (Style one,
woman) HN674
Designer: L. Harradine
Height: 6¾in., 17.2cm.
Issued: 1924-1938
           Colour variation
Price: $675 £450

MASQUERADE (Style two)
HN2251
Designer: M. Davies
Height: 8½in., 21.6cm.
Issued: 1960-1965
Price: $240 £160

MASQUERADE (Style two)
HN2259
Designer: M. Davies
Height: 8½in., 21.6cm.
Issued: 1960-1965
           Colour variation
Price: $240 £160

MASTER HN2325
Designer: M. Davies
Height: 6¼in., 15.9cm.
Issued: 1967-
Price: $172 £69

MASTER SWEEP HN2205
Designer: M. Nicholl
Height: 8½in., 21.6cm.
Issued: 1957-1962
Price: $330 £220

MATADOR AND BULL
HN2324
Designer: M. Davies
Height: 16in., 40.6cm.
Issued: 1964-
Price: $12850 £5140

MATILDA HN2011
Designer: M. Davies
Height: 9¼in., 23.5cm.
Issued: 1949-1953
Price: $525 £350

MAUREEN HN1770
Designer: L. Harradine
Height: 7½in., 19.1cm.
Issued: 1936-1959
Price: $240 £160

MASQUERADE (Style one, woman) HN600   MASQUERADE (Style two) HN2251

MASTER HN2325

MASTER SWEEP HN2205

MATADOR AND BULL HN2324   MATILDA HN2011

MAUREEN HN1771
Designer: L. Harradine
Height: 7½in., 19.1cm.
Issued: 1936-1949
Colour variation
Price: $262 £175

MAUREEN M84
Designer: L. Harradine
Height: 4in., 10.1cm.
Issued: 1939-1949
Price: $210 £140

MAUREEN M85
Designer: L. Harradine
Height: 4in., 10.1cm.
Issued: 1939-1949
Colour variation
Price: $210 £140

MAYOR HN2280
Designer: M. Nicholl
Height: 8¼in., 21.0cm.
Issued: 1963-1971
Price: $225 £150

MAYTIME HN2113
Designer: L. Harradine
Height: 7in., 17.8cm.
Issued: 1953-1967
Price: $127 £85

MEDITATION HN2330
Designer: M. Davies
Height: 5¾in., 14.6cm.
Issued: 1971-1983
Price: $98 £65

MELANIE HN2271
Designer: M. Davies
Height: 7¾in., 19.7cm.
Issued: 1965-1980
Price: $75 £50

MELISSA HN2467
Designer: M. Davies
Height: 6¾in., 17.2cm.
Issued: 1981-
Price: $172 £69

MELODY HN2202
Designer: M. Davies
Height: 6¼in., 15.9cm.
Issued: 1957-1962
Price: $150 £100

MEMORIES HN1855
Designer: L. Harradine
Height: 6in., 15.2cm.
Issued: 1938-1949
Price: $210 £140

MEMORIES HN1856
Designer: L. Harradine
Height: 6in., 15.2cm.
Issued: 1938-1949
Colour variation
Price: $210 £140

MEMORIES HN1857
Designer: L. Harradine
Height: 6in., 15.2cm.
Issued: 1938-1949
Colour variation
Price: $210 £140

MAUREEN HN1771

MAYOR HN2280

MAYTIME HN2113

MEDITATION HN2330

MELANIE HN2271

MELISSA HN2467

MEMORIES HN2030
Designer: L. Harradine
Height: 6in., 15.2cm.
Issued: 1949-1959
        Colour variation
Price: $210 £140

MENDICANT HN1355
Designer: L. Harradine
Height: 8¼in., 21.0cm.
Issued: 1929-1938
Price: $225 £150

MENDICANT HN1365
Designer: L. Harradine
Height: 8¼in., 21.0cm.
Issued: 1929-1969
Price: $127 £85

MEPHISTO HN722
Designer: L. Harradine
Height: 6½in., 16.5cm.
Issued: 1925-1938
Price: $1200 £800

MEPHISTO HN723
Designer: L. Harradine
Height: 6½in., 16.5cm.
Issued: 1925-1938
        Colour variation
Price: $1200 £800

**MEPHISTOPHELES AND
MARGUERITE HN755**
Designer: C. J. Noke
Height: 7¾in., 19.7cm.
Issued: 1925-1949
Price: $1125 £750

**MEPHISTOPHELES AND
MARGUERITE HN775**
Designer: C. J. Noke
Height: 7¾in., 19.7cm.
Issued: 1925-1949
        Colour variation
Price: $1125 £750

MERIEL HN1931
Designer: L. Harradine
Height: 7¼in., 18.4cm.
Issued: 1940-1949
Price: $600 £400

MERIEL HN1932
Designer: L. Harradine
Height: 7¼in., 18.4cm.
Issued: 1940-1949
        Colour variation
Price: $600 £400

MERMAID HN97
Designer: H. Tittensor
Height: 7in., 17.8cm.
Issued: 1918-1936
Price: $600 £400

MERMAID HN300
Designer: H. Tittensor
Height: 7in., 17.8cm.
Issued: 1918-1936
Price: $600 £400

MEMORIES HN2030

MENDICANT HN1365

MEPHISTO HN723

MEPHISTOPHELES AND
MARGUERITE HN775

MERIEL HN1932

MERMAID HN97

205

MERYLL HN1917
Designer: L. Harradine
Height: 6¾in., 17.2cm.
Issued: 1939-1940
Price: $900 £600
(Also called Toinette)

MEXICAN DANCER HN2866
Designer: M. Davies
Height: 8¼in., 21.0cm.
Issued: 1979 in a limited
edition of 750
Price: $450 £300

MICHELLE HN2234
Designer: M. Davies
Height: 7in., 17.8cm.
Issued: 1967-
Price: $157 £63

MIDINETTE (Style one)
HN1289
Designer: L. Harradine
Height: 9in., 22.9cm.
Issued: 1928-1938
Price: $1125 £750

MIDINETTE (Style one)
HN1306
Designer: L. Harradine
Height: 9in., 22.9cm.
Issued: 1928-1938
Colour variation
Price: $1125 £750

MIDINETTE (Style two)
HN2090
Designer: L. Harradine
Height: 7¼in., 18.4cm.
Issued: 1952-1965
Price: $225 £150

MIDSUMMER NOON HN1899
Designer: L. Harradine
Height: 4¾in., 12.0cm.
Issued: 1939-1949
Price: $525 £350

MIDSUMMER NOON HN1900
Designer: L. Harradine
Height: 4¾in., 12.0cm.
Issued: 1939-1949
Colour variation
Price: $525 £350

MIDSUMMER NOON HN2033
Designer: L. Harradine
Height: 4¾in., 12.0cm.
Issued: 1949-1955
Colour variation
Price: $525 £350

MILADY HN1970
Designer: L. Harradine
Height: 6½in., 16.5cm.
Issued: 1941-1949
Price: $450 £300

MILKING TIME HN3
Designer: P. Stabler
Height: Unknown
Issued: 1913-1938
Price: $1950 £1300

MERYLL HN1917

MEXICAN DANCER HN2866

MICHELLE HN2234

MIDINETTE (Style one) HN1289

MIDSUMMER NOON HN1899

MILADY HN1970

MILKING TIME HN306
Designer: P. Stabler
Height: Unknown
Issued: 1913-1938
Colour variation
Price: $1950 £1300

MILKMAID HN2057A
Designer: L. Harradine
Height: 6½in., 16.5cm.
Issued: 1975-1982
Price: $90 £60
Also called The Jersey
Milkmaid

MILLICENT HN1714
Designer: L. Harradine
Height: 8in., 20.3cm.
Issued: 1935-1949
Price: $450 £300

MILLICENT HN1715
Designer: L. Harradine
Height: 8in., 20.3cm.
Issued: 1935-1949
Colour variation
Price: $450 £300

MILLICENT HN1860
Designer: L. Harradine
Height: 8in., 20.3cm.
Issued: 1938-1949
Colour variation
Price: $450 £300

MINUET HN2019
Designer: M. Davies
Height: 7¼in., 18.4cm.
Issued: 1949-1971
Price: $187 £125

MINUET HN2066
Designer: M. Davies
Height: 7¼in., 18.4cm.
Issued: 1950-1955
Colour variation
Price: $300 £200

MIRABEL HN1743
Designer: L. Harradine
Height: 7¾in., 19.7cm.
Issued: 1935-1949
Price: $375 £250

MIRABEL HN1744
Designer: L. Harradine
Height: 7¾in., 19.7cm.
Issued: 1935-1949
Colour variation
Price: $375 £250

MIRABEL M68
Designer: L. Harradine
Height: 4in., 10.1cm.
Issued: 1936-1949
Price: $210 £140

MIRABEL M74
Designer: L. Harradine
Height: 4in., 10.1cm.
Issued: 1936-1949
Colour variation
Price: $210 £140

MILKMAID HN2057A

MILLICENT HN1714

MINUET HN2019

MIRABEL HN1743

MIRANDA HN1818
Designer: L. Harradine
Height: 8½in., 21.6cm.
Issued: 1937-1949
Price: $525 £350

MIRANDA HN1819
Designer: L. Harradine
Height: 8½in., 21.6cm.
Issued: 1937-1949
Colour variation
Price: $525 £350

MIRROR HN1852
Designer: L. Harradine
Height: 7½in., 18.4cm.
Issued: 1938-1949
Price: $525 £350

MIRROR HN1853
Designer: L. Harradine
Height: 7½in., 18.4cm.
Issued: 1938-1949
Colour variation
Price: $525 £350

MISS DEMURE HN1402
Designer: L. Harradine
Height: 7½in., 19.1cm.
Issued: 1930-1975
Price: $127 £85

MISS DEMURE HN1440
Designer: L. Harradine
Height: 7in., 17.8cm.
Issued: 1930-1949
Colour variation
Price: $165 £110

MISS DEMURE HN1463
Designer: L. Harradine
Height: 7in., 17.8cm.
Issued: 1931-1949
Colour variation
Price: $165 £110

MISS DEMURE HN1499
Designer: L. Harradine
Height: 7in., 17.8cm.
Issued: 1932-1938
Colour variation
Price: $225 £150

MISS DEMURE HN1560
Designer: L. Harradine
Height: 7in., 17.7cm.
Issued: 1933-1949
Price: $120 £80

MISS FORTUNE HN1897
Designer: L. Harradine
Height: 6in., 15.2cm.
Issued: 1938-1949
Price: $300 £200

MISS FORTUNE HN1898
Designer: L. Harradine
Height: 5¾in., 14.6cm.
Issued: 1938-1949
Colour variation
Price: $300 £200

MIRANDA HN1818

MIRROR HN1852

MISS DEMURE HN1402

MISS FORTUNE HN1897

MISS MUFFET HN1936
Designer: L. Harradine
Height: 5½in., 13.3cm.
Issued: 1940-1967
Price: $105 £70

MISS MUFFET HN1937
Designer: L. Harradine
Height: 5½in., 13.3cm.
Issued: 1940-1952
Colour variation
Price: $135 £90

MISS 1926 HN1205
Designer: L. Harradine
Height: 7¼in., 18.4cm.
Issued: 1926-1938
Price: $1200 £800

MISS 1926 HN1207
Designer: L. Harradine
Height: 7¼in., 18.4cm.
Issued: Unknown
Colour variation
Price: $1200 £800

MISS WINSOME HN1665
Designer: L. Harradine
Height: 6¾in., 17.2cm.
Issued: 1934-1949
Price: $180 £120

MISS WINSOME HN1666
Designer: L. Harradine
Height: 6¾in., 17.2cm.
Issued: 1934-1938
Colour variation
Price: $225 £150

M'LADY'S MAID HN1795
Designer: L. Harradine
Height: 9in., 22.9cm.
Issued: 1936-1949
Price: $750 £500

M'LADY'S MAID HN1822
Designer: L. Harradine
Height: 9in., 22.9cm.
Issued: 1937-1949
Colour variation
Price: $750 £500

MODENA HN1845
Designer: L. Harradine
Height: 7¼in., 18.4cm.
Issued: 1938-1949
Price: $525 £350

MODENA HN1846
Designer: L. Harradine
Height: 7¼in., 18.4cm.
Issued: 1938-1949
Colour variation
Price: $525 £350

MODERN PIPER HN756
Designer: L. Harradine
Height: 8½in., 21.6cm.
Issued: 1925-1938
Price: $1200 £800

MISS MUFFET HN1936

MISS 1926 HN1205

MISS WINSOME HN1665

MODERN PIPER HN756

FIGURES

MOIRA HN1347
Designer: L. Harradine
Height: 6½in., 16.5cm.
Issued: 1929-1938
Price: $1275 £850

MOLLY MALONE HN1455
Designer: L. Harradine
Height: 7in., 17.8cm.
Issued: 1931-1938
Price: $1275 £850

MONICA HN1458
Designer: L. Harradine
Height: 4in., 10.1cm.
Issued: 1931-1949
Price: $112 £75

MONICA HN1459
Designer: L. Harradine
Height: 4in., 10.1cm.
Issued: 1931-1949
Price: $112 £75

MONICA HN1467
Designer: L. Harradine
Height: 4in., 10.1cm.
Issued: 1931-
Colour variation
Price: $102 £41

MONICA M66
Designer: L. Harradine
Height: 3in., 7.6cm.
Issued: 1935-1949
Price: $180 £120

MONICA M72
Designer: L. Harradine
Height: 3in., 7.6cm.
Issued: 1936-1949
Colour variation
Price: $180 £120

MONTE CARLO HN2332
Designer: P. Davies
Height: 8¼in., 20.9cm.
Issued: 1982 in a limited
edition of 1500
Price: $225 £150

MOOR HN1308
Designer: C. J. Noke
Height: 16½in., 41.9cm.
Issued: 1929-1938
Price: $750 £500

MOOR HN1366
Designer: C. J. Noke
Height: 16½in., 41.9cm.
Issued: 1930-1949
Colour variation
Price: $750 £500

MOOR HN1425
Designer: C. J. Noke
Height: 16½in., 41.9cm.
Issued: 1930-1949
Colour variation
Price: $750 £500

MOIRA HN1347

MOLLY MALONE HN1455

MONICA HN1458

MONICA M66

MONTE CARLO HN2332

MOOR HN1308

MOOR HN1657
Designer: C. J. Noke
Height: 16½in., 41.9cm.
Issued: 1934-1949
Colour variation
Price: $750 £500

MOOR HN2082
Designer: C. J. Noke
Height: 16¼in., 41.2cm.
Issued: 1952-
Colour variation
Price: $1437 £575
Also called "An Arab"

MOORISH MINSTREL HN34
Designer: C. J. Noke
Height: 13½in., 34.3cm.
Issued: 1913-1938
Price: $1125 £750

MOORISH MINSTREL HN364
Designer: C. J. Noke
Height: 13½in., 34.3cm.
Issued: 1920-1938
Colour variation
Price: $1125 £750

MOORISH MINSTREL HN415
Designer: C. J. Noke
Height: 13½in., 34.3cm.
Issued: 1920-1938
Colour variation
Price: $1125 £750

MOORISH MINSTREL HN797
Designer: C. J. Noke
Height: 13½in., 34.3cm.
Issued: 1926-1949
Colour variation
Price: $1125 £750

**MOORISH PIPER
MINSTREL HN301**
Designer: C. J. Noke
Height: 13½in., 34.3cm.
Issued: 1918-1938
Price: $1125 £750

**MOORISH PIPER
MINSTREL HN328**
Designer: C. J. Noke
Height: 13½in., 34.3cm.
Issued: 1918-1938
Colour variation
Price: $1125 £750

**MOORISH PIPER
MINSTREL HN416**
Designer: C. J. Noke
Height: 13½in., 34.3cm.
Issued: 1920-1938
Colour variation
Price: $1125 £750

**MOTHER AND DAUGHTER
HN2843 (Black)**
Designer: E. Griffiths
Height: 8½in., 21.5cm.
Issued: 1981
Price: $150 £60

 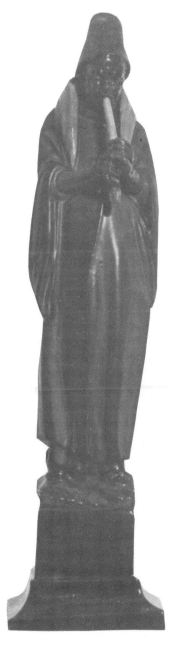

MOORISH MINSTREL HN34   **MOORISH PIPER MINSTREL HN301**

FIGURES

MOTHER AND DAUGHTER
HN2841 (White)
Designer: E. Griffiths
Height: 8½in., 21.5cm.
Issued: 1981
Price: $150 £60

MOTHER'S HELP HN2151
Designer: M. Davies
Height: 5in., 12.7cm.
Issued: 1962-1969
Price: $67 £45

MOTHERHOOD HN28
Designer: P. Stabler
Height: Unknown
Issued: 1913-1938
Price: $1350 £900

MOTHERHOOD HN30
Designer: P. Stabler
Height: Unknown
Issued: 1913-1938
Colour variation
Price: $1350 £900

MOTHERHOOD HN303
Designer: P. Stabler
Height: Unknown
Issued: 1918-1938
Colour variation
Price: $1350 £900

MR. MICAWBER (Style one)
HN532
Designer: L. Harradine
Height: 3½in., 8.9cm.
Issued: 1922-1932
Price: $45 £30

MR. MICAWBER (Style two)
HN557
Designer: L. Harradine
Height: 7in., 17.8cm.
Issued: 1923-1939
Price: $270 £180

MR. MICAWBER (Style two)
HN1895
Designer: L. Harradine
Height: 7in., 17.8cm.
Issued: 1938-1952
Colour variation
Price: $240 £160

MR MICAWBER (Style three)
HN2097
Designer: L. Harradine
Height: 7½in., 19.1cm.
Issued: 1952-1967
Price: $180 £120

MR MICAWBER M42
Designer: L. Harradine
Height: 4in., 10.1cm.
Issued: 1932-1982
Price: $37 £25

MR PICKWICK (Style one)
HN529
Designer: L. Harradine
Height: 3¾in., 9.5cm.
Issued: 1922-1932
Price: $45 £30

MOTHER AND DAUGHTER HN2841 (White)

MOTHER'S HELP HN2151

MR MICAWBER (Style one) HN532

MR MICAWBER (Style two) HN557

MR MICAWBER (Style three) HN2097

MR PICKWICK (Style one) HN529

212

MR PICKWICK (Style two)
HN556
Designer: L. Harradine
Height: 7in., 17.8cm.
Issued: 1923-1939
Price: $270 £180

MR PICKWICK (Style two)
HN1894
Designer: L. Harradine
Height: 7in., 17.8cm.
Issued: 1938-1952
        Colour variation
Price: $240 £160

MR PICKWICK (Style three)
HN2099
Designer: L. Harradine
Height: 7½in., 19.1cm.
Issued: 1952-1967
Price: $180 £120

MR PICKWICK M41
Designer: L. Harradine
Height: 4in., 10.1cm.
Issued: 1932-1982
Price: $37 £25

MRS BARDELL M86
Designer: L. Harradine
Height: 4¼in., 10.1cm.
Issued: 1949-1982
Price: $37 £25

MRS FITZHERBERT HN2007
Designer: M. Davies
Height: 9¼in., 23.5cm.
Issued: 1948-1953
Price: $525 £350

MUSICALE HN2756
Designer: E. Griffiths
Height: 9in., 23cm.
Issued: 1983
Price: $90 £60

MY LOVE HN2339
Designer: M. Davies
Height: 6¼in., 15.9cm.
Issued: 1969-
Price: $182 £73

MY PET HN2238
Designer: M. Davies
Height: 2¾in., 7.0cm.
Issued: 1962-1975
Price: $87 £58

MY PRETTY MAID HN2064
Designer: L. Harradine
Height: 5½in., 14.0cm.
Issued: 1950-1954
Price: $127 £85

MY TEDDY HN2177
Designer: M. Davies
Height: 3¼in., 8.3cm.
Issued: 1962-1967
Price: $150 £100

MR PICKWICK (Style two) HN556   **MR PICKWICK (Style three) HN2099**

MRS BARDELL M86   **MRS FITZHERBERT HN2007**

MY LOVE HN2339   **MY PET HN2238**

MYFANWY JONES HN39
Designer: E. W. Light
Height: 12in., 30.5cm.
Issued: 1914-1938
Price: $1500 £1000
See Welsh Girl

MYFANWY JONES HN92
Designer: E. W. Light
Height: 12in., 30.5cm.
Issued: 1918-1938
            Colour variation
Price: $1500 £1000
See Welsh Girl

MYFANWY JONES HN456
Designer: E. W. Light
Height: 12in., 30.5cm.
Issued: 1921-1938
            Colour variation
Price: $1500 £1000 '
See Welsh Girl

MYFANWY JONES HN514
Designer: E. W. Light;
Height: 12in., 30.5cm.
Issued: 1921-1938
            Colour variation
Price: $1500 £1000
See Welsh Girl

MYFANWY JONES HN516
Designer: E. W. Light
Height: 12in., 30.5cm.
Issued: 1921-1938
            Colour variation
Price: $1500 £1000
See Welsh Girl

MYFANWY JONES HN519
Designer: E. W. Light:
Height: 12in., 30.5cm.
Issued: 1921-1938
            Colour variation
Price: $1500 £1000
See Welsh Girl

MYFANWY JONES HN520
Designer: E. W. Light
Height: 12in., 30.5cm.
Issued: 1921-1938
            Colour variation
Price: $1500 £1000
See Welsh Girl

MYFANWY JONES HN660
Designer: E. W. Light
Height: 12in., 30.5cm.
Issued: 1924-1938
            Colour variation
Price: $1500 £1000
See Welsh Girl

MYFANWY JONES HN668
Designer: E. W. Light
Height: 12in., 30.5cm.
Issued: 1924-1938
            Colour variation
Price: $1500 £1000
See Welsh Girl

MYFANWY JONES HN39

214

MYFANWY JONES HN669
Designer: E. W. Light
Height: 12in., 30.5cm.
Issued: 1924-1938
Colour variation
Price: $1500 £1000
See Welsh Girl

MYFANWY JONES HN701
Designer: E. W. Light
Height: 12in., 30.5cm.
Issued: 1925-1938
Colour variation
Price: $1500 £1000
See Welsh Girl

MYFANWY JONES HN792
Designer: E. W. Light
Height: 12in., 30.5cm.
Issued: 1926-1938
Colour variation
Price: $1500 £1000
See Welsh Girl

N

NADINE HN1885
Designer: L. Harradine
Height: 7¾in., 19.7cm.
Issued: 1938-1949
Price: $450 £300

NADINE HN1886
Designer: L. Harradine
Height: 7¾in., 19.7cm.
Issued: 1938-1949
Colour variation
Price: $450 £300

NANA HN1766
Designer: L. Harradine
Height: 4¾in., 12.0cm.
Issued: 1936-1949
Price: $127 £85

NANA HN1767
Designer: L. Harradine
Height: 4¾in., 12.0cm.
Issued: 1936-1949
Colour variation
Price: $127 £85

NANCY HN2955
Designer: P. Parsons
Height: 7½in., 19.0cm.
Issued: 1982-
Price: $117 £47

NANNY HN2221
Designer: M. Davies
Height: 6in., 15.2cm.
Issued: 1958-
Price: $182 £73

NEGLIGEE HN1219
Designer: L. Harradine
Height: 5in., 12.7cm.
Issued: 1927-1938
Price: $675 £450

NADINE HN1885

NANA HN1766

NANNY HN2221

215

NEGLIGEE HN1228
Designer: L. Harradine
Height: 5in., 12.7cm.
Issued: 1927-1938
          Colour variation
Price: $675 £450

NEGLIGEE HN1272
Designer: L. Harradine
Height: 5in., 12.7cm.
Issued: 1928-1938
          Colour variation
Price: $675 £450

NEGLIGEE HN1273
Designer: L. Harradine
Height: 5in., 12.7cm.
Issued: 1928-1938
          Colour variation
Price: $675 £450

NEGLIGEE HN1454
Designer: L. Harradine
Height: 5in., 12.7cm.
Issued: 1931-1938
          Colour variation
Price: $675 £450

NELL HN3014
Designer: P. Parsons
Height: 4in., 10.0cm.
Issued: 1983-
Price: $107 £43

NELL GWYNN HN1882
Designer: L. Harradine
Height: 6¾in., 17.2cm.
Issued: 1938-1949
Price: $397 £265

NELL GWYNN HN1887
Designer: L. Harradine
Height: 6¾in., 17.2cm.
Issued: 1938-1949
          Colour variation
Price: $397 £265

NELSON HN2928
Designer: S. Keenan
Height: 8¾in., 22.2cm.
Issued: 1981 in a limited
          edition of 950
Price: $150 £100

NEW BONNET HN1728
Designer: L. Harradine
Height: 7in., 17.8cm.
Issued: 1935-1949
Price: $390 £260

NEW BONNET HN1957
Designer: L. Harradine
Height: 7in., 17.8cm.
Issued: 1940-1949
          Colour variation
Price: $390 £260

NEW COMPANIONS HN2770
Designer: W. K. Harper
Height: 7¾in., 19.5cm.
Issued: 1982-
Price: $135 £90

NEGLIGEE HN1454   NELL GWYNN HN1887

NELSON HN2928   NEW BONNET HN1728

NEW BONNET HN1957   NEW COMPANIONS HN2770

**NEWHAVEN FISHWIFE
HN1480**
Designer: H. Fenton
Height: 7¾in., 19.7cm.
Issued: 1931-1938
Price: $1200 £800

NEWSBOY HN2244
Designer: M. Davies
Height: 8½in., 21.6cm.
Issued: 1959-1965
Price: $330 £220

NICOLA HN2839
Designer: M. Davies
Height: 7in., 17.8cm.
Issued: 1978-
Price: $247 £99

NINA HN2347
Designer: M. Davies
Height: 7½in., 19.1cm.
Issued: 1969-1976
Price: $82 £55

NINETTE HN2379
Designer: M. Davies
Height: 7½in., 19.1cm.
Issued: 1971-
Price: $182 £73

NOELLE HN2179
Designer: M. Davies
Height: 6¾in., 17.2cm.
Issued: 1957-1967
Price: $210 £140

NORMA M36
Designer: Unknown
Height: 4½in., 11.4cm.
Issued: 1933-1945
Price: $217 £145

NORMA M37
Designer: Unknown
Height: 4½in., 11.4cm.
Issued: 1933-1945
 Colour variation
Price: $217 £145

**NORTH AMERICAN INDIAN
DANCER HN2809**
Designer: P. Davies
Height: 8½in., 21.5cm.
Issued: 1982 in a limited
 edition of 750
Price: $450 £300

NUDE ON ROCK HN593
Designer: Unknown
Height: Unknown
Issued: 1924-1938
Price: $600 £400

O

ODDS AND ENDS HN1844
Designer: L. Harradine
Height: 7¾in., 19.6cm.
Issued: 1938-1949
Price: $750 £500

NEWHAVEN FISHWIFE HN1480

NEWSBOY HN2244

NINA HN2347

NOELLE HN2179

NORTH AMERICAN INDIAN
DANCER HN2809

ODDS AND ENDS HN1844

OFFICER OF THE LINE
HN2733
Designer: W. K. Harper
Height: 9in., 23.0cm.
Issued: 1983-
Price: $237 £95

OLD BALLOON SELLER
HN1315
Designer: L. Harradine
Height: 7½in., 19.1cm.
Issued: 1929-
Price: $172 £69

**OLD BALLOON SELLER
AND BULLDOG HN1791**
Designer: L. Harradine
Height: 7in., 17.8cm.
Issued: 1932-1938
Price: $300 £200

**OLD BALLOON SELLER
AND BULLDOG HN1912**
Designer: Unknown
Height: Unknown
Issued: 1939-1949
Price: $300 £200

OLD KING HN358
Designer: C. J. Noke
Height: 9¾in., 24.7cm.
Issued: 1919-1938
Price: $600 £400

OLD KING HN623
Designer: C. J. Noke
Height: 9¾in., 24.7cm.
Issued: 1924-1938
Colour variation
Price: $600 £400

OLD KING HN1801
Designer: C. J. Noke
Height: 9¾in., 24.7cm.
Issued: 1937-1954
Price: $450 £300

OLD KING HN2134
Designer: C. J. Noke
Height: 10¾in., 27.3cm.
Issued: 1954-
Colour variation
Price: $497 £199

OLD KING COLE HN2217
Designer: M. Davies
Height: 6½in., 16.5cm.
Issued: 1963-1967
Price: $300 £200

OLD LAVENDER SELLER
HN1492
Designer: L. Harradine
Height: 6in., 15.2cm.
Issued: 1932-1949
Price: $412 £275

OLD LAVENDER SELLER
HN1571
Designer: L. Harradine
Height: 6½in., 16.5cm.
Issued: 1933-1949
Price: $412 £275

OLD BALLOON SELLER HN1315

OLD BALLOON SELLER
AND BULLDOG HN1791

OLD KING HN358

OLD KING HN2134

OLD KING COLE HN2217

OLD LAVENDER SELLER HN1492

218

FIGURES

OLD MAN HN451
Designer: Unknown
Height: Unknown
Issued: 1921-1938
Price: $1275 £850

OLD MEG HN2494
Designer: M. Nicholl
Height: 8¼in., 21.0cm.
Issued: 1974-1976
Price: $112 £75

OLD MOTHER HUBBARD HN2314
Designer: M. Nicholl
Height: 8in., 20.3cm.
Issued: 1964-1975
Price: $180 £120

OLGA HN2463
Designer: J. Bromley
Height: 8¼in., 21.0cm
Issued: 1972-1975
Price: $105 £70

OLIVER TWIST M89
Designer: L. Harradine
Height: 4¼in., 10.8cm.
Issued: 1949-1982
Price: $37 £25

OLIVIA HN1995
Designer: L. Harradine
Height: 7½in., 19.1cm.
Issued: 1947-1951
Price: $270 £180

OMAR KHAYYAM (Style one) HN408
Designer: C. J. Noke
Height: 6in., 15.2cm.
Issued: 1920-1938
Price: $1875 £1250

OMAR KHAYYAM (Style one) HN409
Designer: C. J. Noke
Height: 6in., 15.2cm.
Issued: 1920-1938
         Colour variation
Price: $1875 £1250

OMAR KHAYYAM (Style two) HN2247
Designer: M. Nicholl
Height: 6¼in., 15.9cm.
Issued: 1965-1983
Price: $120 £80

OMAR KHAYYAM AND THE BELOVED HN407
Designer: C. J. Noke
Height: 10in., 25.4cm.
Issued: 1920-1938
Price: $1875 £1250

OMAR KHAYYAM AND THE BELOVED HN419
Designer: C. J. Noke
Height: 6in., 15.2cm.
Issued: 1920-1938
Price: $1875 £1250

OLD MEG HN2494

OLD MOTHER HUBBARD HN2314

OLGA HN2463

OLIVER TWIST M89

OMAR KHAYYAM (Style one) HN408   OMAR KHAYYAM (Style two) HN2247

**OMAR KHAYYAM AND THE
BELOVED HN459**
Designer: C. J. Noke
Height: 10in., 25.4cm.
Issued: 1921-1938
Price: $1875 £1250

**OMAR KHAYYAM AND THE
BELOVED HN598**
Designer: C. J. Noke
Height: 10in., 25.4cm.
Issued: 1924-1938
Price: $1875 £1250

ONCE UPON A TIME HN2047
Designer: L. Harradine
Height: 4¼in., 10.8cm.
Issued: 1949-1955
Price: $150 £100

ONE OF THE FORTY
(Style one) HN417
Designer: H. Tittensor
Height: 8¼in., 21.0cm.
Issued: 1920-1938
Price: $720 £480

ONE OF THE FORTY
(Style one) HN490
Designer: H. Tittensor
Height: 8¼in., 21.0cm.
Issued: 1921-1938
        Colour variation
Price: $720 £480

ONE OF THE FORTY
(Style one) HN495
Designer: H. Tittensor
Height: 8¼in., 21.0cm.
Issued: 1921-1938
        Colour variation
Price: $720 £480

ONE OF THE FORTY
(Style one) HN501
Designer: H. Tittensor
Height: 8¼in., 21cm.
Issued: 1921-1938
        Colour variation
Price: $720 £480

ONE OF THE FORTY
(Style one) HN648
Designer: H. Tittensor
Height: 8¼in., 21.0cm.
Issued: 1924-1938
        Colour variation
Price: $720 £480

ONE OF THE FORTY
(Style one) HN528
Designer: H. Tittensor
Height: 8¼in., 21cm.
Issued: 1921-1938
        Colour variation
Price: $720 £480

ONE OF THE FORTY
(Style one) HN677
Designer: H. Tittensor
Height: 8¼in., 21.0cm.
Issued: 1924-1938
        Colour variation
Price: $720 £480

ONCE UPON A TIME HN2047   ONE OF THE FORTY (Style six) HN423C

ONE OF THE FORTY HN423   ONE OF THE FORTY (Style ten) HN664

ONE OF THE FORTY
(Style one) HN1351
Designer: H. Tittensor
Height: 8¼in., 21.0cm
Issued: 1920-1949
Colour variation
Price: $720 £480

ONE OF THE FORTY
(Style one) HN1352
Designer: H. Tittensor
Height: 8¼in., 21.0cm.
Issued: 1929-1949
Colour variation
Price: $720 £480

ONE OF THE FORTY
(Style two) HN418
Designer: H. Tittensor
Height: 7¼in., 18.4cm.
Issued: 1920-1938
Price: $720 £480

ONE OF THE FORTY
(Style two) HN494
Designer: H. Tittensor
Height: 7¼in., 18.4cm.
Issued: 1921-1938
Colour variation
Price: $720 £480

ONE OF THE FORTY
(Style two) HN498
Designer: H. Tittensor
Height: 7¼in., 18.4cm.
Issued: 1921-1938
Colour variation
Price: $720 £480

ONE OF THE FORTY
(Style two) HN647
Designer: H. Tittensor
Height: 7¼in., 18.4cm.
Issued: 1924-1938
Colour variation
Price: $720 £480

ONE OF THE FORTY
(Style two) HN666
Designer: H. Tittensor
Height: 7¼in., 18.4cm.
Issued: 1924-1938
Colour variation
Price: $720 £480

ONE OF THE FORTY
(Style two) HN704
Designer: H. Tittensor
Height: 7¼in., 18.4cm.
Issued: 1925-1938
Colour variation
Price: $720 £480

ONE OF THE FORTY
(Style two) HN1353
Designer: H. Tittensor
Height: 7¼in., 18.4cm.
Issued: 1929-1949
Colour variation
Price: $720 £480

ONE OF THE FORTY (Style one) HN677

ONE OF THE FORTY
(Style three) HN423
Designer: H. Tittensor
Height: 3in., 7.6cm.
Issued: 1921-1938
Price: $375 £250

ONE OF THE FORTY
(Style four) HN423A
Designer: H. Tittensor
Height: Unknown
Issued: 1921-1938
Price: $375 £250

ONE OF THE FORTY
(Style five) HN423B
Designer: H. Tittensor
Height: 2¾in., 6.9cm.
Issued: 1921-1938
Price: $375 £250

ONE OF THE FORTY
(Style six) HN423C
Designer: H. Tittensor
Height: 2¾in., 6.9cm.
Issued: 1921-1938
Price: $375 £250

ONE OF THE FORTY
(Style seven) HN423D
Designer: H. Tittensor
Height: 2¾in., 6.9cm.
Issued: 1921-1938
Price: $375 £250

ONE OF THE FORTY
(Style eight) HN423E
Designer: H. Tittensor
Height: Unknown
Issued: 1921-1938
Price: $375 £250

ONE OF THE FORTY
(Style nine) HN427
Designer: H. Tittensor
Height: Unknown
Issued: 1921-1938
Price: $720 £480

ONE OF THE FORTY
(Style ten) HN480
Designer: H. Tittensor
Height: 7in., 17.8cm.
Issued: 1921-1938
Price: $720 £480

ONE OF THE FORTY
(Style ten) HN493
Designer: H. Tittensor
Height: 6¾in., 17.1cm.
Issued: 1921-1938
Price: $720 £480

ONE OF THE FORTY
(Style ten) HN497
Designer: H. Tittensor
Height: 6¾in., 17.1cm.
Issued: 1921-1938
Colour variation
Price: $720 £480

ONE OF THE FORTY HN423

ONE OF THE FORTY HN423

ONE OF THE FORTY (Style five) HN423B

ONE OF THE FORTY HN423

ONE OF THE FORTY
(Style ten) HN499
Designer: H. Tittensor
Height: 6¾in., 17.1cm.
Issued: 1921-1938
Colour variation
Price: $720 £480

ONE OF THE FORTY
(Style ten) HN664
Designer: H. Tittensor
Height: 7¾in., 19.7cm.
Issued: 1924-1938
Colour variation
Price: $720 £480

ONE OF THE FORTY
(Style ten) HN714
Designer: H. Tittensor
Height: 6¾in., 17.2cm.
Issued: 1925-1938
Colour variation
Price: $720 £480

ONE OF THE FORTY
(Style eleven) HN481
Designer: H. Tittensor
Height: Unknown
Issued: 1921-1938
Price: $720 £480

ONE OF THE FORTY
(Style eleven) HN483
Designer: H. Tittensor
Height: Unknown
Issued: 1921-1938
Colour variation
Price: $720 £480

ONE OF THE FORTY
(Style eleven) HN491
Designer: H. Tittensor
Height: Unknown
Issued: 1921-1938
Colour variation
Price: $720 £480

ONE OF THE FORTY
(Style eleven) HN646
Designer: H. Tittensor
Height: Unknown
Issued: 1924-1938
Colour variation
Price: $720 £480

ONE OF THE FORTY
(Style eleven) HN667
Designer: H. Tittensor
Height: Unknown
Issued: 1924-1938
Colour variation
Price: $720 £480

ONE OF THE FORTY
(Style eleven) HN712
Designer: H. Tittensor
Height: Unknown
Issued: 1925-1938
Colour variation
Price: $720 £480

ONE OF THE FORTY (Style ten) HN714

FIGURES

ONE OF THE FORTY
(Style eleven) HN1336
Designer: H. Tittensor
Height: Unknown
Issued: 1929-1938
         Colour variation
Price: $720 £480

ONE OF THE FORTY
(Style eleven) HN1350
Designer: H. Tittensor
Height: Unknown
Issued: 1929-1949
         Colour variation
Price: £720 £480

ONE OF THE FORTY
(Style twelve) HN482
Designer: H. Tittensor
Height: 6in., 15.2cm.
Issued: 1921-1938
Price: $720 £480

ONE OF THE FORTY
(Style twelve) HN484
Designer: H. Tittensor
Height: 6in., 15.2cm.
Issued: 1921-1938
         Colour variation
Price: $720 £480

ONE OF THE FORTY
(Style twelve) HN492
Designer: H. Tittensor
Height: 6in., 15.2cm.
Issued: 1921-1938
         Colour variation
Price: $720 £480

ONE OF THE FORTY
(Style twelve) HN645
Designer: H. Tittensor
Height: 6in., 15.2cm.
Issued: 1924-1938
         Colour variation
Price: $720 £480

ONE OF THE FORTY
(Style twelve) HN663
Designer: H. Tittensor
Height: 6in., 15.2cm.
Issued: 1924-1938
         Colour variation
Price: $720 £480

ONE OF THE FORTY
(Style twelve) HN 713
Designer: H. Tittensor
Height: 6in., 15.2cm.
Issued: 1925-1938
         Colour variation
Price: $720 £480

ONE OF THE FORTY
(Style thirteen) HN496
Designer: H. Tittensor
Height: 7¾in., 19.6cn.
Issued: 1921-1938
Price: $720 £480

ONE OF THE FORTY HN 423   ONE OF THE FORTY (Style one) HN1351

ONE OF THE FORTY (Style ten) HN480   ONE OF THE FORTY HN423

ONE OF THE FORTY
(Style thirteen) HN500
Designer: H. Tittensor
Height: 7¾in., 19.7cm.
Issued: 1921-1938
Colour variation
Price: $720 £480

ONE OF THE FORTY
(Style thirteen) HN649
Designer: H. Tittensor
Height: 7¾in., 19.7cm.
Issued: 1924-1938
Colour variation
Price: $720 £480

ONE OF THE FORTY
(Style thirteen) HN665
Designer: H. Tittensor
Height: 7¾in., 19.7cm.
Issued: 1924-1938
Colour variation
Price: $720 £480

ONE OF THE FORTY
(Style thirteen) HN1354
Designer: H. Tittensor
Height: 7¾in., 19.7cm.
Issued: 1929-1949
Colour variation
Price: $720 £480

ONE THAT GOT AWAY
HN2153
Designer: M. Davies
Height: 6¼in., 15.9cm.
Issued: 1955-1959
Price: $120 £80

ORANGE LADY HN1759
Designer: L. Harradine
Height: 8¾in., 22.2cm.
Issued: 1936-1975
Price: $135 £90

ORANGE LADY HN1953
Designer: L. Harradine
Height: 8½in., 21.6cm.
Issued: 1940-1975
Colour variation
Price: $135 £90

ORANGE SELLER HN1325
Designer: L. Harradine
Height: 7in., 17.8cm.
Issued: 1929-1949
Price: $450 £300

ORANGE VENDOR HN72
Designer: C. J. Noke
Height: 6¼in., 15.9cm.
Issued: 1917-1938
Price: $675 £450

ORANGE VENDOR HN508
Designer: C. J. Noke
Height: 6¼in., 15.8cm.
Issued: 1921-1938
Price: $675 £450

ONE THAT GOT AWAY HN2153

ORANGE LADY HN1759

ORANGE LADY HN1953

ORANGE VENDOR HN508

ORANGE VENDOR HN521
Designer: C. J. Noke
Height: 6¼in., 15.8cm.
Issued: 1921-1938
Colour variation
Price: $675 £450

ORANGE VENDOR HN1966
Designer: C. J. Noke
Height: 6¼in., 15.9cm.
Issued: 1941-1949
Colour variation
Price: $562 £375

ORGAN GRINDER HN2173
Designer: M. Nicholl
Height: 8¾in., 22.2cm.
Issued: 1956-1965
Price: $412 £275

OUT FOR A WALK HN86
Designer: H. Tittensor
Height: Unknown
Issued: 1918-1936
Price: $1275 £850

OUT FOR A WALK HN443
Designer: H. Tittensor
Height: Unknown
Issued: 1921-1936
Price: $1275 £850

OUT FOR A WALK HN748
Designer: H. Tittensor
Height: Unknown
Issued: 1925-1936
Price: $1275 £850

ORANGE VENDOR HN1966

ORGAN GRINDER HN2173

OWD WILLUM HN2042
Designer: L. Harradine
Height: 6¾in., 17.2cm.
Issued: 1949-1973
Price: $210 £140

P

PAISLEY SHAWL (Style one) HN1392
Designer: L. Harradine
Height: 8¼in., 21.0cm.
Issued: 1930-1949
Price: $247 £165

PAISLEY SHAWL (Style one) HN1460
Designer: L. Harradine
Height: 8¼in., 21.0cm.
Issued: 1931-1949
Colour variation
Price: $180 £120

PAISLEY SHAWL (Style one) HN1707
Designer: L. Harradine
Height: 8¼in., 21.0cm.
Issued: 1935-1949
Colour variation
Price: $195 £130

OWD WILLIAM HN2042

PAISLEY SHAWL (Style one) HN1392

PAISLEY SHAWL (Style one)
HN1739
Designer: L. Harradine
Height: 8¼in., 21.0cm.
Issued: 1935-1949
Colour variation
Price: $195 £130

PAISLEY SHAWL (Style one)
HN1987
Designer: L. Harradine
Height: 8¼in., 21.0cm.
Issued: 1946-1949
Colour variation
Price: $180 £120

PAISLEY SHAWL (Style two)
HN1914
Designer: L. Harradine
Height: 6½in., 16.5cm.
Issued: 1939-1949
Price: $135 £90

PAISLEY SHAWL (Style two)
HN1988
Designer: L. Harradine
Height: 6¼in., 15.9cm.
Issued: 1946-1975
Colour variation
Price: $135 £90

PAISLEY SHAWL M3
Designer: L. Harradine
Height: 4in., 10.1cm.
Issued: 1932-1938
Price: $180 £120

PAISLEY SHAWL M4
Designer: L. Harradine
Height: 4in., 10.1cm.
Issued: 1932-1945
Colour variation
Price: $150 £100

PAISLEY SHAWL M26
Designer: L. Harradine
Height: 3¾in., 9.5cm.
Issued: 1932-1945
Colour variation
Price: $150 £100

PALIO HN2428
Designer: M. Davies
Height: 17½in., 44.5cm.
Issued: 1971 in a limited
edition of 500
Price: $3000 £2000

PAMELA HN1468
Designer: L. Harradine
Height: 7½in., 19.1cm.
Issued: 1931-1938
Price: $375 £250

PAMELA HN1469
Designer: L. Harradine
Height: 7½in., 19.1cm.
Issued: 1931-1938
Colour variation
Price: $375 £250

PAMELA HN1469

PAMELA HN1564
Designer: L. Harradine
Height: 8in., 20.3cm.
Issued: 1933-1938
          Colour variation
Price: $375 £250

PAN ON ROCK HN621
Designer: Unknown
Height: Unknown
Issued: 1924-1938
Price: $750 £500

PAN ON ROCK HN622
Designer: Unknown
Height: Unknown
Issued: 1924-1938
Price: $750 £500

PANTALETTES HN1362
Designer: L. Harradine
Height: 7¾in., 19.7cm.
Issued: 1929-1938
Price: $255 £170

PANTALETTES HN1412
Designer: L. Harradine
Height: 7¾in., 19.7cm.
Issued: 1930-1949
          Colour variation
Price: $217 £145

PANTALETTES HN1507
Designer: L. Harradine
Height: 7¾in., 19.7cm.
Issued: 1932-1949
          Colour variation
Price: $217 £145

PANTALETTES HN1709
Designer: L. Harradine
Height: 8in., 20.3cm.
Issued: 1935-1938
          Colour variation
Price: $217 £145

PANTALETTES M15
Designer: L. Harradine
Height: 3¾in., 9.5cm.
Issued: 1932-1945
Price: $195 £130

PANTALETTES M16
Designer: L. Harradine
Height: 3¾in., 9.5cm.
Issued: 1932-1945
          Colour variation
Price: $195 £130

PANTALETTES M31
Designer: L. Harradine
Height: 4in., 10.1cm.
Issued: 1932-1945
          Colour variation
Price: $195 £130

PARISIAN HN2445
Designer: M. Nicholl
Height: 8in., 20.3cm.
Issued: 1972-1975
Price: $120 £80

PARISIAN HN2445

PARSON'S DAUGHTER
HN337
Designer: H. Tittensor
Height: 10in., 25.4cm.
Issued: 1919-1938
Price: $375 £250

PARSON'S DAUGHTER
HN338
Designer: H. Tittensor
Height: 10in., 25.4cm.
Issued: 1919-1938
           Colour variation
Price: $375 £250

PARSON'S DAUGHTER
HN441
Designer: H. Tittensor
Height: 10in., 25.4cm.
Issued: 1921-1938
           Colour variation
Price: $375 £250

PARSON'S DAUGHTER
HN564
Designer: H. Tittensor
Height: 9½in., 24.1cm.
Issued: 1923-1949
           Colour variation
Price: $180 £120

PARSON'S DAUGHTER
HN790
Designer: H. Tittensor
Height: 10in., 25.4cm.
Issued: 1926-1938
           Colour variation
Price: $225 £150

PARSON'S DAUGHTER
HN1242
Designer: H. Tittensor
Height: 10in., 25.4cm.
Issued: 1927-1938
           Colour variation
Price: $225 £150

PARSON'S DAUGHTER
HN1356
Designer: H. Tittensor
Height: 9¼in., 23.5cm.
Issued: 1929-1938
           Colour variation
Price: $180 £120

PARSON'S DAUGHTER
HN2018
Designer: H. Tittensor
Height: 9¾in., 24.7cm.
Issued: 1949-1953
           Colour variation
Price: $165 £110

PAST GLORY HN2484
Designer: M. Nicholl
Height: 7½in., 19.1cm.
Issued: 1973-1978
Price: $127 £85

PATCHWORK QUILT
HN1984
Designer: L. Harradine
Height: 6in., 15.2cm.
Issued: 1945-1959
Price: $187 £125

PARSON'S DAUGHTER HN564   **PARSON'S DAUGHTER HN1356**

PAST GLORY HN2484   **PATCHWORK QUILT HN1984**

PATRICIA HN1414
Designer: L. Harradine
Height: 8½in., 21.6cm.
Issued: 1930-1949
Price: $247 £165

PATRICIA HN1431
Designer: L. Harradine
Height: 8½in., 21.6cm.
Issued: 1930-1949
Colour variation
Price: $247 £165

PATRICIA HN1462
Designer: L. Harradine
Height: 8in., 20.3cm.
Issued: 1931-1938
Colour variation
Price: $247 £165

PATRICIA HN1567
Designer: L. Harradine
Height: 8½in., 21.6cm.
Issued: 1933-1949
Colour variation
Price: $270 £180

PATRICIA M7
Designer: L. Harradine
Height: 4in., 10.1cm.
Issued: 1932-1945
Price: $150 £100

PATRICIA M8
Designer: L. Harradine
Height: 4in., 10.1cm.
Issued: 1932-1938
Colour variation
Price: $180 £120

PATRICIA M28
Designer: L. Harradine
Height: 4in., 10.1cm.
Issued: 1932-1945
Colour variation
Price: $150 £100

PATRICIA HN2715
Designer: E. Griffiths
Height: 7½in., 19.0cm.
Issued: 1982-1985
Price: $60 £40

PAULA HN2906
Designer: P. Parsons
Height: 7in., 17.8cm.
Issued: 1980-
Price: $182 £73

PAULINE HN1444
Designer: L. Harradine
Height: 6in., 15.2cm.
Issued: 1931-1938
Price: $180 £120

PAULINE HN2441
Designer: P. Davies
Height: 5in., 12.5cm.
Issued: 1984
Price: $212 £85

PATRICIA HN1414

PATRICIA HN1431

PAULA HN2906

PAULINE HN1444

PAVLOVA HN487
Designer: C. J. Noke
Height: 4¼in., 11.4cm.
Issued: 1921-1938
Price: $1275 £850

PAVLOVA HN676
Designer: Unknown
Height: 4¼in., 10.8cm.
Issued: 1924-1938
Colour variation
Price: $1275 £850

PEACE HN2433 (Black)
Designer: P. Davies
Height: 8in., 20.3cm.
Issued: 1981
Price: $70 £28

PEACE HN2470 (White)
Designer: P. Davies
Height: 8in., 20.3cm.
Issued: 1981
Price: $70 £28

PEARLY BOY (Style one) HN1482
Designer: L. Harradine
Height: 5½in., 14.0cm.
Issued: 1931-1949
Price: $240 £160

PEARLY BOY (Style one) HN1547
Designer: L. Harradine
Height: 5½in., 14.0cm.
Issued: 1933-1949
Colour variation
Price: $240 £160

PEARLY BOY (Style two) HN2035
Designer: L. Harradine
Height: 5¼in., 13.3cm.
Issued: 1949-1959
Price: $127 £85

PEARLY GIRL (Style one) HN1483
Designer: L. Harradine
Height: 5½in., 14.0cm.
Issued: 1931-1949
Price: $240 £160

PEARLY GIRL (Style one) HN1548
Designer: L. Harradine
Height: 5½in., 14.0cm.
Issued: 1933-1949
Colour variation
Price: $240 £160

PEARLY GIRL (Style two) HN2036
Designer: L. Harradine
Height: 5¼in., 13.3cm.
Issued: 1949-1959
Price: $127 £85

PECKSNIFF (Style one) HN535
Designer: L. Harradine
Height: 3¾in., 9.5cm.
Issued: 1922-1932
Price: $45 £30

PAVLOVA HN487

PEACE HN2470 (White)

PEARLY BOY (Style one) HN1482

PEARLY BOY (Style two) HN2035

PEARLY GIRL (Style one) HN1483

PECKSNIFF (Style one) HN535

231

PECKSNIFF (Style two) HN553
Designer: L. Harradine
Height: 7in., 17.8cm.
Issued: 1923-1939
Price: $270 £180

PECKSNIFF (Style two) HN1891
Designer: L. Harradine
Height: 7in., 17.8cm.
Issued: 1938-1952
Price: $240 £160

PECKSNIFF (Style three) HN2098
Designer: L. Harradine
Height: 7¼in., 18.4cm.
Issued: 1952-1967
Price: $180 £120

PECKSNIFF, MR M43
Designer: L. Harradine
Height: 4¼in., 10.8cm.
Issued: 1932-1982
Price: $30 £20

PEDLAR WOLF HN7
Designer: C. J. Noke
Height: 5½in., 14.0cm.
Issued: 1913-1938
Price: $1500 £1000

PEGGY HN1941
Designer: L. Harradine
Height: 5in., 12.7cm.
Issued: 1940-1949
Price: $67 £45

PEGGY HN2038
Designer: L. Harradine
Height: 5in., 12.7cm.
Issued: 1949-1978
Price: $45 £30

PENELOPE HN1901
Designer: L. Harradine
Height: 7in., 17.8cm.
Issued: 1939-1975
Price: $180 £120

PENELOPE HN1902
Designer: L. Harradine
Height: 7in., 17.8cm.
Issued: 1939-1949
Colour variation
Price: $262 £175

PENNY HN2338
Designer: M. Davies
Height: 4¾in., 12.0cm.
Issued: 1968-
Price: $69 £28

PENNY HN2424
Designer: P. Davies
Height: 4¾in., 12.0cm.
Issued: 1983-
Price: $69 £28

PENSIVE MOMENTS HN2704
Designer: M. Davies
Height: 5in., 12.7cm.
Issued: 1975-1982
Price: $82 £55

PECKSNIFF (Style two) HN553

PECKSNIFF (Style three) HN2098

PEDLAR WOLF HN7

PEGGY HN2038

PENELOPE HN1901

PENNY HN2338

PERFECT PAIR HN581
Designer: L. Harradine
Height: 6¾in., 17.2cm.
Issued: 1923-1938
Price: $675 £450

PHILIPPA OF HAINAULT HN2008
Designer: M. Davies
Height: 9¾in., 24.7cm.
Issued: 1948-1953
Price: $525 £350

PHILIPPINE DANCER HN2439
Designer: M. Davies
Height: 9½in., 24.1cm.
Issued: 1978 in a limited edition of 750
Price: $450 £300

PHYLLIS HN1420
Designer: L. Harradine
Height: 9in., 22.9cm.
Issued: 1930-1949
Price: $300 £200

PHYLLIS HN1430
Designer: L. Harradine
Height: 9in., 22.9cm.
Issued: 1930-1938
Colour variation
Price: $300 £200

PHYLLIS HN1486
Designer: L. Harradine
Height: 9in., 22.9cm.
Issued: 1931-1949
Colour variation
Price: $375 £250

PHYLLIS HN1698
Designer: L. Harradine
Height: 9in., 22.9cm.
Issued: 1935-1949
Colour variation
Price: $375 £250

PICARDY PEASANT (man) HN13
Designer: P. Stabler
Height: 9in., 22.9cm.
Issued: 1913-1938
Price: $750 £500

PICARDY PEASANT (man) HN17
Designer: P. Stabler
Height: 9½in., 24.0cm.
Issued: 1913-1938
Colour variation
Price: $750 £500

PICARDY PEASANT (man) HN19
Designer: P. Stabler
Height: 9½in., 24.0cm.
Issued: 1913-1938
Colour variation
Price: $750 £500

PERFECT PAIR HN581

PHILIPPINE DANCER HN2439

PHYLLIS HN1698

PHILIPPA OF HAINAULT HN2008

PHYLLIS HN1420

PICARDY PEASANT (man) HN13

233

PICARDY PEASANT (woman)
HN4
Designer: P. Stabler
Height: 9¼in., 23.5cm.
Issued: 1913-1938
Price: $750 £500

PICARDY PEASANT (woman)
HN5
Designer: P. Stabler
Height: 9¼in., 23.5cm.
Issued: 1913-1938
Colour variation
Price: $750 £500

PICARDY PEASANT (woman)
HN17A
Designer: P. Stabler
Height: 9½in., 24.0cm.
Issued: 1913-1938
Colour variation
Price: $750 £500

PICARDY PEASANT (woman)
HN351
Designer: P. Stabler
Height: 9½in., 24.0cm.
Issued: 1919-1938
Colour variation
Price: $750 £500

PICARDY PEASANT (woman)
HN513
Designer: P. Stabler
Height: 9½in., 24.0cm.
Issued: 1921-1938
Colour variation
Price: $750 £500

PICNIC HN2308
Designer: M. Davies
Height: 3¾in., 9.5cm.
Issued: 1965-
Price: $107 £43

PIED PIPER HN1215
Designer: L. Harradine
Height: 8¼in., 21.0cm.
Issued: 1926-1938
Price: $600 £400

PIED PIPER HN2102
Designer: L. Harradine
Height: 8½in., 21.6cm.
Issued: 1953-1976
Colour variation
Price: $180 £120

PIERETTE (Style one) HN642
Designer: L. Harradine
Height: 7¼in., 18.4cm.
Issued: 1924-1938
Price: $525 £350

PIERETTE (Style one) HN643
Designer: L. Harradine
Height: 7¼in., 18.4cm.
Issued: 1924-1938
Colour variation
Price: $525 £350

PICARDY PEASANT (woman) HN4

PIED PIPER HN1215

PIED PIPER HN2102

PIERETTE (Style one) HN643

234

PIERETTE (Style one) HN644
Designer: L. Harradine
Height: 7¼in., 18.4cm.
Issued: 1924-1938
Colour variation
Price: $450 £300

PIERETTE (Style one) HN691
Designer: L. Harradine
Height: 7¼in., 18.4cm.
Issued: 1925-1938
Colour variation
Price: $675 £450

PIERETTE (Style one) HN721
Designer: L. Harradine
Height: 7¼in., 18.4cm.
Issued: 1925-1938
Colour variation
Price: $525 £350

PIERETTE (Style one) HN731
Designer: L. Harradine
Height: 7¼in., 18.4cm.
Issued: 1925-1938
Colour variation
Price: $450 £300

PIERETTE (Style one) HN732
Designer: L. Harradine
Height: 7¼in., 18.4cm.
Issued: 1925-1938
Colour variation
Price: $450 £300

PIERETTE (Style one) HN784
Designer: L. Harradine
Height: 7¼in., 18.4cm.
Issued: 1926-1938
Colour variation
Price: $450 £300

PIERETTE(Style two)HN795
Designer: L. Harradine
Height: 3½in., 8.9cm.
Issued: 1926-1938
Price: $450 £300

PIERETTE (Style two) HN796
Designer: L. Harradine
Height: 3½in., 8.9cm.
Issued: 1926-1938
Price: $450 £300

PIERETTE (Style three)
HN1391
Designer: L. Harradine
Height: 8½in., 21.6cm.
Issued: 1930-1938
Price: $525 £350

PIERETTE (Style three)
HN1749
Designer: L. Harradine
Height: 8½in., 21.6cm.
Issued: 1936-1949
Colour variation
Price: $525 £350

PILLOW FIGHT HN2270
Designer: M. Davies
Height: 5in., 12.7cm.
Issued: 1965-1969
Price: $187 £125

PIERETTE (Style one) HN644

PIERETTE (Style three) HN1391

PIERETTE (Style three) HN1749

PILLOW FIGHT HN2270

FIGURES

PINKIE HN1552
Designer: L. Harradine
Height: 5in., 12.7cm.
Issued: 1933-1938
Price: $127 £85

PINKIE HN1553
Designer: L. Harradine
Height: 5in., 12.7cm.
Issued: 1933-1938
    Colour variation
Price: $127 £85

PIPER HN2907
Designer: M. Abberley
Height: 8in., 20.3cm.
Issued: 1980-
Price: $262 £105

PIRATE KING HN2901
Designer: W. K. Harper
Height: 10in., 25.4cm.
Issued: 1981-
Price: $352 £235

PIROUETTE HN2216
Designer: M. Davies
Height: 5¾in., 14.6cm.
Issued: 1959-1967
Price: $135 £90

PLEASE KEEP STILL HN2967
Designer: P. Parsons
Height: 4½in., 11.5cm.
Issued: 1982-1985
Price: $60 £40

POACHER HN2043
Designer: L. Harradine
Height: 6in., 15.2cm.
Issued: 1949-1959
Price: $210 £140

POCAHONTAS HN2930
Designer: S. Keenan
Height: 8in., 20.3cm.
Issued: 1982 in a limited
    edition of 950
Price: $150 £100

POKE BONNET HN362
Designer: C, J. Noke
Height: 8¾in., 22.2cm.
Issued: 1919-1938
Price: $600 £400

POKE BONNET HN612
Designer: C. J. Noke
Height: 9½in., 24.1cm.
Issued: 1924-1938
    Colour variation
Price: $600 £400

POKE BONNET HN765
Designer: C. J. Noke
Height: 8¾in., 22.2cm.
Issued: 1925-1938
    Colour variation
Price: $600 £400
Also called 'Grandma's Days'
and Lilac Shawl'

PINKIE HN1552

PIPER HN2907

PIROUETTE HN2216

POACHER HN2043

POCAHONTAS HN2930

POKE BONNET HN612

POLISH DANCER HN2836
Designer: M. Davies
Height: 9½in., 24.1cm.
Issued: 1980 in a limited
edition of 750
Price: $450 £300

POLKA HN2156
Designer: M. Davies
Height: 7½in., 19.1cm.
Issued: 1955-1969
Price: $180 £120

POLLY PEACHUM (Style one)
HN463
Designer: L. Harradine
Height: 6¼in., 15.9cm.
Issued: 1921-1949
Price: $225 £150

POLLY PEACHUM (Style one)
HN465
Designer: L. Harradine
Height: 6½in., 16.5cm.
Issued: 1921-1949
Colour variation
Price: $225 £150

POLLY PEACHUM (Style one)
HN550
Designer: L. Harradine
Height: 6½in., 16.5cm.
Issued: 1922-1949
Colour variation
Price: $225 £150

POLLY PEACHUM (Style one)
HN589
Designer: L. Harradine
Height: 6½in., 16.5cm.
Issued: 1924-1949
Colour variation
Price: $225 £150

POLLY PEACHUM (Style one)
HN614
Designer: L. Harradine
Height: 6½in., 16.5cm.
Issued: 1924-1949
Colour variation
Price: $225 £150

POLLY PEACHUM (Style one)
HN680
Designer: L. Harradine
Height: 6½in., 16.5cm.
Issued: 1924-1949
Colour variation
Price: $225 £150

POLLY PEACHUM (Style one)
HN693
Designer: L. Harradine
Height: 6½in., 16.5cm.
Issued: 1925-1949
Colour variation
Price: $225 £150

POLLY PEACHUM (Style two)
HN489
Designer: L. Harradine
Height: 4¼in., 10.8cm.
Issued: 1921-1938
Price: $240 £160

POLISH DANCER HN2836   POLKA HN2156

POLLY PEACHUM (Style one) HN550

237

POLLY PEACHUM (Style two)
HN549
Designer: L. Harradine
Height: 4¼in., 10.8cm.
Issued: 1922-1949
          Colour variation
Price: $240 £160

POLLY PEACHUM (Style two)
HN620
Designer: L. Harradine
Height: 4¼in., 10.8cm.
Issued: 1924-1938
          Colour variation
Price: $225 £150

POLLY PEACHUM (Style two)
HN694
Designer: L. Harradine
Height: 4¼in., 10.8cm.
Issued: 1925-1949
          Colour variation
Price: $225 £150

POLLY PEACHUM (Style two)
HN734
Designer: L. Harradine
Height: 4¼in., 10.8cm.
Issued: 1925-1949
          Colour variation
Price: $225 £150

POLLY PEACHUM
(Style three) HN698
Designer: L. Harradine
Height: 2¼in., 5.7cm.
Issued: 1925-1949
Price: $225 £150

POLLY PEACHUM
(Style three) HN699
Designer: L. Harradine
Height: 2¼in., 5.7cm.
Issued: 1925-1949
          Colour variation
Price: $225 £150

POLLY PEACHUM
(Style three) HN757
Designer: L. Harradine
Height: 2¼in., 5.7cm.
Issued: 1925-1949
          Colour variation
Price: $150 £100

POLLY PEACHUM
(Style three) HN758
Designer: L. Harradine
Height: 2¼in., 5.7cm.
Issued: 1925-1949
          Colour variation
Price: $150 £100

POLLY PEACHUM
(Style three) HN759
Designer: L. Harradine
Height: 2¼in., 5.7cm.
Issued: 1925-1949
          Colour variation
Price: $150 £100

POLLY PEACHUM (Style two) HN549

POLLY PEACHUM (Style three) HN698

POLLY PEACHUM
(Style three) HN760
Designer: L Harradine
Height: 2¼in., 5.7cm.
Issued: 1925-1949
Colour variation
Price: $150 £100

POLLY PEACHUM
(Style three) HN761
Designer: L. Harradine
Height: 2¼in., 5.7cm.
Issued: 1925-1949
Colour variation
Price: $150 £100

POLLY PEACHUM
(Style three) HN762
Designer: L. Harradine
Height: 2¼in., 5.7cm.
Issued: 1925-1949
Colour variation
Price: $150 £100

POLLY PEACHUM M21
Designer: L. Harradine
Height: 2¼in., 5.7cm.
Issued: 1932-1945
Price: $150 £100

POLLY PEACHUM M22
Designer: L. Harradine
Height: 2¼in., 5.7cm.
Issued: 1932-1938
Colour variation
Price: $180 £120

POLLY PEACHUM M23
Designer: L. Harradine
Height: 2¼in., 5.7cm.
Issued: 1932-1938
Colour variation
Price: $180 £120

**POLLY PUT THE KETTLE
ON HN3021**
Designer: P. Parsons
Height: 8in., 20.0cm.
Issued: 1984-
Price: $107 £43

POLLYANNA HN2965
Designer: P. Parsons
Height: 6¾in., 17.0cm.
Issued: 1982-1985
Price: $60 £40

POPE JOHN PAUL II HN2888
Designer: E. Griffiths
Height: 10in., 25.4cm.
Issued: 1982
Price: $157 £63

POTTER HN1493
Designer: C. J. Noke
Height: 7in., 17.8cm.
Issued: 1932-
Price: $337 £135

POLLY PEACHUM (Style three) HN762

POTTER HN1493

239

POTTER HN1518
Designer: C. J. Noke
Height: 6¾in., 17.2cm.
Issued: 1932-1949
           Colour variation
Price: $225 £150

POTTER HN1522
Designer: C. J. Noke
Height: 6¾in., 17.2cm.
Issued: 1932-1949
           Colour variation
Price: $225 £150

PREMIERE HN2343
Designer: M. Davies
Height: 7½in., 19.1cm.
Issued: 1969-1978
Price: $90 £60

PRETTY LADY HN69
Designer: H. Tittensor
Height: 9½in., 24.1cm.
Issued: 1916-1938
Price: $900 £600

PRETTY LADY HN70
Designer: H. Tittensor
Height: 9½in., 24.1cm.
Issued: 1916-1938
           Colour variation
Price: $900 £600

PRETTY LADY HN302
Designer: H. Tittensor
Height: 9½in., 24.1cm.
Issued: 1918-1938
           Colour variation
Price: $900 £600

PRETTY LADY HN330
Designer: H. Tittensor
Height: 9½in., 24.1cm.
Issued: 1918-1938
           Colour variation
Price: $900 £600

PRETTY LADY HN361
Designer: H. Tittensor
Height: 9½in., 24.1cm.
Issued: 1919-1938
           Colour variation
Price: $900 £600

PRETTY LADY HN384
Designer: H. Tittensor
Height: 9½in., 24.1cm.
Issued: 1920-1938
           Colour variation
Price: $900 £600

PRETTY LADY HN565
Designer: H. Tittensor
Height: 10in., 25.4cm.
Issued: 1923-1938
           Colour variation
Price: $900 £600

PRETTY LADY HN700
Designer: H. Tittensor
Height: 9½in., 24.1cm.
Issued: 1925-1938
           Colour variation
Price: $900 £600

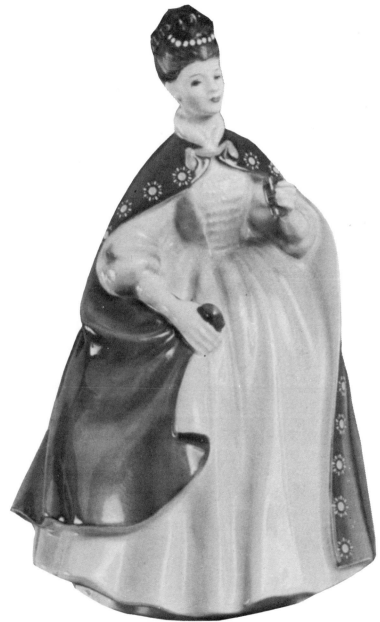

PREMIERE HN2343

PRETTY LADY HN763
Designer: H. Tittensor
Height: 9½in., 24.1cm.
Issued: 1925-1938
Colour variation
Price: $900 £600

PRETTY LADY HN783
Designer: H. Tittensor
Height: 9½in., 24.1cm.
Issued: 1926-1938
Colour variation
Price: $900 £600

PRETTY POLLY HN2768
Designer: W. K. Harper
Height: 6in., 15.0cm.
Issued: 1984-
Price: $167 £67

PRIMROSES HN1617
Designer: L. Harradine
Height: 6½in., 16.5cm.
Issued: 1934-1949
Price: $300 £200

PRINCE OF WALES HN1217
Designer: L. Harradine
Height: 7½in., 19.1cm.
Issued: 1926-1938
Price: $1050 £700

PRINCE OF WALES HN2883
Designer: E. Griffiths
Height: 8in., 20.3cm.
Issued: 1981 in a limited
edition of 1500
Price: $750 £500

PRINCE OF WALES HN2884
Designer: E. Griffiths
Height: 8in., 20.3cm.
Issued: 1981 in a limited
edition of 1500
Price: $675 £450

PRINCESS HN391
Designer: Unknown
Height: Unknown
Issued: 1920-1938
Price: $1875 £1250

PRINCESS HN392
Designer: Unknown
Height: Unknown
Issued: 1920-1938
Colour variation
Price: $1875 £1250

PRINCESS HN420
Designer: Unknown
Height: Unknown
Issued: 1920-1938
Colour variation
Price: $1875 £1250

PRINCESS HN430
Designer: Unknown
Height: Unknown
Issued: 1921-1938
Colour variation
Price: $1875 £1250

PRIMROSES HN1617

PRINCE OF WALES HN1217

PRINCE OF WALES HN2883

PRINCE OF WALES HN2884

PRINCESS HN431
Designer: Unknown
Height: Unknown
Issued: 1921-1938
Colour variation
Price: $1875 £1250

PRINCESS HN633
Designer: Unknown
Height: Unknown
Issued: 1924-1938
Colour variation
Price: $1875 £1250

**PRINCESS BADOURA
HN2081**
Designer: H. Tittensor, H. E.
Stanton and F. Van
Allen Phillips
Height: 20in., 50.8cm.
Issued: 1952-
Price: $17100 £6840

**PRINCESS OF WALES
HN2887**
Designer: E. Griffiths
Height: 7¾in., 19.6cm.
Issued: 1982 in a limited
edition of 1500
Price: $225 £150

PRISCILLA HN1337
Designer: L. Harradine
Height: 8in., 20.3cm.
Issued: 1929-1938
Price: $270 £180

PRISCILLA HN1340
Designer: L. Harradine
Height: 8in., 20.3cm.
Issued: 1929-1949
Colour variation
Price: $202 £135

PRISCILLA HN1495
Designer: L. Harradine
Height: 8in., 20.3cm.
Issued: 1932-1949
Colour variation
Price: $217 £145

PRISCILLA HN1501
Designer: L. Harradine
Height: 8in., 20.3cm.
Issued: 1932-1938
Colour variation
Price: $270 £180

PRISCILLA HN1559
Designer: L. Harradine
Height: 8in., 20.3cm.
Issued: 1933-1949
Colour variation
Price: $202 £135

PRISCILLA M13
Designer: L. Harradine
Height: 4in., 10.1cm.
Issued: 1932-1938
Price: $150 £100

PRISCILLA HN1337

FIGURES

PRISCILLA M14
Designer: L. Harradine
Height: 3¾in., 9.5cm.
Issued: 1932-1945
Colour variation
Price: $150 £100

PRISCILLA M24
Designer: L. Harradine
Height: 3¾in., 9.5cm.
Issued: 1932-1945
Colour variation
Price: $150 £100

**PRIVATE, CONNECTICUT
REGIMENT 1777 HN2845**
Designer: E. J. Griffiths
Height: 11¼in., 28.5cm.
Issued: 1978 in a limited
edition of 350
Price: $375 £250

**PRIVATE, DELAWARE
REGIMENT 1776 HN2761**
Designer: E. J. Griffiths
Height: 12in., 30.5cm.
Issued: 1977 in a limited
edition of 350
Price: $375 £250

**PRIVATE, 1ST GEORGIA
REGIMENT 1777 HN2779**
Designer: E. J. Griffiths
Height: 11in., 27.9cm.
Issued: 1975 in a limited
edition of 350
Price: $375 £250

**PRIVATE, MASSACHUSETTS
REGIMENT 1778 HN2760**
Designer: E. J. Griffiths
Height: 12½in., 31.7cm.
Issued: 1977 in a limited
edition of 350
Price: $375 £250

**PRIVATE, PENNSYLVANIA
RIFLE BATTALION 1776
HN2846**
Designer: E. J. Griffiths
Height: 11¼in., 28.5cm.
Issued: 1978 in a limited
edition of 350
Price: $375 £250

**PRIVATE, RHODE ISLAND
REGIMENT 1781 HN2759**
Designer: E. J. Griffiths
Height: 11¾in., 29.8cm.
Issued: 1977 in a limited
edition of 350
Price: $375 £250

**PRIVATE, 2ND SOUTH
CAROLINA REGIMENT
1781 HN2717**
Designer: E. J. Griffiths
Height: 11½in., 29.2cm.
Issued: 1975 in a limited
edition of 350
Price: $375 £250

PRISCILLA M14

PRISCILLA M24

**PRIVATE, CONNECTICUT
REGIMENT 1777 HN2845**

**PRIVATE, DELAWARE
REGIMENT 1776 HN2761**

**PRIVATE, RHODE ISLAND
REGIMENT 1781 HN2759**

**PRIVATE, 2ND SOUTH CAROLINA
REGIMENT 1781 HN2717**

FIGURES

PRIVATE, 3RD NORTH CAROLINA REGIMENT 1778 HN2754
Designer: E. J. Griffiths
Height: 11in., 27.9cm.
Issued: 1976 in a limited edition of 350
Price: $375 £250

PROFESSOR HN2281
Designer: M. Nicholl
Height: 7¼in., 18.4cm.
Issued: 1965-1980
Price: $82 £55

PROMENADE HN2076
Designer: M. Davies
Height: 8in., 20.3cm.
Issued: 1951-1953
Price: $1200 £800

PROPOSAL (Man) HN725
Designer: Unknown
Height: 5½in., 14.0cm.
Issued: 1925-1938
Price: $675 £450

PROPOSAL (Man) HN1209
Designer: Unknown
Height: 5½in., 14.0cm.
Issued: 1926-1938
Colour variation
Price: $675 £450

PROPOSAL (Woman) HN715
Designer: Unknown
Height: 5¾in., 14.6cm.
Issued: 1925-1938
Price: $675 £450

PROPOSAL (Woman) HN716
Designer: Unknown
Height: 5¾in., 14.6cm.
Issued: 1925-1938
Colour variation
Price: $675 £450

PROPOSAL (Woman) HN788
Designer: Unknown
Height: 5¾in., 14.6cm.
Issued: 1926-1938
Colour variation
Price: $675 £450

PRUDENCE HN1883
Designer: L. Harradine
Height: 6¾in., 17.2cm.
Issued: 1938-1949
Price: $300 £200

PRUDENCE HN1884
Designer: L. Harradine
Height: 6¾in., 17.2cm.
Issued: 1938-1949
Colour variation
Price: $300 £200

PRUE HN1996
Designer: L. Harradine
Height: 6¾in., 17.2cm.
Issued: 1947-1955
Price: $180 £120

PRIVATE, 3RD NORTH CAROLINA REGIMENT 1778 HN2754

PROFESSOR HN2281

PROMENADE HN2076

PROPOSAL (Man) HN725

PROPOSAL (Woman) HN715

PRUDENCE HN1883

FIGURES

PUFF AND POWDER HN397
Designer: L. Harradine
Height: Unknown
Issued: 1920-1938
Price: $1350 £900

PUFF AND POWDER HN398
Designer: L. Harradine
Height: Unknown
Issued: 1920-1938
Colour variation
Price: $1350 £900

PUFF AND POWDER HN400
Designer: L. Harradine
Height: Unknown
Issued: 1920-1938
Colour variation
Price: $1350 £900

PUFF AND POWDER HN432
Designer: L. Harradine
Height: Unknown
Issued: 1921-1938
Colour variation
Price: $1350 £900

PUFF AND POWDER HN433
Designer: L. Harradine
Height: Unknown
Issued: 1921-1938
Colour variation
Price: $1350 £900

PUNCH AND JUDY MAN HN2765
Designer: W. K. Harper
Height: 9in., 22.9cm.
Issued: 1981-
Price: $297 £119

PUPPETMAKER HN2253
Designer: M. Nicholl
Height: 8in., 20.3cm.
Issued: 1962-1973
Price: $277 £185

PUSSY HN18
Designer: F. C. Stone
Height: 7¾in., 19.7cm.
Issued: 1913-1938
Price: $1500 £1000

PUSSY HN325
Designer: F. C. Stone
Height: 7½in., 19.1cm.
Issued: 1918-1938
Colour variation
Price: $1500 £1000

PUSSY HN507
Designer: F. C. Stone
Height: 7½in., 19.0cm.
Issued: 1921-1938
Colour variation
Price: $1500 £1000

PYJAMAS HN1942
Designer: L. Harradine
Height: 5¼in., 13.3cm.
Issued: 1940-1949
Price: $150 £100

PUNCH AND JUDY MAN HN2765

PUPPETMAKER HN2253

PUSSY HN18

PYJAMAS HN1942

FIGURES

Q

QUALITY STREET HN1211
Designer: Unknown
Height: 7¼in., 18.4cm.
Issued: 1926-1938
Price: $600 £400

QUALITY STREET HN1211A
Designer: Unknown
Height: 7¼in., 18.4cm.
Issued: 1926-1938
Colour variation
Price: $600 £400

QUEEN ELIZABETH II HN2502
Designer: M. Davies
Height: 7¾in., 19.7cm.
Issued: 1973 in a limited edition of 750
Price: $1275 £850

QUEEN MOTHER HN2882
Designer: E. Griffiths
Height: 8in., 20.3cm.
Issued: 1980 in a limited edition of 1500
Price: $525 £350

QUEEN OF SHEBA HN2328
Designer: P. Davies
Height: 9in., 22.8cm.
Issued: 1982 in a limited edition of 750
Price: $1275 £850

QUEEN OF THE DAWN HN2437
Designer: P. Davies
Height: 8½in., 21.5cm.
Issued: 1983-
Price: $157 £63

QUEEN OF THE ICE HN2435
Designer: P. Davies
Height: 8in., 20.0cm.
Issued: 1983-
Price: $157 £63

R

RACHEL HN2919
Designer: P. Gee
Height: 7½in., 19.1cm.
Issued: 1980-1984
Price: $82 £55

RACHEL HN2936
Designer: P. Gee
Height: 7¾in., 19.5cm.
Issued: 1985-
Colour variation
Price: $182 £73

RAG DOLL HN2142
Designer: M. Davies
Height: 4¾in., 12.0cm.
Issued: 1954-
Price: $77 £31

QUALITY STREET HN1211

QUEEN ELIZABETH II HN2502

QUEEN MOTHER HN2882

QUEEN OF SHEBA HN2328

RACHEL HN2919

RAG DOLL HN2142

RAG DOLL SELLER HN2944
Designer: R. Tabbenor
Height: 7in., 17.5cm.
Issued: 1984-
Price: $167 £67

REBECCA HN2805
Designer: M. Davies
Height: 7¼in., 18.4cm.
Issued: 1980-
Price: $337 £135

REFLECTIONS HN1820
Designer: L. Harradine
Height: 5in., 12.7cm.
Issued: 1937-1938
Price: $525 £350

REFLECTIONS HN1821
Designer: L. Harradine
Height: 5in., 12.7cm.
Issued: 1937-1938
   Colour variation
Price: $525 £350

REFLECTIONS HN1847
Designer: L. Harradine
Height: 4½in., 11.4cm.
Issued: 1938-1949
   Colour variation
Price: $525 £350

REFLECTIONS HN1848
Designer: L. Harradine
Height: 5in., 12.7cm.
Issued: 1938-1949
   Colour variation
Price: $525 £350

REGAL LADY HN2709
Designer: M. Davies
Height: 7½in., 19.1cm.
Issued: 1975-1984
Price: $90 £60

REGENCY HN1752
Designer: L. Harradine
Height: 8in., 20.3cm.
Issued: 1936-1949
Price: $300 £200

REGENCY BEAU HN1972
Designer: H. Fenton
Height: 8in., 20.3cm.
Issued: 1941-1949
Price: $675 £450

RENDEZVOUS HN2212
Designer: M. Davies
Height: 7¼in., 18.4cm.
Issued: 1962-1971
Price: $180 £120

REPOSE HN2272
Designer: M. Davies
Height: 5¼in., 13.3cm.
Issued: 1972-1978
Price: $127 £85

REST AWHILE HN2728
Designer: W. K. Harper
Height: 8in., 20.3cm.
Issued: 1981-1984
Price: $75 £50

REBECCA HN2805   REFLECTIONS HN1820

REGAL LADY HN2709

REGENCY HN1752

REGENCY BEAU HN1972   RENDEZVOUS HN2212

FIGURES

RETURN OF PERSEPHONE
HN31
Designer: C. Vyse
Height: 16in., 40.6cm.
Issued: 1913-1938
Price: $2250 £1500

REVERIE HN2306
Designer: M. Davies
Height: 6½in., 16.5cm.
Issued: 1964-1982
Price: $90 £60

RHAPSODY HN2267
Designer: M. Davies
Height: 6¾in., 17.2cm.
Issued: 1961-1973
Price: $120 £80

RHODA HN1573
Designer: L. Harradine
Height: 10¼in., 26.7cm.
Issued: 1933-1949
Price: $262 £175

RHODA HN1574
Designer: L. Harradine
Height: 10¼in., 26.7cm.
Issued: 1933-1938
           Colour variation
Price: $262 £175

RHODA HN1688
Designer: L. Harradine
Height: 10¼in., 26.7cm.
Issued: 1935-1949
           Colour variation
Price: $262 £175

RHYTHM HN1903
Designer: L. Harradine
Height: 6¾in., 17.2cm.
Issued: 1939-1949
Price: $750 £500

RHYTHM HN1904
Designer: L. Harradine
Height: 6¾in., 17.2cm.
Issued: 1939-1949
           Colour variation
Price: $750 £500

RITA HN1448
Designer: L. Harradine
Height: 7in., 17.8cm.
Issued: 1931-1938
Price: $450 £300

RITA HN1450
Designer: L. Harradine
Height: 7in., 17.8cm.
Issued: 1931-1938
           Colour variation
Price: $450 £300

RIVER BOY HN2128
Designer: M. Davies
Height: 4in., 10.1cm.
Issued: 1962-1975
Price: $82 £55

RETURN OF PERSEPHONE HN31

REVERIE HN2306

RHAPSODY HN2267

RHODA HN1574

RHYTHM HN1903

RIVER BOY HN2128

ROBERT BURNS HN42
Designer: E. W. Light
Height: 18in., 45.7cm.
Issued: 1914-1938
Price: $2250 £1500

ROBIN M38
Designer: Unknown
Height: 2½in., 6.4cm.
Issued: 1933-1945
Price: $210 £140

ROBIN M39
Designer: Unknown
Height: 2½in., 6.4cm.
Issued: 1933-1945
Colour variation
Price: $210 £140

ROBIN HOOD HN2773
Designer: W. K. Harper
Height: 8in., 20.0cm.
Issued: 1985-
Price: $157 £63

ROCKING HORSE HN2072
Designer: L. Harradine
Height: 7in., 17.8cm.
Issued: 1951-1953
Price: $1200 £800

ROMANCE HN2430
Designer: M. Davies
Height: 5¼in., 13.3cm.
Issued: 1972-1980
Price: $82 £55

ROMANY SUE HN1757
Designer: L. Harradine
Height: 9¼in., 23.5cm.
Issued: 1936-1949
Price: $570 £380

ROMANY SUE HN1758
Designer: L. Harradine
Height: 9½in., 24.1cm.
Issued: 1936-1949
Colour variation
Price: $570 £380

ROSABELL HN1620
Designer: L. Harradine
Height: 6¾in., 17.1cm.
Issued: 1934-1938
Price: $450 £300

ROSALIND HN2393
Designer: M. Davies
Height: 5½in., 14.0cm.
Issued: 1970-1975
Price: $90 £60

ROSAMUND (Style one) HN1320
Designer: L. Harradine
Height: 7¼in., 18.4cm.
Issued: 1929-1938
Price: $1200 £800

ROBERT BURNS HN42

ROBIN M38

ROCKING HORSE HN2072

ROMANCE HN2430

ROMANY SUE HN1757

ROSALIND HN2393

ROSAMUND (Style two)
HN1497
Designer: L. Harradine
Height: 8½in., 21.6cm.
Issued: 1932-1938
Price: $600 £400

ROSAMUND (Style two)
HN1551
Designer: L. Harradine
Height: 8½in., 21.6cm.
Issued: 1933-1938
Colour variation
Price: $600 £400

ROSAMUND M32
Designer: L. Harradine
Height: 4¼in., 10.8cm.
Issued: 1932-1945
Price: $195 £130

ROSAMUND M33
Designer: L. Harradine
Height: 4in., 10.1cm.
Issued: 1932-1945
Colour variation
Price: $195 £130

ROSE HN1368
Designer: L. Harradine
Height: 4½in., 11.4cm.
Issued: 1930-
Price: $69 £28

ROSE HN1387
Designer: L. Harradine
Height: 4½in., 11.4cm.
Issued: 1930-1938
Colour variation
Price: $112 £75

ROSE HN1416
Designer: L. Harradine
Height: 4½in., 11.4cm.
Issued: 1930-1949
Colour variation
Price: $90 £60

ROSE HN1506
Designer: L. Harradine
Height: 4½in., 11.4cm.
Issued: 1932-1938
Colour variation
Price: $112 £75

ROSE HN1654
Designer: L. Harradine
Height: 4½in., 11.4cm.
Issued: 1934-1938
Colour variation
Price: $112 £75

ROSE HN2123
Designer: L. Harradine
Height: 4½in., 11.4cm.
Issued: 1983-
Price: $69 £28

ROSEANNA HN1921
Designer: L. Harradine
Height: 8in., 20.3cm.
Issued: 1940-1949
Price: $270 £180

ROSEANNA HN1921

250

ROSEANNA HN1926
Designer: L. Harradine
Height: 8in., 20.3cm.
Issued: 1940-1959
Colour variation
Price: $195 £130

ROSEBUD (Style one) HN1580
Designer: L. Harradine
Height: 3in., 7.6cm.
Issued: 1933-1938
Price: $330 £220

ROSEBUD (Style one) HN1581
Designer: L. Harradine
Height: 3in., 7.6cm.
Issued: 1933-1938
Colour variation
Price: $330 £220

ROSEBUD (Style two) HN1983
Designer: L. Harradine
Height: 7½in., 19.1cm.
Issued: 1945-1952
Price: $210 £140

ROSEMARY HN2091
Designer: L. Harradine
Height: 7in., 17.8cm.
Issued: 1952-1959
Price: $210 £140

ROSINA HN1358
Designer: L. Harradine
Height: 5¾in., 14.6cm.
Issued: 1929-1938
Price: $330 £220

ROSINA HN1364
Designer: L. Harradine
Height: 5¼in., 13.3cm.
Issued: 1929-1938
Colour variation
Price: $330 £220

ROSINA HN1556
Designer: L. Harradine
Height: 5¾in., 14.6cm.
Issued: 1933-1938
Colour variation
Price: $330 £220

ROWENA HN2077
Designer: L. Harradine
Height: 7¼in., 18.4cm.
Issued: 1951-1955
Price: $255 £170

**ROYAL CANADIAN
MOUNTED POLICE 1873
(BUST.) HN2555**
Designer: Unknown
Height: 8¼in., 21.0cm.
Issued: 1973 in a limited
edition of 1500
Price: $150 £100

**ROYAL CANADIAN
MOUNTED POLICE 1973
HN2547**
Designer: Unknown
Height: 8in., 20.3cm.
Issued: 1973 in a limited
edition of 1500
Price: $150 £100

ROSEBUD (Style one) HN1580

ROSEBUD (Style two) HN1983

ROSEMARY HN2091

ROSINA HN1358

ROWENA HN2077

ROYAL CANADIAN MOUNTED
POLICE 1973 HN2547

FIGURES

ROYAL GOVERNOR'S COOK HN2233
Designer: M. Davies
Height: 6in., 15.2cm.
Issued: 1960-1984
Price: $120 £80

RUBY HN1724
Designer: L. Harradine
Height: 5¼in., 13.3cm.
Issued: 1935-1949
Price: $142 £95

RUBY HN1725
Designer: L. Harradine
Height: 5¼in., 13.3cm.
Issued: 1935-1949
Colour variation
Price: $142 £95

RUMPELSTILTSKIN HN3025
Designer: R. Jefferson
Height: 8in., 20.0cm.
Issued: 1983-
Price: $157 £63

RUSTIC SWAIN HN1745
Designer: L. Harradine
Height: 5¼in., 13.3cm.
Issued: 1935-1949
Price: $1125 £750

RUSTIC SWAIN HN1746
Designer: L. Harradine
Height: 5¼in., 13.3cm.
Issued: 1935-1949
Colour variation
Price: $1125 £750

RUTH HN2799
Designer: M. Davies
Height: 6in., 15.2cm.
Issued: 1976-1982
Price: $39 £26

RUTH THE PIRATE MAID HN2900
Designer: W. K. Harper
Height: 11¾in., 29.8cm.
Issued: 1981-
Price: $352 £235

S

SABBATH MORN HN1982
Designer: L. Harradine
Height: 7¼in., 18.4cm.
Issued: 1945-1959
Price: $262 £175

SAILOR'S HOLIDAY HN2442
Designer: M. Nicholl
Height: 6¼in., 15.9cm.
Issued: 1972-1978
Price: $105 £70

SAIREY GAMP M46
Designer: L. Harradine
Height: 4in., 10.1cm.
Issued: 1932-1982
Price: $45 £30

ROYAL GOVERNOR'S COOK HN2233

RUBY HN1724

RUSTIC SWAIN HN1745

RUTH THE PIRATE MAID HN2900

SABBATH MORN HN1982

SAILOR'S HOLIDAY HN2442

FIGURES

SAIREY GAMP (Style one)
HN533
Designer: L. Harradine
Height: 4in., 10.1cm.
Issued: 1922-1932
Price: $45 £30

SAIREY GAMP (Style two)
HN558
Designer: L. Harradine
Height: 7in., 17.8cm.
Issued: 1923-1939
Price: $270 £180

SAIREY GAMP (Style two)
HN1896
Designer: L. Harradine
Height: 7in., 17.8cm.
Issued: 1938-1952
Colour variation
Price: $195 £130

SAIREY GAMP (Style three)
HN2100
Designer: L. Harradine
Height: 7¼in., 18.4cm.
Issued: 1952-1967
Price: $165 £110

SALOME HN1775
Designer: R. Garbe
Height: Unknown
Issued: 1933 in a limited
edition of 100
Price: $2250 £1500

SALOME HN1828
Designer: R. Garbe
Height: Unknown
Issued: 1937-1949
Colour variation
Price: $2250 £1500

SAM WELLER HN531
Designer: L. Harradine
Height: 4in., 10.1cm.
Issued: 1922-1932
Price: $45 £30

SAM WELLER M48
Designer: L. Harradine
Height: 4in., 10.1cm.
Issued: 1932-1982
Price: $30 £20

SAMANTHA HN2954
Designer: P. Parsons
Height: 7in., 17.5cm.
Issued: 1982-1984
Price: $60 £40

SAMWISE HN2925
Designer: D. Lyttleton
Height: 4½in., 11.5cm.
Issued: 1982-1984
Price: $30 £20

SANDRA HN2275
Designer: M. Davies
Height: 7¾in., 19.7cm.
Issued: 1969-
Price: $147 £59

SAIREY GAMP (Style one) HN533

SAIREY GAMP (Style two) HN558

SAIREY GAMP (Style three) HN2100

SAM WELLER HN531

SAMANTHA HN2954

SAMWISE HN2925

SANDRA HN2401
Designer: P. Davies
Height: 8in., 20.0cm.
Issued: 1983-
Price: $147 £59

SANTA CLAUS HN2725
Designer: W. K. Harper
Height: 9½in., 24.0cm.
Issued: 1982-
Price: $262 £105

SARA HN2265
Designer: M. Davies
Height: 7½in., 19.1cm.
Issued: 1981-
Price: $222 £89

SAUCY NYMPH HN1539
Designer: Unknown
Height: 4½in., 11.4cm.
Issued: 1933-1949
Price: $187 £125

SAVE SOME FOR ME HN2959
Designer: P. Parsons
Height: 7¼in., 18.0cm.
Issued: 1982-1985
Price: $67 £45

SCHOOLMARM HN2223
Designer: M. Davies
Height: 6¾in., 17.2cm.
Issued: 1958-1980
Price: $97 £65

SCOTCH GIRL HN1269
Designer: L. Harradine
Height: 7½in., 19.1cm.
Issued: 1928-1938
Price: $1170 £780

SCOTTIES HN1281
Designer: L. Harradine
Height: 5½in., 14.0cm.
Issued: 1928-1938
Price: $750 £500

SCOTTIES HN1349
Designer: L. Harradine
Height: 5¼in., 13.3cm.
Issued: 1929-1949
Colour variation
Price: $600 £400

SCOTTISH HIGHLAND
DANCER HN2436
Designer: M. Davies
Height: 9½in., 24.1cm.
Issued: 1978 in a limited
edition of 750
Price: $450 £300

SCRIBE HN305
Designer: C. J. Noke
Height: 6in., 15.2cm.
Issued: 1918-1936
Price: $750 £500

SCRIBE HN324
Designer: C. J. Noke
Height: 6in., 15.2cm.
Issued: 1918-1938
Colour variation
Price: $750 £500

SANTA CLAUS HN2725

SARA HN2265

SAUCY NYMPH HN1539

SCOTCH GIRL HN1269

SCOTTIES HN1281

SCOTTISH HIGHLAND DANCER HN2436

SCRIBE HN1235
Designer: C. J. Noke
Height: 6in., 15.2cm.
Issued: 1927-1938
Colour variation
Price: $750 £500

SCROOGE M87
Designer: L. Harradine
Height: 4in., 10.1cm.
Issued: 1949-1982
Price: $30 £20

SEA HARVEST HN2257
Designer: M. Nicholl
Height: 7½in., 19.1cm.
Issued: 1969-1976
Price: $112 £75

SEA SHORE HN2263
Designer: M. Davies
Height: 3½in., 8.9cm.
Issued: 1961-1965
Price: $150 £100

SEA SPRITE (Style one) HN1261
Designer: L. Harradine
Height: 5in., 12.7cm.
Issued: 1927-1938
Price: $247 £165

SEA SPRITE (Style two) HN2191
Designer: M. Davies
Height: 7in., 17.8cm.
Issued: 1958-1962
Price: $240 £160

SEAFARER HN2455
Designer: M. Nicholl
Height: 8½in., 21.6cm.
Issued: 1972-1976
Price: $112 £75

SECRET THOUGHTS HN2382
Designer: M. Davies
Height: 6¼in., 15.9cm.
Issued: 1971-
Price: $222 £89

SENTIMENTAL PIERROT HN36
Designer: C. J. Noke
Height: 5½in., 14.0cm.
Issued: 1914-1938
Price: $1200 £800

SENTIMENTAL PIERROT HN307
Designer: C. J. Noke
Height: 5½in., 14.0cm.
Issued: 1918-1938
Price: $1200 £800

SENTINEL HN523
Designer: Unknown
Height: 17½in., 44.4cm.
Issued: 1921-1938
Price: $2700 £1800

SERENA HN1868
Designer: L. Harradine
Height: 11in., 27.9cm.
Issued: 1938-1949
Price: $412 £275

SCRIBE HN1235

SCROOGE M87

SEA SHORE HN2263

SECRET THOUGHTS HN2382

SENTIMENTAL PIERROT HN36

SERENA HN1868

SERENADE HN2753
Designer: E. Griffiths
Height: 9in., 23.0cm.
Issued: 1983-
Price: $75 £50

SERGEANT, 6TH
MARYLAND REGIMENT
1777 HN2815
Designer: E. J. Griffiths
Height: 13¾in., 34.9cm.
Issued: 1976 in a limited
edition of 350
Price: $375 £250

SERGEANT, VIRGINIA 1ST
REGIMENT CONTINENTAL
LIGHT DRAGOONS, 1777
HN2844
Designer: E. J. Griffiths
Height: 14¼in., 36.1cm.
Issued: 1978 in a limited
edition of 350
Price: $375 £250

SHARON HN3047
Designer: P. Parsons
Height: 5½in., 14.0cm.
Issued: 1984-
Price: $107 £43

SHEILA HN2742
Designer: D. Tootle
Height: 8¼in., 21.0cm.
Issued: 1984-
Price: $142 £57

SHE LOVES ME NOT HN2045
Designer: L. Harradine
Height: 5½in., 14.0cm.
Issued: 1949-1962
Price: $105 £70

SHEPHERD (Style one) HN81
Designer: C. J. Noke
Height: 13¼in., 33.6cm.
Issued: 1918-1938
Price: $1650 £1100

SHEPHERD (Style one) HN617
Designer: C. J. Noke
Height: 13¼in., 33.6cm.
Issued: 1924-1938
Colour variation
Price: $1650 £1100

SHEPHERD·(Style one) HN632
Designer: C. J. Noke
Height: 13¼in., 33.6cm.
Issued: 1924-1938
Colour variation
Price: $1650 £1100

SHEPHERD (Style two) HN709
Designer: Unknown
Height: 3½in., 8.8cm.
Issued: 1925-1938
Price: $450 £300

SHEPHERD (Style three)
HN751
Designer: Unknown
Height: 7½in., 19.1cm.
Issued: 1925-1938
Price: $450 £300

SERGEANT, 6TH MARYLAND
REGIMENT 1777 HN2815

SERGEANT, VIRGINIA 1ST REGIMENT
CONTINENTAL LIGHT DRAGOONS,
1777 HN2844

SHE LOVES ME NOT HN2045

SHEPHERD (Style three) HN751

SHEPHERD (Style four)
HN1975
Designer: H. Fenton
Height: 8½in., 21.6cm.
Issued: 1945-1975
Price: $112 £75

SHEPHERD M17
Designer: Unknown
Height: 3¾in., 9.5cm.
Issued: 1932-1938
Price: $450 £300

SHEPHERD M19
Designer: Unknown
Height: 3¾in., 9.5cm.
Issued: 1932-1938
        Colour variation
Price: $450 £300

SHEPHERDESS (Style one)
HN708
Designer: Unknown
Height: 3½in., 8.8cm.
Issued: 1925-1948
Price: $450 £300

SHEPHERDESS (Style two)
HN735
Designer: Unknown
Height: 7in., 17.8cm.
Issued: 1925-1938
Price: $675 £450

SHEPHERDESS (Style two)
HN750
Designer: Unknown
Height: 7in., 17.8cm.
Issued: 1925-1938
        Colour variation
Price: $675 £450

SHEPHERDESS M18
Designer: Unknown
Height: 3½in., 8.9cm.
Issued: 1932-1938
Price: $450 £300

SHEPHERDESS M20
Designer: Unknown
Height: 3¾in., 9.5cm.
Issued: 1932-1938
        Colour variation
Price: $450 £300

SHIRLEY HN2702
Designer: P. Davies
Height: 7¼in., 18.0cm.
Issued: 1985-
Price: $142 £57

SHORE LEAVE HN2254
Designer: M. Nicholl
Height: 7½in., 19.1cm.
Issued: 1965-1978
Price: $112 £75

SHY ANNE HN60
Designer: L. Perugini
Height: 7¾in., 19.7cm.
Issued: 1916-1938
Price: $1200 £800

SHEPHERD (Style four) HN1975   SHEPHERDESS (Style one) HN708

SHEPHERDESS M18   SHORE LEAVE HN2254

257

SHY ANNE HN64
Designer: L. Perugini
Height: 7¾in., 19.7cm.
Issued: 1916-1938
Colour variation
Price: $1200 £800

SHY ANNE HN65
Designer: L. Perugini
Height: 7¾in., 19.7cm.
Issued: 1916-1938
Colour variation
Price: $1200 £800

SHY ANNE HN568
Designer: L. Perugini
Height: 7½in., 19.1cm.
Issued: 1923-1938
Colour variation
Price: $1200 £800

SHY ANNE HN568

SHYLOCK HN317

SHYLOCK HN79
Designer: C. J. Noke
Height: Unknown
Issued: 1917-1938
Price: $1350 £900

SHYLOCK HN317
Designer: C. J. Noke
Height: Unknown
Issued: 1918-1938
Colour variation
Price: $1350 £900

SIBELL HN1668
Designer: L. Harradine
Height: 6½in., 16.5cm.
Issued: 1934-1949
Price: $412 £275

SIBELL HN1695
Designer: L. Harradine
Height: 6½in., 16.5cm.
Issued: 1935-1949
Colour variation
Price: $412 £275

SIBELL HN1695

SIESTA HN1305

SIBELL HN1735
Designer: L. Harradine
Height: 6½in., 16.5cm.
Issued: 1935-1949
Colour variation
Price: $412 £275

SIESTA HN1305
Designer: L. Harradine
Height: 4¾in., 12.0cm.
Issued: 1928-1938
Price: $1275 £850

SILKS AND RIBBONS
HN2017
Designer: L. Harradine
Height: 6in., 15.2cm.
Issued: 1949-
Price: $157 £63

SILVERSMITH OF
WILLIAMSBURG HN2208
Designer: M. Davies
Height: 6¼in., 15.9cm.
Issued: 1960-1983
Price: $90 £60

SILKS AND RIBBONS HN2017

SILVERSMITH OF WILLIAMSBURG
HN2208

SIMONE HN2378
Designer: M. Davies
Height: 7¼in., 18.4cm.
Issued: 1971-1982
Price: $82 £55

SIR EDWARD HN2370
Designer: Unknown
Height: 11in., 27.9cm.
Issued: 1979 in a limited
edition of 500
Price: $262 £175

SIR RALPH HN2371
Designer: Unknown
Height: 10¾in., 27.3cm.
Issued: 1979 in a limited
edition of 500
Price: $262 £175

SIR THOMAS HN2372
Designer: Unknown
Height: 11in., 27.9cm.
Issued: 1979 in a limited
edition of 500
Price: $262 £175

**SIR THOMAS LOVELL
HN356**
Designer: C. J. Noke
Height: 7¾in., 19.7cm.
Issued: 1919-1938
Price: $1050 £700

**SIR WALTER RALEIGH
HN1742**
Designer: L. Harradine
Height: 10½in., 26.7cm.
Issued: 1935-1949
Price: $450 £300

**SIR WALTER RALEIGH
HN1751**
Designer: L. Harradine
Height: 11½in., 29.2cm.
Issued: 1936-1949
Colour variation
Price: $450 £300

**SIR WALTER RALEIGH
HN2015**
Designer: L. Harradine
Height: 11½in., 29.2cm.
Issued: 1948-1955
Colour variation
Price: $390 £260

**SIR WINSTON CHURCHILL
HN3057**
Designer: A. Hughes
Height: 10½in., 26.5cm.
Issued: 1985-
Price: $127 £51

SISTERS HN3018
Designer: P. Parsons
Height: 8½in., 21.5cm.
Issued: 1983-
Price: $95 £38

SIMONE HN2378

SIR EDWARD HN2370

SIR RALPH HN2371

SIR THOMAS HN2372

SIR THOMAS LOVELL HN356

SIR WALTER RALEIGH HN2015

SISTERS HN3019
Designer: P. Parsons
Height: 8½in., 21.5cm.
Issued: 1983-
Colour variation
Price: $95 £38

SKATER HN2117
Designer: M. Davies
Height: 7¼in., 18.4cm.
Issued: 1953-1971
Price: $210 £140

SLEEP HN24
Designer: P. Stabler
Height: 8¼in., 21.0cm.
Issued: 1913-1938
Price: $1275 £850

SLEEP HN24A
Designer: P. Stabler
Height: 8¼in., 21.0cm.
Issued: 1913-1938
Colour variation
Price: $1275 £850

SLEEP HN25
Designer: P. Stabler
Height: 8¼in., 21.0cm.
Issued: 1913-1938
Colour variation
Price: $1275 £850

SLEEP HN25A
Designer: P. Stabler
Height: 8¼in., 21.0cm.
Issued: 1913-1938
Colour variation
Price: $1275 £850

SLEEP HN424
Designer: P. Stabler
Height: 6in., 15.2cm.
Issued: 1921-1938
Colour variation
Price: $1275 £850

SLEEP HN692
Designer: P. Stabler
Height: 8¼in., 21.0cm.
Issued: 1925-1938
Colour variation
Price: $1275 £850

SLEEP HN710
Designer: P. Stabler
Height: 8¼in., 21.0cm.
Issued: 1925-1938
Colour variation
Price: $1275 £850

SLEEPY DARLING HN2953
Designer: P. Parsons
Height: 7¼in., 18.4cm.
Issued: Only available in
1981
Price: $112 £75
(Collectors Club Issue)

SLEEPY SCHOLAR HN15
Designer: W. White
Height: 6¾in., 17.2cm.
Issued: 1913-1938
Price: $1200 £800

SKATER HN2117

SLEEP HN24

SLEEPY DARLING HN2953

SLEEPY SCHOLAR HN15

FIGURES

SLEEPY SCHOLAR HN16
Designer: W. White
Height: 6¾in., 17.2cm.
Issued: 1913-1938
Colour variation
Price: $1200 £800

SLEEPY SCHOLAR HN29
Designer: W. White
Height: 6¾in., 17.2cm.
Issued: 1913-1938
Colour variation
Price: $1200 £800

SLEEPYHEAD HN2114
Designer: M. Davies
Height: 5in., 12.7cm.
Issued: 1953-1955
Price: $675 £450

SMILING BUDDHA HN454
Designer: C. J. Noke
Height: 6¼in., 15.9cm.
Issued: 1921-1938
Price: $900 £600

SNAKE CHARMER HN1317
Designer: Unknown
Height: 4in., 10.1cm.
Issued: 1929-1938
Price: $900 £600

SOIRÉE HN2312
Designer: M. Davies
Height: 7½in., 19.1cm.
Issued: 1967-1984
Price: $82 £55

SOLITUDE HN2810
Designer: M. Davies
Height: 5½in., 14.0cm.
Issued: 1977-1983
Price: $98 £65

SONATA HN2438
Designer: P. Davies
Height: 6½in., 16.5cm.
Issued: 1983-
Price: $75 £50

SONG OF THE SEA HN2729
Designer: W. K. Harper
Height: 7¼in., 18.0cm.
Issued: 1983-
Price: $172 £69

SONIA HN1692
Designer: L. Harradine
Height: 6¼in., 15.9cm.
Issued: 1935-1949
Price: $412 £275

SONIA HN1738
Designer: L. Harradine
Height: 6½in., 16.5cm.
Issued: 1935-1949
Colour variation
Price: $412 £275

SONNY HN1313
Designer: L. Harradine
Height: 3½in., 8.9cm.
Issued: 1929-1938
Price: $480 £320

SLEEPYHEAD HN2114　　　**SMILING BUDDHA HN454**

SNAKE CHARMER HN1317

SOIRÉE HN2312

SOLITUDE HN2810　　　**SONIA HN1692**

SONNY HN1314
Designer: L. Harradine
Height: 3½in., 8.9cm.
Issued: 1929-1938
Colour variation
Price: $480 £320

SOPHIE HN2833
Designer: M. Davies
Height: 6in., 15.2cm.
Issued: 1977-
Price: $107 £43

SOUTHERN BELLE HN2229
Designer: M. Davies
Height: 7½in., 19.1cm.
Issued: 1958-
Price: $172 £69

SOUTHERN BELLE HN2425
Designer: P. Davies
Height: 7½in., 19.0cm.
Issued: 1983-
Colour variation
Price: $172 £69

**SPANISH FLAMENCO
DANCER HN2831**
Designer: M. Davies
Height: 7¼in., 18.4cm.
Issued: 1977 in a limited
edition of 750
Price: $525 £350

SPANISH LADY HN1262
Designer: L. Harradine
Height: 8½in., 21.6cm.
Issued: 1927-1938
Price: $900 £600

SPANISH LADY HN1290
Designer: L. Harradine
Height: 8¼in., 21.0cm.
Issued: 1928-1938
Colour variation
Price: $900 £600

SPANISH LADY HN1293
Designer: L. Harradine
Height: 8¼in., 21.0cm.
Issued: 1928-1938
Colour variation
Price: $900 £600

SPANISH LADY HN1294
Designer: L. Harradine
Height: 8¼in., 21.0cm.
Issued: 1928-1938
Colour variation
Price: $900 £600

SPANISH LADY HN1309
Designer: L. Harradine
Height: 8¼in., 21.0cm.
Issued: 1929-1938
Colour variation
Price: $900 £600

SPINNING HN2390
Designer: P. Davies
Height: 7½in., 19cm.
Issued: 1984 in a limited
edition of 750
Price: $600 £400

SONNY HN1314

SOPHIE HN2833

SOUTHERN BELLE HN2229

SPANISH FLAMENCO
DANCER HN2831

SPANISH LADY HN1262

SPANISH LADY HN1294

SPIRIT OF THE WIND
HN1777
Designer: R. Garbe
Height: Unknown
Issued: 1933 in a limited
edition of 50
Price: $1950 £1300

SPIRIT OF THE WIND
HN1825
Designer: R. Garbe
Height: Unknown
Issued: 1937-1949
Colour variation
Price: $1950 £1300

SPOOK HN50
Designer: H. Tittensor
Height: 7in., 17.8cm.
Issued: 1916-1938
Price: $1050 £700

SPOOK HN51
Designer: H. Tittensor
Height: 7in., 17.8cm.
Issued: 1916-1938
Colour variation
Price: $1050 £700

SPOOK HN51A
Designer: H. Tittensor
Height: 7in., 17.8cm.
Issued: 1916-1938
Colour variation
Price: $1050 £700

SPOOK HN51B
Designer: H. Tittensor
Height: 7in., 17.8cm.
Issued: 1916-1938
Colour variation
Price: $1050 £700

SPOOK HN58
Designer: H. Tittensor
Height: 7in., 17.8cm.
Issued: 1916-1938
Colour unknown
Price: $1050 £700

SPOOK HN512
Designer: H. Tittensor
Height: 7in., 17.8cm.
Issued: 1921-1938
Colour variation
Price: $1050 £700

SPOOK HN625
Designer: H. Tittensor
Height: 7in., 17.8cm.
Issued: 1924-1938
Colour variation
Price: $1050 £700

SPOOK HN1218
Designer: H. Tittensor
Height: 7in., 17.8cm.
Issued: 1926-1938
Colour variation
Price: $1050 £700

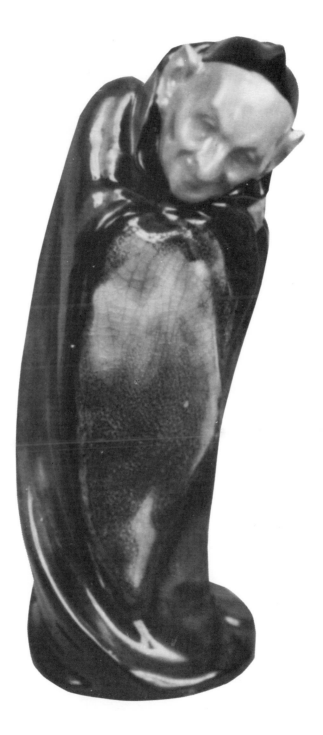

SPOOK HN51

263

FIGURES

SPOOKS HN88
Designer: C. J. Noke
Height: 7¼in., 18.4cm.
Issued: 1918-1936
Price: $1500 £1000

SPOOKS HN89
Designer: C. J. Noke
Height: 7¼in., 18.4cm.
Issued: 1918-1936
Colour variation
Price: $1500 £1000

SPOOKS HN372
Designer: C. J. Noke
Height: 7¼in., 18.4cm.
Issued: 1920-1936
Colour variation
Price: $1500 £1000

SPRING (Style one) HN312
Designer: Unknown
Height: 7½in., 19.1cm.
Issued: 1918-1938
Price: $1350 £900

SPRING (Style one) HN472
Designer: Unknown
Height: 7½in., 19.1cm.
Issued: 1921-1938
Colour variation
Price: $1350 £900

SPRING (Style two) HN1774
Designer: R. Garbe
Height: 21in., 53.3cm.
Issued: 1933 in a limited
edition of 100
Price: $1875 £1250

SPRING (Style two) HN1827
Designer: R. Garbe
Height: 21in., 53.3cm.
Issued: 1937-1949
Colour variation
Price: $1875 £1250

SPRING (Style three) HN2085
Designer: M. Davies
Height: 7¾in., 19.6cm.
Issued: 1952-1959
Price: $277 £185

SPRING FLOWERS HN1807
Designer: L. Harradine
Height: 7¼in., 18.4cm.
Issued: 1937-1959
Price: $240 £160

SPRING FLOWERS HN1945
Designer: L. Harradine
Height: 7¼in., 18.4cm.
Issued: 1940-1949
Colour variation
Price: $300 £200

SPRING MORNING HN1922
Designer: L. Harradine
Height: 7½in., 19.1cm.
Issued: 1940-1973
Price: $150 £100

SPOOKS HN88

SPRING (Style one) HN472

SPRING (Style two) HN1827

SPRING (Style three) HN2085

SPRING FLOWERS HN1807

SPRING FLOWERS HN1945

FIGURES

SPRING MORNING HN1923
Designer: L. Harradine
Height: 7½in., 19.1cm.
Issued: 1940-1949
Colour variation
Price: $195 £130

SPRINGTIME HN1971
Designer: L. Harradine
Height: 6in., 15.2cm.
Issued: 1941-1949
Price: $600 £400

SQUIRE HN1814
Designer: Unknown
Height: 9¾in., 24.7cm.
Issued: 1937-1949
Price: $1500 £1000
Also called "Hunting Squire"

ST. GEORGE (Style one) HN385
Designer: S. Thorogood
Height: 16in., 40.6cm.
Issued: 1920-1938
Price: $1500 £1000

ST. GEORGE (Style one) HN386
Designer: S. Thorogood
Height: 16in., 40.6cm.
Issued: 1920-1938
Colour variation
Price: $1500 £1000

ST. GEORGE (Style one) HN1800
Designer: S. Thorogood
Height: 16in., 40.6cm.
Issued: 1934-1950
Colour variation
Price: $1200 £800

ST. GEORGE (Style one) HN2067
Designer: S. Thorogood
Height: 15¾in., 40.0cm.
Issued: 1950-1976
Colour variation
Price: $1125 £750

ST. GEORGE (Style two) HN2051
Designer: M. Davies
Height: 7½in., 19.1cm.
Issued: 1950-
Price: $285 £190

ST. GEORGE (Style three) HN2856
Designer: W. K. Harper
Height: 16in., 40.6cm.
Issued: 1978-
Price: $7825 £3130

STAYED AT HOME HN2207
Designer: M. Davies
Height: 5in., 12.7cm.
Issued: 1958-1969
Price: $112 £75

SPRING MORNING HN1923

SPRINGTIME HN1971

SQUIRE HN1814

ST. GEORGE (Style one) HN386

ST. GEORGE (Style two) HN2051

ST. GEORGE (Style three) HN2856

STEPHANIE HN2807
Designer: M. Davies
Height: 7¼in., 18.4cm.
Issued: 1977-1982
Price: $75 £50

STEPHANIE HN2811
Designer: P. Davies
Height: 7½in., 19.0cm.
Issued: 1983-
Price: $172 £69

STICK 'EM UP HN2981
Designer: A. Hughes
Height: 7in., 17.5cm.
Issued: 1984-1985
Price: $61 £41

STIGGINS HN536
Designer: L. Harradine
Height: 3¾in., 9.5cm.
Issued: 1922-1932
Price: $45 £30

STIGGINS M50
Designer: L. Harradine
Height: 4in., 10.1cm.
Issued: 1932-1982
Price: $30 £20

STITCH IN TIME HN2352
Designer: M. Nicholl
Height: 6¼in., 15.9cm.
Issued: 1966-1980
Price: $90 £60

STOP PRESS HN2683
Designer: M. Nicholl
Height: 7½in., 19.1cm.
Issued: 1977-1980
Price: $90 £60

SUITOR HN2132
Designer: M. Davies
Height: 7¼in., 18.4cm.
Issued: 1962-1971
Price: $180 £120

SUMMER (Style one) HN313
Designer: Unknown
Height: 7½in., 19.1cm.
Issued: 1918-1938
Price: $1200 £800

SUMMER (Style one) HN473
Designer: Unknown
Height: 7½in., 19.1cm.
Issued: 1921-1938
Price: $1200 £800

SUMMER (Style two) HN2086
Designer: M. Davies
Height: 7¼in., 18.4cm.
Issued: 1952-1959
Price: $270 £180

SUMMER'S DAY HN2181
Designer: M. Davies
Height: 5¾in., 14.6cm.
Issued: 1957-1962
Price: $210 £140

STEPHANIE HN2807

STIGGINS HN536

STITCH IN TIME HN2352

STOP PRESS HN2683

SUMMER (Style one) HN313

SUMMER (Style two) HN2086

FIGURES

SUNDAY BEST HN2206
Designer: M. Davies
Height: 7½in., 19.1cm.
Issued: 1979-1984
Price: $82 £55

SUNDAY BEST HN2698
Designer: P. Davies
Height: 7½in., 19.1cm.
Issued: 1985-
Price: $127 £51

SUNDAY MORNING HN2184
Designer: M. Davies
Height: 7½in., 19.1cm.
Issued: 1963-1969
Price: $195 £130

SUNSHINE GIRL HN1344
Designer: L. Harradine
Height: 5in., 12.7cm.
Issued: 1929-1938
Price: $1275 £850

SUNSHINE GIRL HN1348
Designer: L. Harradine
Height: 5in., 12.7cm.
Issued: 1929-1938
        Colour variation
Price: $1275 £850

SUSAN HN2056
Designer: L. Harradine
Height: 7in., 17.8cm.
Issued: 1950-1959
Price: $180 £120

SUSAN HN2952
Designer: P. Parsons
Height: 8½in., 21.5cm.
Issued: 1982-
Price: $247 £99

SUSANNA HN1233
Designer: L. Harradine
Height: 6in., 15.2cm.
Issued: 1927-1938
Price: $420 £280

SUSANNA HN1288
Designer: L. Harradine
Height: 6in., 15.2cm.
Issued: 1928-1938
Price: $420 £280

SUSANNA HN1299
Designer: L. Harradine
Height: 6in., 15.2cm.
Issued: 1928-1938
        Colour variation
Price: $420 £280

SUZETTE HN1487
Designer: L. Harradine
Height: 7½in., 19.1cm.
Issued: 1931-1950
Price: $180 £120

SUZETTE HN1577
Designer: L. Harradine
Height: 7½in., 19.1cm.
Issued: 1933-1949
        Colour variation
Price: $180 £120

SUNDAY BEST HN2206

SUNDAY MORNING HN2184

SUNSHINE GIRL HN1348

SUSAN HN2952

SUSANNA HN1233

SUZETTE HN1487

SUZETTE HN1585
Designer: L. Harradine
Height: 7½in., 19.1cm.
Issued: 1933-1938
Colour variation
Price: $240 £160

SUZETTE HN1696
Designer: L. Harradine
Height: 7½in., 19.1cm.
Issued: 1935-1949
Colour variation
Price: $180 £120

SUZETTE HN2026
Designer: L. Harradine
Height: 7¼in., 18.4cm.
Issued: 1949-1959
Colour variation
Price: $180 £120

SWEET AND FAIR HN1864
Designer: L. Harradine
Height: 7½in., 19.1cm.
Issued: 1938-1949
Price: $337 £225

SWEET AND FAIR HN1865
Designer: L. Harradine
Height: 7¼in., 18.4cm.
Issued: 1938-1949
Colour variation
Price: $337 £225

SWEET AND TWENTY
(Style one) HN1298
Designer: L. Harradine
Height: 5¾in., 14.6cm.
Issued: 1928-1969
Price: $165 £110

SWEET AND TWENTY
(Style one) HN1360
Designer: L. Harradine
Height: 6in., 15.2cm.
Issued: 1929-1938
Colour variation
Price: $270 £180

SWEET AND TWENTY
(Style one) HN1437
Designer: L. Harradine
Height: 6in., 15.2cm.
Issued: 1930-1938
Colour variation
Price: $270 £180

SWEET AND TWENTY
(Style one) HN1438
Designer: L. Harradine
Height: 6in., 15.2cm.
Issued: 1930-1938
Colour variation
Price: $270 £180

SWEET AND TWENTY
(Style one) HN1549
Designer: L. Harradine
Height: 6in., 15.2cm.
Issued: 1933-1949
Colour variation
Price: $140 £90

SUZETTE HN2026   **SWEET AND FAIR HN1864**

SWEET AND TWENTY (Style one) HN1298

SWEET AND TWENTY
(Style one) HN1563
Designer: L. Harradine
Height: 6in., 15.2cm.
Issued: 1933-1938
Colour variation
Price: $270 £180

SWEET AND TWENTY
(Style one) HN1649
Designer: L. Harradine
Height: 6in., 15.2cm.
Issued: 1934-1949
Colour variation
Price: $270 £180

SWEET AND TWENTY
(Style two) HN1589
Designer: L. Harradine
Height: 3½in., 8.9cm.
Issued: 1933-1949
Price: $150 £100

SWEET AND TWENTY
(Style two) HN1610
Designer: L. Harradine
Height: 3½in., 8.9cm.
Issued: 1933-1938
Colour variation
Price: $195 £130

SWEET ANNE HN1318
Designer: L. Harradine
Height: 7½in., 19.1cm.
Issued: 1929-1949
Price: $127 £85

SWEET ANNE HN1330
Designer: L. Harradine
Height: 7¼in., 18.4cm.
Issued: 1929-1949
Colour variation
Price: $150 £100

SWEET ANNE HN1331
Designer: L. Harradine
Height: 7¼in., 18.4cm.
Issued: 1929-1949
Colour variation
Price: $150 £100

SWEET ANNE HN1453
Designer: L. Harradine
Height: 7in., 17.8cm.
Issued: 1931-1949
Colour variation
Price: $150 £100

SWEET ANNE HN1496
Designer: L. Harradine
Height: 7in., 17.8cm.
Issued: 1932-1967
Colour variation
Price: $127 £85

SWEET ANNE HN1631
Designer: L. Harradine
Height: 7in., 17.8cm.
Issued: 1934-1938
Colour variation
Price: $240 £160

SWEET ANNE HN1318

FIGURES

SWEET ANNE HN1701
Designer: L. Harradine
Height: 7in., 17.8cm.
Issued: 1935-1938
Colour variation
Price: $240 £160

SWEET ANNE M5
Designer: L. Harradine
Height: 4in., 10.1cm.
Issued: 1932-1945
Price: $150 £100

SWEET ANNE M6
Designer: L. Harradine
Height: 4in., 10.1cm.
Issued: 1932-1945
Colour variation
Price: $150 £100

SWEET ANNE M5

SWEET ANNE M27
Designer: L. Harradine
Height: 4in., 10.1cm.
Issued: 1932-1945
Colour variation
Price: $150 £100

SWEET APRIL HN2215

SWEET APRIL HN2215
Designer: M. Davies
Height: 7¼in., 18.4cm.
Issued: 1965-1967
Price: $195 £130

SWEET DREAMS HN2380
Designer: M. Davies
Height: 5in., 12.7cm.
Issued: 1971-
Price: $157 £63

SWEET LAVENDER HN1373
Designer: L. Harradine
Height: 9in., 22.8cm.
Issued: 1930-1949
Price: $375 £250

SWEET DREAMS HN2380

SWEET MAID (Style one)
HN1504
Designer: L. Harradine
Height: 8in., 20.3cm.
Issued: 1932-1938
Price: $300 £200

SWEET LAVENDER HN1373

SWEET MAID (Style one)
HN1505
Designer: L. Harradine
Height: 8in., 20.3cm.
Issued: 1932-1938
Colour variation
Price: $300 £200

SWEET MAID (Style two)
HN2092
Designer: L. Harradine
Height: 7in., 17.8cm.
Issued: 1952-1955
Price: $150 £100

SWEET SEVENTEEN HN2734
Designer: D. V. Tootle
Height: 7½in., 19.1cm.
Issued: 1975-
Price: $172 £69

SWEET MAID (Style one) HN1505

SWEET MAID (Style two) HN2092

FIGURES

SWEET SIXTEEN HN2231
Designer: M. Davies
Height: 7¼in., 18.4cm.
Issued: 1958-1965
Price: $195 £130

SWEET SUZY HN1918
Designer: L. Harradine
Height: 6½in., 16.5cm.
Issued: 1939-1949
Price: $270 £180

SWEETING HN1935
Designer: L. Harradine
Height: 6in., 15.2cm.
Issued: 1940-1973
Price: $67 £45

SWEETING HN1938
Designer: L. Harradine
Height: 6in., 15.2cm.
Issued: 1940-1949
Colour variation
Price: $67 £45

SWIMMER HN1270
Designer: L. Harradine
Height: 7¼in., 18.4cm.
Issued: 1928-1938
Price: $900 £600

SWIMMER HN1326
Designer: L. Harradine
Height: 7½in., 19.1cm.
Issued: 1929-1938
Colour variation
Price: $975 £650

SWIMMER HN1329
Designer: L. Harradine
Height: 7½in., 19.1cm.
Issued: 1929-1938
Colour variation
Price: $975 £650

SYLVIA HN1478
Designer: L. Harradine
Height: 10½in., 26.7cm.
Issued: 1931-1938
Price: $270 £180

SYMPATHY HN2838 (Black)
Designer: P. Davies
Height: 11¾in., 29.8cm.
Issued: 1981
Price: $107 £43

SYMPATHY HN2876 (White)
Designer: P. Davies
Height: 11¾in., 29.8cm.
Issued: 1981
Price: $107 £43

SYMPHONY HN2287
Designer: D. B. Lovegrove
Height: 5¼in., 13.3cm.
Issued: 1961-1965
Price: $180 £120

SWEET SIXTEEN HN2231

SWEET SUZY HN1918

SWEETING HN1935

SWIMMER HN1270

SYLVIA HN1478

SYMPATHY HN2838 (Black)

271

T

TAILOR HN2174
Designer: M. Nicholl
Height: 5in., 12.7cm.
Issued: 1956-1959
Price: $450 £300

TAKING THINGS EASY HN2677
Designer: M. Nicholl
Height: 6¾in., 17.2cm.
Issued: 1975-
Price: $237 £95

TALL STORY HN2248
Designer: M. Nicholl
Height: 6½in., 16.5cm.
Issued: 1968-1975
Price: $112 £75

TAPESTRY WEAVING HN3048
Designer: P. Parsons
Height: 7½in., 19.0cm.
Issued: 1985 in a limited edition of 750
Price: $987 £395

TEATIME HN2255
Designer: M. Nicholl
Height: 7¼in., 18.4cm.
Issued: 1972-
Price: $172 £69

TEENAGER HN2203
Designer: M. Davies
Height: 7¼in., 18.4cm.
Issued: 1957-1962
Price: $270 £180

TENDERNESS HN2713
Designer: E. Griffiths
Height: 11¾in., 29.5cm.
Issued: 1982-
Price: $107 £43

TENDERNESS HN2714
Designer: E. Griffiths
Height: 11¾in., 29.5cm.
Issued: 1982-
Colour variation
Price: $107 £43

TERESA HN1682
Designer: L. Harradine
Height: 5¾in., 14.6cm.
Issued: 1935-1949
Price: $525 £350

TERESA HN1683
Designer: L. Harradine
Height: 5¾in., 14.6cm.
Issued: 1935-1938
Colour variation
Price: $600 £400

TESS HN2865
Designer: M. Davies
Height: 5¾in., 14.6cm.
Issued: 1978-1983
Price: $42 £28

TAILOR HN2174

TAKING THINGS EASY HN2677

TALL STORY HN2248

TEATIME HN2255

TERESA HN1682

TESS HN2865

FIGURES

TÊTE-À-TÊTE (Style one)
HN798
Designer: L. Harradine
Height: 5¾in., 14.6cm.
Issued: 1926-1938
Price: $600 £400

TÊTE-À-TÊTE (Style one)
HN799
Designer: L. Harradine
Height: 5¾in., 14.6cm.
Issued: 1926-1938
Colour variation
Price: $600 £400

TÊTE-À-TÊTE (Style two)
HN1236
Designer: C. J. Noke
Height: 3in., 7.6cm.
Issued: 1927-1938
Price: $487 £325

TÊTE-À-TÊTE HN1237
Designer: C. J. Noke
Height: 3in., 7.6cm.
Issued: 1927-1938
Colour variation
Price: $487 £325

THANK YOU HN2732
Designer: W. K. Harper
Height: 8¼in., 21.0cm.
Issued: 1983-
Price: $172 £69

THANKS DOC HN2731
Designer: W. K. Harper
Height: 8¾in., 22.2cm.
Issued: 1975-
Price: $222 £89

THANKSGIVING HN2446
Designer: M. Nicholl
Height: 8in., 20.3cm.
Issued: 1972-1976
Price: $90 £60

THIS LITTLE PIG HN1793
Designer: L. Harradine
Height: 4in., 10.1cm.
Issued: 1936-
Price: $77 £31

THIS LITTLE PIG HN1794
Designer: L. Harradine
Height: 4in., 10.1cm.
Issued: 1936-1949
Colour variation
Price: $127 £85

THIS LITTLE PIG HN2125
Designer: L. Harradine
Height: 4in., 10.0cm.
Issued: 1984-
Colour variation
Price: $51 £21

TILDY HN1576
Designer: L. Harradine
Height: 5in., 12.7cm.
Issued: 1933-1938
Price: $375 £250

TÊTE-À-TÊTE (Style one) HN798

THANKSGIVING HN2446

THIS LITTLE PIG HN1794

THANKS DOC HN2731

THIS LITTLE PIG HN1793

TILDY HN1576

TILDY HN1859
Designer: L. Harradine
Height: 5½in., 14.0cm.
Issued: 1938-1949
Colour variation
Price: $300 £200

TINKLE BELL HN1677
Designer: L. Harradine
Height: 4¾in., 12.0cm.
Issued: 1935-
Price: $77 £31

TINSMITH HN2146
Designer: M. Nicholl
Height: 6½in., 16.5cm.
Issued: 1962-1967
Price: $277 £185

TINY TIM HN539
Designer: L. Harradine
Height: 3½in., 8.9cm.
Issued: 1922-1932
Price: $45 £30

TINY TIM M56
Designer: L. Harradine
Height: 3¾in., 9.5cm.
Issued: 1932-1983
Price: $30 £20

TO BED HN1805
Designer: L. Harradine
Height: 6in., 15.2cm.
Issued: 1937-1959
Price: $150 £100

TO BED HN1806
Designer: L. Harradine
Height: 6in., 15.2cm.
Issued: 1937-1949
Colour variation
Price: $150 £100

TOINETTE HN1940
Designer: L. Harradine
Height: 6¾in., 17.1cm.
Issued: 1940-1949
Price: $900 £600
Also called "Meryll"

TOM HN2864
Designer: M. Davies
Height: 5¾in., 14.6cm.
Issued: 1978-1982
Price: $42 £28

TOM BOMBADIL HN2924
Designer: D. Lyttleton
Height: 5¾in., 14.6cm.
Issued: 1982-1984
Price: $37 £25

TOM BROWN HN2941
Designer: R. Tabbenor
Height: 6¾in., 17.0cm.
Issued: 1983-1985
Price: $37 £25

TOM SAWYER HN2926
Designer: D. Lyttleton
Height: 5¼in., 13.0cm.
Issued: 1982-1985
Price: $37 £25

TINKLE BELL HN1677

TINSMITH HN2146

TINY TIM HN539

TO BED HN1805

TOINETTE HN1940

TOM HN2864

TOM, TOM THE PIPERS SON HN3032
Designer: A. Hughes
Height: 7in., 17.5cm.
Issued: 1984-
Price: $107 £43

TONY WELLER (Style one) HN346
Designer: C. J. Noke
Height: 10½in., 26.7cm.
Issued: 1919-1938
Price: $1140 £760

TONY WELLER (Style one) HN368
Designer: C. J. Noke
Height: 10½in., 26.7cm.
Issued: 1920-1938
Colour variation
Price: $1140 £760

TONY WELLER (Style one) HN684
Designer: C. J. Noke
Height: 10¼in., 26.0cm.
Issued: 1924-1938
Colour variation
Price: $1050 £700

TONY WELLER (Style two) HN544
Designer: L. Harradine
Height: 3½in., 8.9cm.
Issued: 1922-1932
Price: $45 £30

TONY WELLER (Style two) M47
Designer: L. Harradine
Height: 4in., 10.1cm.
Issued: 1932-1982
Price: $30 £20

TOOTLES HN1680
Designer: L. Harradine
Height: 4¾in., 12.0cm.
Issued: 1935-1975
Price: $52 £35

TOP O'THE HILL HN1833
Designer: L. Harradine
Height: 7in., 17.8cm.
Issued: 1937-1971
Price: $127 £85

TOP O'THE HILL HN1834
Designer: L. Harradine
Height: 7in., 17.8cm.
Issued: 1937-
Colour variation
Price: $172 £69

TOP O'THE HILL HN1849
Designer: L. Harradine
Height: 7¼in., 18.4cm.
Issued: 1938-1975
Colour variation
Price: $112 £75

TOWN CRIER HN2119
Designer: M. Davies
Height: 8½in., 21.6cm.
Issued: 1953-1976
Price: $165 £110

TONY WELLER (Style one) HN346

TOOTLES HN1680

TOP O' THE HILL HN1833

TOWN CRIER HN2119

FIGURES

TOYMAKER HN2250
Designer: M. Nicholl
Height: 6in., 15.2cm.
Issued: 1959-1973
Price: $300 £200

TOYS HN1316
Designer: L. Harradine
Height: Unknown
Issued: 1929-1938
Price: $1200 £800

TRACY HN2736
Designer: D. Tootle
Height: 7½in., 19.0cm.
Issued: 1983-
Price: $117 £47

TRANQUILITY HN2426
(Black)
Designer: P. Davies
Height: 12in., 30.5cm.
Issued: 1981
Price: $107 £43

TRANQUILITY HN2469
(White)
Designer: P. Davies
Height: 12in., 30.5cm.
Issued: 1981
Price: $107 £43

TREASURE ISLAND HN2243
Designer: M. Davies
Height: 4¾in., 12.0cm.
Issued: 1962-1975
Price: $90 £60

TROTTY VECK M91
Designer: L. Harradine
Height: 4¼in., 10.8cm.
Issued: 1949-1982
Price: $30 £20

TULIPS HN466
Designer: Unknown
Height: 9½in., 24.1cm.
Issued: 1921-1938
Price: $750 £500

TULIPS HN488
Designer: Unknown
Height: 9½in., 24.1cm.
Issued: 1921-1938
Colour variation
Price: $750 £500

TULIPS HN672
Designer: Unknown
Height: 9½in., 24.1cm.
Issued: 1924-1938
Colour variation
Price: $750 £500

TULIPS HN747
Designer: Unknown
Height: 9½in., 24.1cm.
Issued: 1925-1938
Colour variation
Price: $750 £500

TOYMAKER HN2250

TREASURE ISLAND HN2243

TROTTY VECK M91

TULIPS HN1334
Designer: Unknown
Height: 9½in., 24.1cm.
Issued: 1929-1938
Colour variation
Price: $750 £500

TUPPENCE A BAG HN2320
Designer: M. Nicholl
Height: 5½in., 14.0cm.
Issued: 1968-
Price: $172 £69

TWILIGHT HN2256
Designer: M. Nicholl
Height: 5in., 12.7cm.
Issued: 1971-1976
Price: $90 £60

TWO-A-PENNY HN1359
Designer: L. Harradine
Height: 8¼in., 21.0cm.
Issued: 1929-1938
Price: $750 £500

TZ'U HSI, THE EMPRESS DOWAGER HN2391
Designer: P. Davies
Height: 8in., 20.0cm.
Issued: 1983-
Price: $525 £350

U

UNCLE NED HN2094
Designer: H. Fenton
Height: 6¾in., 17.2cm.
Issued: 1952-1965
Price: $240 £160

UNDER THE GOOSEBERRY BUSH HN49
Designer: C. J. Noke
Height: 3½in., 8.9cm.
Issued: 1916-1938
Price: $750 £500

"UPON HER CHEEKS SHE WEPT" HN59
Designer: L. Perugini
Height: 9in., 22.8cm.
Issued: 1916-1938
Price: $1200 £800

"UPON HER CHEEKS SHE WEPT" HN511
Designer: L. Perugini
Height: 9in., 22.8cm.
Issued: 1921-1938
Colour variation
Price: $1200 £800

"UPON HER CHEEKS SHE WEPT" HN522
Designer: L. Perugini
Height: 9in., 22.8cm.
Issued: 1921-1938
Price: $1200 £800

TUPPENCE A BAG HN2320

TWILIGHT HN2256

TWO-A-PENNY HN1359

UNCLE NED HN2094

UNDER THE GOOSEBERRY BUSH HN49

"UPON HER CHEEKS SHE WEPT" HN59

URIAH HEEP (Style one)
HN545
Designer: L. Harradine
Height: 4in., 10.1cm.
Issued: 1922-1932
Price: $45 £30

URIAH HEEP (Style one)
M45
Designer: L. Harradine
Height: 4in., 10.1cm.
Issued: 1932-1982
Price: $30 £20

URIAH HEEP (Style two)
HN554
Designer: L. Harradine
Height: 7¼in., 18.4cm.
Issued: 1923-1939
Price: $270 £180

URIAH HEEP (Style two)
HN1892
Designer: L. Harradine
Height: 7in., 17.8cm.
Issued: 1938-1952
Price: $210 £140

URIAH HEEP (Style three)
HN2101
Designer: L. Harradine
Height: 7½in., 19.1cm.
Issued: 1952-1967
Price: $180 £120

V

VALERIE HN2107
Designer: M. Davies
Height: 4¾in., 12.0cm.
Issued: 1953-
Price: $102 £41

VANESSA HN1836
Designer: L. Harradine
Height: 7½in., 19.1cm.
Issued: 1938-1949
Price: $270 £180

VANESSA HN1838
Designer: L. Harradine
Height: 7½in., 19.1cm.
Issued: 1938-1949
Colour variation
Price: $270 £180

VANITY HN2475
Designer: M. Davies
Height: 5¼in., 13.3cm.
Issued: 1973-
Price: $102 £41

VENETA HN2722
Designer: W. K. Harper
Height: 8in., 20.3cm.
Issued: 1974-1980
Price: $82 £55

URIAH HEEP (Style one) HN545

URIAH HEEP (Style two) HN554

VALERIE HN2107

VANESSA HN1836

VANITY HN2475

VENETA HN2722

FIGURES

VERA HN1729
Designer: L. Harradine
Height: 4¼in., 10.8cm.
Issued: 1935-1938
Price: $450 £300

VERA HN1730
Designer: L. Harradine
Height: 4¼in., 10.8cm.
Issued: 1935-1938
Colour variation
Price: $450 £300

VERENA HN1835
Designer: L. Harradine
Height: 8¼in., 21.0cm.
Issued: 1938-1949
Price: $375 £250

VERENA HN1854
Designer: L. Harradine
Height: 8¼in., 21.0cm.
Issued: 1938-1949
Colour variation
Price: $375 £250

VERONICA (Style one)
HN1517
Designer: L. Harradine
Height: 8in., 20.3cm.
Issued: 1932-1951
Price: $150 £100

VERONICA (Style one)
HN1519
Designer: L. Harradine
Height: 8in., 20.3cm.
Issued: 1932-1938
Colour variation
Price: $202 £135

VERONICA (Style one)
HN1650
Designer: L. Harradine
Height: 8in., 20.3cm.
Issued: 1934-1949
Colour variation
Price: $202 £135

VERONICA (Style one)
HN1943
Designer: L. Harradine
Height: 8in., 20.3cm.
Issued: 1940-1949
Colour variation
Price: $165 £110

VERONICA (Style two)
HN1915
Designer: L. Harradine
Height: 5¾in., 14.6cm.
Issued: 1939-1949
Price: $225 £150

VERONICA M64
Designer: L. Harradine
Height: 4½in., 10.8cm.
Issued: 1934-1949
Price: $180 £120

VERA HN1729

VERENA HN1835   VERONICA (Style one) HN1517

VERONICA M70
Designer: L. Harradine
Height: 4¼in., 10.8cm.
Issued: 1936-1949
Colour variation
Price: $180 £120

VICTORIA HN2471
Designer: M. Davies
Height: 6½in., 16.5cm.
Issued: 1973-
Price: $172 £69

VICTORIAN LADY HN726
Designer: L. Harradine
Height: 7½in., 19.1cm.
Issued: 1925-1938
Price: $225 £150

VICTORIAN LADY HN727
Designer: L. Harradine
Height: 7½in., 19.1cm.
Issued: 1925-1938
Colour variation
Price: $225 £150

VICTORIAN LADY HN728
Designer: L. Harradine
Height: 7¾in., 19.7cm.
Issued: 1925-1952
Colour variation
Price: $150 £100

VICTORIAN LADY HN736
Designer: L. Harradine
Height: 7¾in., 19.7cm.
Issued: 1925-1938
Colour variation
Price: $225 £150

VICTORIAN LADY HN739
Designer: L. Harradine
Height: 7¾in., 19.7cm.
Issued: 1925-1938
Colour variation
Price: $225 £150

VICTORIAN LADY HN740
Designer: L. Harradine
Height: 7¾in., 19.7cm.
Issued: 1925-1938
Colour variation
Price: $225 £150

VICTORIAN LADY HN742
Designer: L. Harradine
Height: 7¾in., 19.7cm.
Issued: 1925-1938
Colour variation
Price: $225 £150

VICTORIAN LADY HN745
Designer: L. Harradine
Height: 7¾in., 19.7cm.
Issued: 1925-1938
Colour variation
Price: $225 £150

VICTORIAN LADY HN1208
Designer: L. Harradine
Height: 7¾in., 19.7cm.
Issued: 1926-1938
Colour variation
Price: $225 £150

VICTORIAN LADY HN740

VICTORIAN LADY HN1258
Designer: L. Harradine
Height: 7¾in., 19.7cm.
Issued: 1927-1938
          Colour variation
Price: $225 £150

VICTORIAN LADY HN1276
Designer: L. Harradine
Height: 7½in., 19.1cm.
Issued: 1928-1938
          Colour variation
Price: $225 £150

VICTORIAN LADY HN1277
Designer: L. Harradine
Height: 7¾in., 19.7cm.
Issued: 1928-1938
          Colour variation
Price: $225 £150

VICTORIAN LADY HN1345
Designer: L. Harradine
Height: 7¾in., 19.7cm.
Issued: 1929-1949
          Colour variation
Price: $165 £110

VICTORIAN LADY HN1452
Designer: L. Harradine
Height: 7¾in., 19.7cm.
Issued: 1931-1949
          Colour variation
Price: $150 £100

VICTORIAN LADY HN1529
Designer: L. Harradine
Height: 7¾in., 19.7cm.
Issued: 1932-1938
          Colour variation
Price: $225 £150

VICTORIAN LADY M1
Designer: L. Harradine
Height: 3¾in., 9.5cm.
Issued: 1932-1945
Price: $150 £100

VICTORIAN LADY M2
Designer: L. Harradine
Height: 3¾in., 9.5cm.
Issued: 1932-1945
          Colour variation
Price: $150 £100

VICTORIAN LADY M25
Designer: L. Harradine
Height: 3¾in., 9.5cm.
Issued: 1932-1945
          Colour variation
Price: $150 £100

VIKING HN2375
Designer: J. Bromley
Height: 8¾in., 22.2cm.
Issued: 1973-1976
Price: $142 £95

VIOLA D'AMORE HN2797
Designer: M. Davies
Height: 6in., 15.2cm.
Issued: 1976 in a limited
          edition of 750
Price: $450 £300

VIKING HN2375

VIOLIN HN2432
Designer: M. Davies
Height: 6¼in., 15.9cm.
Issued: 1972 in a limited
edition of 750
Price: $450 £300

VIRGINALS HN2427
Designer: M. Davies
Height: 6¼in., 15.9cm.
Issued: 1971 in a limited
edition of 750
Price: $450 £300

VIRGINIA HN1693
Designer: L. Harradine
Height: 7½in., 19.1cm.
Issued: 1935-1949
Price: $397 £265

VIRGINIA HN1694
Designer: L. Harradine
Height: 7½in., 19.1cm.
Issued: 1935-1949
Colour variation
Price: $397 £265

VIVIENNE HN2073
Designer: L. Harradine
Height: 7¾in., 19.7cm.
Issued: 1951-1967
Price: $187 £125

**VOTES FOR WOMEN
HN2816**
Designer: W. K. Harper
Height: 9¾in., 24.7cm.
Issued: 1978-1981
Price: $90 £60

W

**WANDERING MINSTREL
HN1224**
Designer: L. Harradine
Height: 7in., 17.8cm.
Issued: 1927-1938
Price: $1200 £800

**WARDROBE MISTRESS
HN2145**
Designer: M. Davies
Height: 5¾in., 14.6cm.
Issued: 1954-1967
Price: $210 £140

WAYFARER HN2362
Designer: M. Nicholl
Height: 5½in., 14.0cm.
Issued: 1970-1976
Price: $105 £70

WEDDING MORN HN1866
Designer: L. Harradine
Height: 10½in., 26.7cm.
Issued: 1938-1949
Price: $750 £500

VIOLIN HN2432

VIRGINALS HN2427

VIRGINIA HN1693

VIVIENNE HN2073

WANDERING MINSTREL HN1224

WARDROBE MISTRESS HN2145

WEDDING MORN HN1867
Designer: L. Harradine
Height: 10½in., 26.7cm.
Issued: 1938-1949
Colour variation
Price: $750 £500

WEE WILLIE WINKIE HN2050
Designer: M. Davies
Height: 5¼in., 13.3cm.
Issued: 1949-1953
Price: $195 £130

WEE WILLIE WINKIE HN3031
Designer: A. Hughes
Height: 7¾in., 19.5cm.
Issued: 1984-
Price: $107 £43

WELSH GIRL HN39
Designer: E. W. Light
Height: 12in., 30.5cm.
Issued: 1914-1938
Price: $1500 £1000

WELSH GIRL HN92
Designer: E. W. Light
Height: 12in., 30.5cm.
Issued: 1918-1938
Colour variation
Price: $1500 £1000

WELSH GIRL HN456
Designer: E. W. Light
Height: 12in., 30.5cm.
Issued: 1921-1938
Colour variation
Price: $1500 £1000

WELSH GIRL HN514
Designer: E. W. Light
Height: 12in., 30.5cm.
Issued: 1921-1938
Colour variation
Price: $1500 £1000

WELSH GIRL HN516
Designer: E. W. Light
Height: 12in., 30.5cm.
Issued: 1921-1938
Colour variation
Price: $1500 £1000

WELSH GIRL HN519
Designer: E. W. Light
Height: 12in., 30.5cm.
Issued: 1921-1938
Colour variation
Price: $1500 £1000

WELSH GIRL HN520
Designer: E. W. Light
Height: 12in., 30.5cm.
Issued: 1921-1938
Colour variation
Price: $1500 £1000

WEE WILLIE WINKIE HN2050

FIGURES

WELSH GIRL HN660
Designer: E. W. Light
Height: 12in., 30.5cm.
Issued: 1924-1938
           Colour variation
Price: $1500 £1000

WELSH GIRL HN668
Designer: E. W. Light
Height: 12in., 30.5cm.
Issued: 1924-1938
           Colour variation
Price: $1500 £1000

WELSH GIRL HN669
Designer: E. W. Light
Height: 12in., 30.5cm.
Issued: 1924-1938
           Colour variation
Price: $1500 £1000

WELSH GIRL HN701
Designer: E. W. Light
Height: 12in., 30.5cm.
Issued: 1925-1938
           Colour variation
Price: $1500 £1000

WELSH GIRL HN792
Designer: E. W. Light
Height: 12in., 30.5cm.
Issued: 1926-1938
           Colour variation
Price: $1500 £1000

WENDY HN2109
Designer: L. Harradine
Height: 5in., 12.7cm.
Issued: 1953-
Price: $77 ´ £31

WEST INDIAN DANCER HN2384
Designer: P. Davies
Height: 8¾in., 22.2cm.
Issued: 1981 in a limited
           edition of 750
Price: $450 £300

WEST WIND HN1776
Designer: R. Garbe
Height: 14½in., 36.8cm.
Issued: 1933 in a limited
           edition of 25
Price: $2850 £1900

WEST WIND HN1826
Designer: R. Garbe
Height: 14½in., 36.8cm.
Issued: 1937-1949
Price: $2850 £1900

WIGMAKER OF WILLIAMSBURG HN2239
Designer: M. Davies
Height: 7½in., 19.1cm.
Issued: 1960-1983
Price: $82 £55

WELSH GIRL HN669   WENDY HN2109

WEST INDIAN DANCER HN2384   WIGMAKER OF WILLIAMSBURG HN2239

WILLY-WON'T-HE HN1561
Designer: L. Harradine
Height: 6in., 15.2cm.
Issued: 1933-1949
Price: $210 £140

WILLY-WON'T-HE HN1584
Designer: L. Harradine
Height: 6in., 15.2cm.
Issued: 1933-1949
       Colour variation
Price: $210 £140

WILLY-WON'T-HE HN2150
Designer: L. Harradine
Height: 5½in., 14.0cm.
Issued: 1955-1959
       Colour variation
Price: $187 £125

WINDFLOWER (Style one) HN1763
Designer: L. Harradine
Height: 7¼in., 18.4cm.
Issued: 1936-1949
Price: $270 £180

WINDFLOWER (Style one) HN1764
Designer: L. Harradine
Height: 7¼in., 18.4cm.
Issued: 1936-1949
       Colour variation
Price: $270 £180

WINDFLOWER (Style one) HN2029
Designer: L. Harradine
Height: 4¾in., 12.0cm.
Issued: 1949-1955
       Colour variation
Price: $270 £180

WINDFLOWER (Style two) HN1920
Designer: L. Harradine
Height: 11in., 27.9cm.
Issued: 1939-1949
Price: $270 £180

WINDFLOWER (Style two) HN1939
Designer: L. Harradine
Height: 11in., 27.9cm.
Issued: 1940-1949
       Colour variation
Price: $270 £180

WINDFLOWER M78
Designer: L. Harradine
Height: 4in., 10.1cm.
Issued: 1939-1949
Price: $187 £125

WINDFLOWER M79
Designer: L. Harradine
Height: 4in., 10.1cm.
Issued: 1939-1949
       Colour variation
Price: $187 £125

WILLY-WON'T-HE HN1584

FIGURES

WINDMILL LADY HN1400
Designer: L. Harradine
Height: 8½in., 21.6cm.
Issued: 1930-1938
Price: $900 £600

WINNER HN1407
Designer: Unknown
Height: 6¾in., 17.2cm.
Issued: 1930-1938
Price: $1800 £1200

WINSOME HN2220
Designer: M. Davies
Height: 8in., 20.3cm.
Issued: 1960-1985
Price: $75 £50

WINTER (Style one) HN315
Designer: Unknown
Height: 7½in., 19.1cm.
Issued: 1918-1938
Price: $1125 £750

WINTER (Style one) HN475
Designer: Unknown
Height: 7½in., 19.1cm.
Issued: 1921-1938
Colour variation
Price: $1125 £750

WINTER (Style two) HN2088
Designer: M. Davies
Height: 6¼in., 15.9cm.
Issued: 1952-1959
Price: $270 £180

WISTFUL HN2396
Designer: M. Davies
Height: 6½in., 16.5cm.
Issued: 1979-
Price: $337 £135

WIZARD HN2877
Designer: A. Maslankowski
Height: 9¾in., 24.8cm.
Issued: 1979-
Price: $222 £89

WOMAN HOLDING CHILD HN462
Designer: Unknown
Height: 9¼in., 23.5cm.
Issued: 1921-1938
Price: $1275 £850

WOMAN HOLDING CHILD HN570
Designer: Unknown
Height: 9¼in., 23.5cm.
Issued: 1923-1938
Colour variation
Price: $1275 £850

WOMAN HOLDING CHILD HN703
Designer: Unknown
Height: 9¼in., 23.5cm.
Issued: 1925-1938
Colour variation
Price: $1275 £850

WINDMILL LADY HN1400

WINNER HN1407

WINSOME HN2220

WINTER (Style one) HN315

WINTER (Style two) HN2088

WISTFUL HN2396

FIGURES

WOMAN HOLDING CHILD
HN743
Designer: Unknown
Height: 9¼in., 23.5cm.
Issued: 1925-1938
Colour variation
Price: $1275 £850

WOMAN OF THE TIME OF
HENRY VI HN43
Designer: E. W. Light
Height: 9¼in., 23.4cm.
Issued: 1914-1938
Price: $1500 £1000

WOOD NYMPH HN2192
Designer: M. Davies
Height: 7¼in., 18.4cm.
Issued: 1958-1962
Price: $240 £160

WOMAN OF THE TIME OF HENRY VI HN43   WOOD NYMPH HN2192

Y

YEARNING HN2920 (White)
Designer: P. Gee
Height: 11¾in., 29.8cm.
Issued: 1982
Price: $107 £43

YEARNING HN2921 (Black)
Designer: P. Gee
Height: 11¾in., 29.8cm.
Issued: 1982
Price: $107 £43

YEOMAN OF THE GUARD
HN688
Designer: L. Harradine
Height: 5¾in., 14.6cm.
Issued: 1924-1938
Price: $750 £500

YEOMAN OF THE GUARD HN688

YOUNG KNIGHT HN94

YEOMAN OF THE GUARD
HN2122
Designer: L. Harradine
Height: 5¾in., 14.6cm.
Issued: 1954-1959
Price: $600 £400

YOUNG KNIGHT HN94
Designer: C. J. Noke
Height: 9½in., 24.1cm.
Issued: 1918-1936
Price: $1800 £1200

YOUNG LOVE HN2735
Designer: D. V. Tootle
Height: 10in., 25.4cm.
Issued: 1975-
Price: $637 £255

YOUNG MASTER HN2872
Designer: M. Davies
Height: 7in., 17.8cm.
Issued: 1980-
Price: $337 £135

YOUNG LOVE HN2735

YOUNG MASTER HN2872

**YOUNG MISS
NIGHTINGALE HN2010**
Designer: M. Davies
Height: 9¼in., 23.5cm.
Issued: 1948-1953
Price: $525 £350

YOUNG WIDOW HN1399
Designer: L. Harradine
Height: 8in., 20.3cm.
Issued: 1930-1938
Price: $975 £650
Also called "Little Mother"
(Style two)

YUM-YUM (Style one) HN1268
Designer: L. Harradine
Height: 5in., 12.7cm.
Issued: 1928-1938
Price: $360 £240

YUM-YUM (Style one) HN1287
Designer: L. Harradine
Height: 5in., 12.7cm.
Issued: 1928-1939
        Colour variation
Price: $360 £240

YUM-YUM (Style two) HN2899
Designer: W. K. Harper
Height: 10¾in., 27.3cm.
Issued: 1980-
Price: $352 £235

YUM-YUM (Style two) HN2899   **YOUNG MISS NIGHTINGALE HN2010**

KINGSWARE

Doulton Kingsware jug depicting Dickens' characters, designed by C. J. Noke. $90 £60

Pied Piper, a Royal Doulton Kingsware teapot, with silver mounts, circa 1905. $130 £85

Nelson, a Royal Doulton Kingsware triangular flask, 8in. high, 6in. wide, 1914. $90 £60

Oyez, Oyez, ewer shaped Kingsware flask made for Dewar's Scotch Whisky, 10½in. high, issued 1909. $105 £70

Royal Doulton Kingsware wall plaque decorated with a portrait of a gentleman in relief, 15¾in. diam. $375 £250

Doctor Johnson, a Kingsware flask made for Watson's Scotch Whisky, issued 1905, 8¼in. high. $105 £70

Pied Piper, a Royal Doulton Kingsware milk jug with silver mounts, circa 1905. $75 £50

Royal Doulton Kingsware tobacco jar decorated in relief with a gentleman smoking, 8¼in. high. $75 £50

Jovial Monk, a Kingsware flask made for Dewar's Scotch Whisky, issued 1908, 7¾in. high. $100 £65

Pied Piper, a Royal Doulton Kingsware coffee pot, with silver mounts, circa 1905. $135 £90

Royal Doulton Kingsware Duke of York water jug, 7¼in. high. $120 £80

Monk, a Royal Doulton Kingsware flask decorated with a monk tasting wine, 8¼in. high. $150 £100

Wizard, a Royal Doulton Kingsware flask decorated with a wizard standing over a cauldron, designed by Noke, 10in. high, issued 1904. $190 £125

Gillie and Fisherman, a Royal Doulton Kingsware whisky flask, 8in. high. $120 £80

Coachman, a Doulton Kingsware flagon, issued 1932, 10½in. high. $135 £90

A Kingsware two-handled vase, 'Here's Health Unto His Majesty', 13in. high. $195 £130

Royal Doulton Kingsware flask bearing a portrait of Richard Arkwright, 1732-1792, 9in. high. $165 £110

Royal Doulton Kingsware sugar bowl with silver mounts, circa 1905. $75 £50

Royal Doulton Kingsware teapot, issued 1932, DN2870. $85 £55

Royal Doulton Kingsware ash-tray and match-holder, issued 1932. $57 £38

Micawber, a Kingsware yellow glaze flagon, 7½in. high.$90 £60

Royal Doulton Kingsware mug with silver rim, 4in. high. $66 £44

Alchemist, a Doulton Kingsware flask, signed Noke, issued 1913, 8¼in. high. $115 £75

Ben Jonson, a Kingsware flask made for Dewar's Scotch Whisky, issued 1909, 7in. high. $105 £70

Huntsman, a Royal Doulton Kingsware loving cup, issued 1932, 8in. high. $130 £85

Nelson, a Kingsware flask made for Dewar's Scotch Whisky, issued 1914, 8½in. high. $105 £70

KINGSWARE

Memories, a Kingsware water jug depicting Dickens' characters. $85 £55

Royal Doulton Kingsware teapot, issued 1932, DN1286. $85 £55

Friar, a Royal Doulton Kingsware shaving mug. $90 £60

Alchemist, a Kingsware yellow glaze flagon, 8½in. high. $100 £65

Royal Doulton Kingsware whisky flask in the form of Tony Weller, 3½in. high. $300 £200

George The Guard, a Kingsware pear shaped ewer made for Dewar's, 8¼in. high, issued 1908. $130 £85

Royal Doulton Kingsware single handled jug depicting golfers, 9in. high. $330 £220

Fisherman, a Kingsware yellow glaze flagon, 7in. high. $85 £55

Royal Doulton Kingsware tea caddy, DN2693. $180 £120

Watchman, a Kingsware globular shaped flask, 8in. high, with modelled head. $140 £95

Royal Doulton Kingsware single-handled jug depicting a golfer and his caddie. $330 £220

Tony Weller, a Royal Doulton Kingsware flask with the inscription, 'Tony Weller Bevare of the Vidders', 8in. high. $135 £90

Pied Piper, a Royal Doulton Kingsware flask with silver mounts, circa 1905, 8in. high. $135 £90

LOVING CUPS & JUGS

ADMIRAL LORD NELSON LOVING CUP
Designed by C. J. Noke & H. Fenton, 10½in. high,
Issued 1935 in a limited edition of 600.
$525 £350

THE APOTHECARY LOVING CUP
Designed by C. J. Noke & H. Fenton, 6in. high,
Issued 1934 in a limited edition of 600.
$412 £275

CAPTAIN COOK LOVING CUP
Designed by C. J. Noke & H. Fenton, 9½in. high,
Issued 1933 in a limited edition of 350.
$1200 £800

CAPTAIN PHILLIP JUG
Designed by C. J. Noke & H. Fenton, 9¼in. high,
Issued 1938 in a limited edition of 350.
$675 £450

CHARLES DICKENS JUG
Designed by C. J. Noke & H. Fenton, 10½in. high,
Issued 1936 in a limited edition of 1000.
$405 £270

DICKENS DREAM JUG
Designed by C. J. Noke, 10½in. high,
Issued 1933 in a limited edition of 1000.
$525 £350

GEORGE WASHINGTON BICENTENARY JUG
Designed by C. J. Noke & H. Fenton, 10¾in. high, Issued 1932 in a limited edition of 1000, Colour variation on handle.
$3750 £2500

GEORGE WASHINGTON BICENTENARY JUG
Designed by C. J. Noke & H. Fenton, 10¾in. high,
Issued 1932 in a limited edition of 1000,
Variation of handle style. $1875 £1250

GUY FAWKES JUG
Designed by H. Fenton, 7½in. high,
Issued 1934 in a limited edition of 600. $450 £300

JACKDAW OF RHEIMS JUG
Designer - Unknown, 11in. high,
Issued - Trial Jug circa 1934. $4500 £3000

JAN VAN RIEBECK LOVING CUP
Designed by C. J. Noke & H. Fenton, 10¼in. high,
Issued circa 1935 in a limited edition of 300.
                                              $2250 £1500

JOHN PEEL LOVING CUP
Designer - Unknown, 9in. high,
Issued 1933 in a limited edition of 500.
$675 £450

KING EDWARD VIII CORONATION LOVING CUP
(Small)
Designed by C. J. Noke, 6½in. high,
Issued 1937 in a limited edition of 1000.
$300 £200

KING EDWARD VIII CORONATION LOVING CUP
(Large)
Designed by C. J. Noke & H. Fenton, 10in. high,
Issued 1937 in a limited edition of 2000.
$450 £300

KING GEORGE V AND QUEEN MARY SILVER JUBILEE LOVING CUP
Designed by C. J. Noke & H. Fenton, 10in. high,
Issued 1935 in a limited edition of 1000.
$450 £300

**KING GEORGE VI AND QUEEN ELIZABETH
CORONATION LOVING CUP (Large)**
Designed by C. J. Noke & H. Fenton, 10½in. high,
Issued 1937 in a limited edition of 2000.
$450 £300

**KING GEORGE VI AND QUEEN ELIZABETH
CORONATION LOVING CUP (Small)**
Designed by C. J. Noke & H. Fenton, 6½in. high,
Issued 1937 in a limited edition of 2000.
$375 £250

MASTER OF FOXHOUNDS PRESENTATION JUG
Designed by C. J. Noke, 13in. high, Issued 1930 in a limited edition of 500. $450 £300

MAYFLOWER LOVING CUP
Designed by David Biggs, 10¼in. high,
Issued 1970 in a limited edition of 500.
$150 £100

PIED PIPER JUG
Designed by C. J. Noke & H. Fenton, 10in. high,
Issued 1934 in a limited edition of 600.
$525 £350

POTTERY IN THE PAST LOVING CUP
Designed by Graham Tongue, 6in. high,
Issued 1983,
$75 £50

QUEEN ELIZABETH II CORONATION JUG
Designer - Unknown, 6¼in. high,
Issued 1953 unlimited.
$125 £85

QUEEN ELIZABETH II CORONATION LOVING CUP
Designed by C. J. Noke & H. Fenton, 10½in. high, Issued 1953 in a limited edition of 1000.
$450 £300

QUEEN ELIZABETH SILVER JUBILEE LOVING CUP
Designed by R. Johnson, 10½in. high, Issued 1977 in a limited edition of 250. $450 £300

REGENCY COACH JUG
Designed by C. J. Noke, 10in. high, Issued 1931 in a limited edition of 500.
$525 £350

ROBIN HOOD LOVING CUP
Designed by C. J. Noke & H. Fenton, 8½in. high, Issued 1938 in a limited edition of 600.
$525 £350

SIR FRANCIS DRAKE JUG
Designed by C. J. Noke & H. Fenton, 10½in. high,
Issued 1933 in a limited edition of 500.
$525 £350

THE THREE MUSKETEERS LOVING CUP
Designed by C. J. Noke & H. Fenton, 10in. high,
Issued 1936 in a limited edition of 600.
$600 £400

TOWER OF LONDON JUG
Designed by C. J. Noke & H. Fenton, 9½in. high,
Issued 1933 in a limited edition of 500.
$525 £350

TREASURE ISLAND JUG
Designed by C. J. Noke & H. Fenton, 7½in. high,
Issued 1934 in a limited edition of 600.
$525 £350

THE VILLAGE BLACKSMITH JUG
Designed by C. J. Noke, 7¾in. high, Issued 1936 in a limited edition of 600. $450 £300

THE WANDERING MINSTREL LOVING CUP
Designed by C. J. Noke & H. Fenton, 5½in. high, Issued 1934 in a limited edition of 600. $300 £200

WILLIAM SHAKESPEARE JUG
Designed by C. J. Noke, 10¾in. high,
Issued 1933 in a limited edition of 1000.
$420 £280

WILLIAM WORDSWORTH LOVING CUP
Designed by C. J. Noke, 6½in. high,
Issued 1933 unlimited. $480 £320

MISCELLANEOUS WARE

ASH BOWLS

AULD MAC D6006
Size: 3in., 7.5cm.
Issued: 1939-1960
Price: $75 £50

FARMER JOHN D6007
Size: 3in., 7.5cm.
Issued: 1939-1960
Price: $75 £50

OLD CHARLEY D5925
Size: 3in., 7.5cm.
Issued: 1938-1960
Price: $75 £50

PADDY D5926
Size: 3in., 7.5cm.
Issued: 1938-1960
Price: $75 £50

PARSON BROWN D6008
Size: 3in., 7.5cm.
Issued: 1939-1960
Price: $75 £50

SAIREY GAMP D6009
Size: 3in., 7.5cm.
Issued: 1939-1960
Price: $75 £50

ASH TRAYS

DICK TURPIN D5601
Size: 2¾in., 7cm.
Issued: 1936-1960
Price: $75 £50

JOHN BARLEYCORN D5602
Size: 2¾in., 7cm.
Issued: 1936-1960
Price: $75 £50

OLD CHARLEY D5599
Size: 2¾in., 7cm.
Issued: 1936-1960
Price: $75 £50

PARSON BROWN D5600
Size: 2¾in., 7cm.
Issued: 1936-1960
Price: $75 £50

DICK TURPIN

JOHN BARLEYCORN

OLD CHARLEY

PARSON BROWN

BOOKENDS

MR MICAWBER HN1615
Size: 4in., 10cm.
Issued: 1934-c.1939
Price: $240 £160

MR PICKWICK HN1623
Size: 4in., 10cm.
Issued: 1934-c.1939
Price: $240 £160

SAIREY GAMP HN1625
Size: 4in., 10cm.
Issued: 1934-c.1939
Price: $240 £160

TONY WELLER HN1616
Size: 4in., 10cm.
Issued: 1934-c.1939
Price: $240 £160

MR MICAWBER

MR PICKWICK

SAIREY GAMP

TONY WELLER

BUSTS

BUZ FUZ D6048
Issued: 1939-1960
Price: $60 £40

MR MICAWBER D6050
Issued: 1939-1960
Price: $60 £40

MR PICKWICK D6049
Issued: 1939-1960
Price: $60 £40

SAIREY GAMP D6047
Issued: 1939-1960
Price: $60 £40

SAM WELLER D6052
Issued: 1939-1960
Price: $60 £40

TONY WELLER D6051
Issued: 1939-1960
Price: $60 £40

DICKENS TINIES

ARTFUL DODGER D6678
Designer: P. Gee
Issued: 1982
Price: $27 £18

BILL SYKES D6684
Designer: M. Abberley
Issued: 1982
Price: $27 £18

BETSY TROTWOOD D6684
Designer: M. Abberley
Issued: 1982
Price: $27 £18

CHARLES DICKENS D6688
Designer: E. Griffiths
Issued: 1982
Price: $27 £18

DAVID COPPERFIELD D6680
Designer: M. Abberley
Issued: 1982
Price: $27 £18

FAGIN D6679
Designer: R. Tabbenor
Issued: 1982
Price: $27 £18

LITTLE NELL D6681
Designer: M. Abberley
Issued: 1982
Price: $27 £18

MR BUMBLE D6686
Designer: R. Tabbenor
Issued: 1982
Price: $27 £18

MRS BARDELL D6687
Designer: R. Tabbenor
Issued: 1982
Price: $27 £18

OLIVER TWIST D6677
Designer: R. Tabbenor
Issued: 1982
Price: $27 £18

SCROOGE D6682
Designer: M. Abberley
Issued: 1982
Price: $27 £18

URIAH HEEP D6682
Designer: R. Tabbenor
Issued: 1982
Price: $27 £18

MUSICAL JUGS

AULD MAC D5889
Issued: 1938-c.1939
Price: $720 £480

OLD CHARLEY D5858
Issued: 1937-c.1939
Price: $600 £400

OLD KING COLE D6014
Issued: 1939
Price: $1500 £1000

OLD KING COLE (Yellow Crown) D6014
Issued: 1939
Price: $1875 £1250

PADDY D5887
Issued: 1938-1939
Price: $675 £450

TONY WELLER D5888
Issued: 1938-1939
Price: $637 £425

OLD KING COLE

NAPKIN RINGS

FAT BOY M59
Issued: 1935-1939
Price: $225 £150

MR MICAWBER M58
Issued: 1935-1939
Price: $225 £150

MR PICKWICK M57
Issued: 1935-1939
Price: $225 £150

SAIREY GAMP M62
Issued: 1935-1939
Price: $225 £150

SAM WELLER M61
Issued: 1935-1939
Price: $225 £150

TONY WELLER M60
Issued: 1935-1939
Price: $225 £150

FAT BOY

MR MICAWBER

MR PICKWICK

SAIREY GAMP

SAM WELLER

TONY WELLER

SUGAR BOWLS

OLD CHARLEY D6012
Size: 2½in., 6.5cm.
Issued: 1939
Price: $180 £120

SAIREY GAMP D6011
Size: 2½in., 6.5cm.
Issued: 1939
Price: $180 £120

TONY WELLER D6013
Size: 2½in., 6.5cm.
Issued: 1939
Price: $180 £120

OLD CHARLEY

SAIREY GAMP   TONY WELLER

TABLE LIGHTERS

BACCHUS D6505
Size: 3½in., 9cm.
Issued: 1964-1974
Price: $90 £60

BEEFEATER D6233
Size: 3½in., 9cm.
Issued: 1958-1973
Price: $90 £60

BUZ FUZ D5838
Size: 3½in., 9cm.
Issued: 1958
Price: $112 £75

BACCHUS   **BEEFEATER**   **BUZ FUZ**

CAPTAIN AHAB D6506
Size: 3½in., 9cm.
Issued: 1964-1974
Price: $90 £60

CAP'N CUTTLE D5842
Size: 3½in., 9cm.
Issued: 1958
Price: $120 £80

FALSTAFF D6385
Size: 3½in., 9cm.
Issued: 1958-1973
Price: $90 £60

CAPTAIN AHAB   **CAP'N CUTTLE**   **FALSTAFF**

LAWYER D6504
Size: 3½in., 9cm.
Issued: 1962-1974
Price: $90 £60

LONG JOHN SILVER D6386
Size: 3½in., 9cm.
Issued: 1958-1973
Price: $90 £60

MR MICAWBER D5843
Size: 3½in., 9cm.
Issued: 1958
Price: $112 £75

LAWYER   **LONG JOHN SILVER**   **MR MICAWBER**

MR PICKWICK D5839
Size: 3½in., 9cm.
Issued: 1958-1961
Price: $97 £65

OLD CHARLEY D5527
Size: 3½in., 9cm.
Issued: 1959-1973
Price: $90 £60

POACHER D6464
Size: 3½in., 9cm.
Issued: 1958-1973
Price: $90 £60

PORTHOS D6453
Size: 3½in., 9cm.
Issued: 1958
Price: $195 £130

RIP VAN WINKLE D6463
Size: 3½in., 9cm.
Issued: 1958
Price: $225 £150

MR PICKWICK   **POACHER**   **RIP VAN WINKLE**

TEAPOTS

OLD CHARLEY D6017
Size: 7in., 18cm.
Issued: 1939
Price: $1275 £850

SAIREY GAMP D6015
Size: 7in., 18cm.
Issued: 1939
Price: $1275 £850

TONY WELLER D6016
Size: 7in., 18cm.
Issued: 1939
Price: $1275 £850

TOOTHPICK HOLDERS

OLD CHARLEY D6152
Size: 2¼in., 5.5cm.
Issued: 1940-1941
Price: $75 £50

PADDY D6151
Size: 2¼in., 5.5cm.
Issued: 1940-1941
Price: $75 £50

SAIREY GAMP D6150
Size: 2¼in., 5.5cm.
Issued: 1940-1941
Price: $75 £50

TOBACCO JARS

OLD CHARLEY D5844
Size: 5½in., 14cm.
Issued: 1938-1941
Price: $420 £280

PADDY D5854
Size: 5½in., 14cm.
Issued: 1938-1941
Price: $450 £300

OLD CHARLEY

PADDY

WALL VASES

JESTER D6111
Size: 7¼in., 18cm.
Issued: 1940-1941
Price: $525 £350

OLD CHARLEY D6110
Size: 7¼in., 18cm.
Issued: 1940-1941
Price: $525 £350

JESTER

OLD CHARLEY

PANELS

In the early 20th century the Doulton works began producing decorative pottery tiles in large numbers for the embellishment of both interiors and exteriors of shops, bars and other establishments.

Making pictures and decorations from tiles was however far from being a new idea for as far back as the Egyptian Pharaohs the device had been used and some very beautiful tiles can still be seen in mosques of Iran and other Moslem countries. The Persian tile with its intricate foliage decoration and brilliant colours was an artistic masterpiece.

Doulton's idea of making whole pictures from tiles however was a new departure and their creations were used in the decoration of hospital wards, especially children's wards, where the artists let their fancies run free. The results were wonderful creations of nursery rhymes and fantasy children's scenes which must have diverted the minds of many small patients.

Tiled walls were not only decorative but they also had the advantage of being easily washed down and cleaned for it was a time when medical authorities were beginning to realise the importance of hygiene in hospitals.

By the 1950's however, modernisation programmes meant that tiled walls were either torn out or covered over with boarding. Those that have survived are now being preserved as works of art. Prices range from a few hundred pounds to many thousands depending upon the size and subject matter.

HERE WE GO GATHERING NUTS IN MAY

SIMPLE SIMON MET A PIEMAN

LADY QUEEN ANNE

MARY, MARY, QUITE CONTRARY

SLEEPING PRINCESS

LITTLE RED RIDING HOOD

THERE WAS AN OLD WOMAN WHO LIVED IN A SHOE

OLD KING COLE WAS A MERRY OLD SOUL

CINDERELLA

HIGGLEDY, PIGGLEDY, MY BLACK HEN

JACK AND JILL

THE QUEEN OF HEARTS

SEE-SAW, MARGERY DAW

PUSS IN BOOTS

THE GOOSE GIRL

LITTLE BO-PEEP

LITTLE MISS MUFFET

LITTLE BOY BLUE

HANSEL AND GRETEL

PUSS IN BOOTS

AGRICULTURE & HORTICULTURE

The Prince awakens
the SLEEPING BEAUTY

SLEEPING BEAUTY

OLD MOTHER HUBBARD

LITTLE JACK HORNER   DING, DONG, BELL, PUSSY'S IN THE WELL

ELEPHANT & CASTLE CROSSROADS

SERIES WARE

Shakespearean character plate depicting 'Hamlet', 10¼in. diam. $48 £32

'Old Moreton Hall' Series ware teapot, 5½in. high. $63 £42

'Old London' jug in low relief designed by C. J. Noke, issued 1949-1960, D6291. $112 £75

'Gibson Girl' rack plate designed by Charles Dana Gibson, circa 1901. $60 £40

Royal Doulton Series ware coffee pot, 7½in. tall, D5506, 1934. $45 £30

Royal Doulton rack plate 'Short Headed Salmon', signed J. Birbeck, 9½in. diam., circa 1909. $105 £70

Old English Inns Series milk jug depicting 'The Cat and The Fiddle'. $42 £28

'Country Garden' Series dish depicting the 'Maid at the Well', circa 1929. $45 £30

Dickens' ware 'Friar' shape jug depicting 'Little Nell', 6¾in. high. $50 £34

Sir Roger de Coverley rack plate 'The Saracen's Head', 10¼in. diam. $48 £32

Sir Roger de Coverley Series ware teapot, 5½in. high. $66 £44

'Jackdaw of Rheims' rack plate, D2532, issued 1906-1930. $45 £30

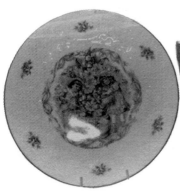

'Valentine's Day', Series ware rack plate, 1985, 6¼in. diam. $15 £10

Oliver Twist jug designed by C. J. Noke, depicting 'Fagin and Bumble', D5617. $97 £65

'Short Headed Salmon', a Royal Doulton rack plate, signed by J. Birbeck, 9½in. diam., circa 1913. $105 £70

'Gibson Girl' rack plate, by Charles Dana Gibson, circa 1901. $60 £40

Dickens' ware water jug modelled in low relief depicting Mr Pickwick. $75 £50

Robert Burns rack plate 'Here's Health to them that's awa', 10¼in. diam. $48 £32

Proverbs rack plate 'Nothing Venture, Nothing Win', 10¼in. diam. $82 £55

Dickens' ware 'Cleveland' shape teapot depicting 'Fagin', 5¼in. high. $66 £44

Dickens' ware rack plate depicting 'Tony Weller', 10¼in. diam. $39 £26

Series ware rack plate 'The Seasons', 'Winter'. $18 £12

Royal Doulton jug in low relief by Charles Crombie, depicting a golfer, 9¼in. high, circa 1910. $340 £225

'Gibson Girl' rack plate designed by Charles Dana Gibson, circa 1901. $60 £40

Robert Burns portrait plate with a ploughman in the background, 10¼in. diam. $42 £28

'Nightwatchman', a Series ware jug by C. J. Noke, 8½in. high, D1198, 1903. $57 £38

Old English Inns Series ware rack plate depicting 'The Leather Bottle, Cobham', 10in. diam. $39 £26

Old English Inns Series ware rack plate depicting 'The Bear's Head', 10in. diam. $39 £26

Water jug in low relief depicting 'Tony Weller', D6397. $68 £45

Dickens' ware rack plate depicting 'The Fat Boy', 10¼in. diam. $39 £26

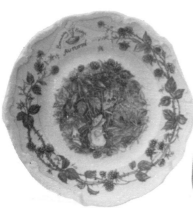

Rack plate 'Autumn' from 'The Seasons'. $18 £12

A Jacobean jug 'Ye Old Belle' depicting a serving wench and two cavaliers, 6½in. high. $63 £42

'Gibson Girl' rack plate with lover's knot and heart border, circa 1901. $60 £40

Series ware rack plate 'Mother Kangaroo and Toby', 10½in. diam. $15 £10

Dickens' ware rack plate depicting 'Sairey Gamp', 10¼in. diam. $39 £26

'Edinburgh Castle', rack plate, 10½in. diam. $15 £10

'Widow and Her Friends' Series rack plate by Charles Dana Gibson, circa 1901. $57 £38

Water jug in low relief depicting a scene from David Copperfield, D6292, issued 1947-1960. $112 £75

'Arabian Nights' rack plate, 'The Arrival of the Unknown Princess', 10¼in. diam. $42 £28

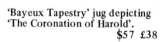

Old Moreton Hall rack plate depicting 'Queen Elizabeth', 10¼in. diam. $42 £28

'Bayeux Tapestry' jug depicting 'The Coronation of Harold'. $57 £38

Charles Dickens portrait plate with a border of Dickens' characters, 10¼in. diam. $48 £32

Shakespearean character plate depicting 'Ophelia', 10¼in. diam. $48 £32

'St. George and the Dragon' rack plate, D5108, issued 1931-1945. $45 £30

Souter Series plate, 'The Tiff', with Art Nouveau border. $75 £50

Dickens' ware water jug in low
relief depicting 'Bill Sykes',
D6396. $75 £50

'Old Curiosity Shop' jug in low
relief, designed by C. J. Noke,
D5584, issued 1937-1960.
                         $90 £60

Oliver Twist tankard in low
relief, designed by C. J. Noke,
issued 1949-1960. $90 £60

Royal Doulton two-handled
vase, designed by Charles
Crombie, depicting two golfers
and a caddie, 8in. high.
           $340 £225

'Country Garden', Series ware
tray 'Old Man with Scythe', 1929.
                         $45 £30

Dickens' ware 'Friar' shape jug
depicting 'Poor Joe', 4¾in. high.
                     $42 £28

Proverbs rack plate 'Fine Feathers
Make Fine Birds', 10¼in. diam.
                    $82 £55

Oliver Twist jug, 'I want some
more', by C. J. Noke, issued
1949-1960. $97 £65

Castles and Churches rack plate
depicting 'Dunolly Castle', D4643.
                     $48 £32

STONEWARE

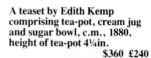

A salt cellar with incised blue leaves and bead work, c.m., 1877, 2¼in. high. $67 £45

An hexagonal salt cellar, the interior glazed blue, o.u.m., circa 1872, 3in. diameter.
$112 £75

A teaset by Edith Kemp comprising tea-pot, cream jug and sugar bowl, c.m., 1880, height of tea-pot 4¼in.
$360 £240

A vase painted with yellow fruit and dark brown foliage on a brown field, c.m.l. & c., circa 1912, 9in. high. $90 £60

A pair of candlesticks with incised geometric patterns in blue and brown on a buff ground, o.u.m., circa 1872, 11in. high. $480 £320

A mounted jug, the mottled brown ground with applied geometric and leaf patterns, c.m., 1878, 9½in. high.
$105 £70

A tapered jug, with applied blue and green stylised flower heads, c.m., 1880, 9½in. high.
$127 £85

A Punch and Judy clockcase, the buff stoneware with a bright blue glaze, c.m.l. & c., circa 1905, 11½in. high.
$1125 £750

A jug, the light buff body with incised diamonds and applied blue slip flowers, impressed Doulton Lambeth, circa 1868, 9½in. high. $135 £90

A pepper pot by Alice Budden with incised leaves and bead work, c.m., 1880, 2½in. high. $105 £70

A massive pair of candlesticks by Alice E. Budden, incised overall, r.m., 1881, 11¾in. high. $480 £320

A jug by Jane S. Hurst with applied green and white geometric patterns in high relief, r.m., 1881, 9½in. high. $150 £100

A vase by Elizabeth Atkins, the buff ground with an incised scale pattern and four panels, r.m., 1883, 7in. high. $165 £110

A pair of vases by Margaret Aitken, the white ground with incised flowering foliage painted in green and white pâte-sur-pâte, r.m., 1881, 8in. high. $330 £220

A vase by Harry Barnard, the cream ground with incised bands of chevrons on which are painted tadpoles, r.m., 1882, 10¼in. high. $210 £140

A vase by Alberta L. Green with incised green leaves growing from a central ochre band, r.m., circa 1882, 8¾in. high. $120 £80

A pair of vases by Bertha Evans, the mottled blue ground with incised brown scrolls, r.m., 1883, 7in. high. $300 £200

A vase by Ellen Gathercole, the incised brown ground with green plants having white flowers, r.m., 1882, 8¼in. high. $195 £130

A vase possibly by Emily Welch, the grey-green ground with applied blue flowering branches, r.m., circa 1885, 11¾in. high. $195 £130

A pair of vases by Mary Capes painted with green flowers outlined in gilt, r.m., 1884, 7¾in. high. $255 £170

A white stoneware jug with an incised diamond pattern, glazed alternately blue and brown with applied flower heads, o.u.m., the silver cover hallmarked 1872, 7in. high. $255 £170

A jug by Ellen Gathercole decorated in the traditional manner with applied vignettes of sporting scenes, r.m., 1882, 8¾in. high. $390 £260

A pair of candlesticks by Nellie Garbott with incised brown and blue leaves, c.m., 1879, 6¾in. high. $390 £260

A large vase by Harry Barnard, the buff ground with incised foliage, r.m., 1881, 14¼in. high. $1275 £850

A vase by Annie Gentle, with painted white lattice-work and incised green and yellow foliage, c.m., 1879, 9¾in. high. $135 £90

A pair of vases by Margaret Aitken, with incised and carved brown and blue leaves, r.m., 1882, 7½in. $360 £240

A vase by Eliza S. Banks, with carved panels of blue foliage surrounded by painted white flowers, r.m., 1882, 8½in. high. $202 £135

STONEWARE

An unattributed jug moulded as a uniformed man with peaked hat, r.m., circa 1888, 9¼in. high. $375 £250

A small circular clockcase in buff stoneware with applied rough cast chips, circa 1890, 7¼in. high. $255 £170

An unattributed pair of vases, each with incised pale green and yellow foliage, r.m., circa 1885, 11½in. high. $480 £320

An unattributed beaker, the buff ground with painted white foliage and coloured lines, c.m.l. & c., circa 1902, 5½in. high. $90 £60

A late vase with stylised blue flowers and green leaves edged in white, c.m. & l., circa 1922, 7½in. high. $60 £40

A vase painted with formal purple flowers and green leaves against a white ground, c.m.l. & c., circa 1912, 7¾in. high.
          $97 £65

An unattributed salt cellar, the bowl with incised brown leaves, c.m., circa 1880, 3½in. high.
          $165 £110

A monumental clockcase glazed in shades of blue and brown with carved and incised details and applied bead work, c.m., 1879, 15½in. high.
          $1725 £1150

An unattributed vase with upright blue handles, c.m., 1879, 7½in. high. $142 £95

344

A vase, the mottled blue ground with incised lines, modelled in high relief with a dragon biting the neck, r.m., 1886, 10in. high. $255 £170

An early architectural clockcase glazed ochre and blue, with incised blue, green, and purple leaves, o.m., 1875, 14½in. high. $1275 £850

An unattributed jug, the combed buff ground with incised green fish and plants, DLE, circa 1895, 13¼in. high. $330 £220

A vase with black and purple designs on a white ground, c.m.l. & c., circa 1920, 8¼in. high. $90 £60

An architectural clockcase glazed in dark brown, blue and green, r.m., 1884, 10¼in. high. $975 £650

A cylindrical vase with blue, green and black geometric designs on a lovat ground, c.m.l. & c., circa 1920, 7¾in. high. $90 £60

An unattributed jug, the buff ground with white bead work and incised blue and brown leaves, c.m., 1879, 7¾in. high. $165 £110

An unattributed hexagonal open-work basket pierced with brown lattice, r.m., 1880, 5¼in. high. $180 £120

An unattributed horn cup moulded with a blue and ochre sphinx, c.m., 1876, 9in. high. $390 £260

A tapered jug with mottled brown glaze and applied blue flower heads, o.m., 1875, 10½in. high. $105 £70

A bulbous jug with applied geometric and floral patterns in purple and green, c.m., 1879, 7¼in. high. $285 £190

A jug by Harriet E. Hibbut, the blue ground with an applied carpet of large flowers predominantly blue, c.m., 1880, 9¼in. high. $120 £80

A vase by Bessie Youatt, the white ground with an incised spiral green leafy branch, c.m., 1879, 8in. high. $195 £130

A pair of vases by Emily A. London with a blue hatched ground, r.m., 1883, 4½in. high. $142 £95

A vase by Bessie Youatt, the white neck finely combed and the body painted with brown leaves, c.m., 1880, 9½in. high. $240 £160

A pâte-sur-pâte jug, the buff ground with finely incised and applied green leaves and bead work, r.m., circa 1882, 8½in. high. $112 £75

A shaped jug with applied blue geometric patterns in high relief, c.m., 1877, 8½in. high. $165 £110

A jug with an overall incised diamond pattern, glazed alternately in brown and blue, r.m., circa 1882, 8¾in. high. $90 £60

A jug, with applied dark green and white shell motifs within various applied borders, c.m., 1880, 9½in. high. $120 £80

A modelled owl with detachable head, the feathers formed by applied motifs in shades of blue, ochre and brown, r.m., circa 1880, 8in. high. $420 £280

A vase, the light buff body stencilled overall with impressed concentric circles, r.m., circa 1882, 12¼in. high. $120 £80

A jug by Bessie Youatt, incised and applied with a ring of blue flower heads, c.m., 1879, 8½in. high. $210 £140

A pair of vases by Bessie Youatt, each with four incised shaped panels, r.m., 1883, 10¾in. high. $540 £360

A baluster-shaped jug with incised blue shield-shaped panels on a brown ground, r.m., 1882, 9½in. high. $135 £90

A jug by Emma Shute with applied pale blue and white motifs, c.m., 1880, 9¼in. high. $75 £50

A mug by Constance E. Redford, the buff ground with white dots and incised blue scrolls, r.m., 1882, 5in. high. $112 £75

A jug by Harriett E. Hibbut, the mottled brown body with applied grey and blue leaves, and flower heads, c.m., 1976, 9in. high. $105 £70

A cylindrical jug with a dark brown glaze and applied flower heads, blue triangles and white beads, c.m., 1878, 6¾in. high. $127 £85

A vase by Mary Aitken of baluster shape, with overall applied bands of graduated beads, r.m., 1880, 14½in. high. $120 £80

A small bowl by Emily Welch with impressed gilt concentric circles, r.m., circa 1888, 4in. high. $217 £145

A brown glazed jug with incised acorns, flowers, and leaves, filled with blue slip, o.u.m., circa 1871, 8in. high. $135 £90

A cruet set by Charlotte Lamb, both bottles with incised flowering plants, c.m., 1879, 4¼in. high. $270 £180

A blue stoneware jug with carved stylised leaves and a band of applied flower heads, the base incised F.M. and impressed with the letter B, o.u.m., circa 1871, 7¼in. high. $135 £90

An incised jug, the light buff body with cattle and a goat below leaf bands filled with brown slip, o.u.m., circa 1871, 7in. high. $285 £190

A small bowl by Sarah Fisher, the cover pierced with green and blue scrolls, c.m., 1879, 4in. high. $195 £130

A baluster-shaped jug with a mottled blue glaze, applied blue leaf motifs, and brown bead work, r.m., 1883, 8¼in. high. $142 £95

A mounted jug with applied geometric patterns and a frieze of multi-coloured applied circles, r.m., 1880, 9½in. high. $127 £85

An egg cup stand by Mary Davies, the ochre stand with incised green foliate scrolls, r.m., 1884, 6in. diameter. $210 £140

A jug, the cream body with incised and applied blue lily of the valley, o.u.m., circa 1871, 7¼in. high. $180 £120

An inscribed vase by Alice Groom, the buff body with incised green and brown leaves and blue flowers, r.m., 1886, 6½in. high. $195 £130

A large vase attributed to Cund, with two modelled monkeys clinging to the sides, r.m., 1881, 18in. high. $1275 £850

A jug by Jane S. Hurst with overall applied green and grey motifs, c.m., 1879, 9¼in. high. $120 £80

A pair of vases by Nellie Garbott with incised pale blue flowers on a dark blue ground, r.m., 1881, 6in. high. $240 £160

A jug covered with a pale brown glaze, with applied clusters of green shells. o.m., 1875, 6½in. high. $135 £90

A slip-cast vase by William Rowe with green leaves and a black and white checkered design, s.c.m., circa 1920, 9in. high. $82 £55

Nelson's Centenary, a moulded statuette of the admiral glazed green, c.m.l. & c., circa 1905, 8¼in. high. $375 £250

A vase modelled with shaped panels in relief, on each an applied moulded portrait glazed. dark green, r.m., 1888, 9⅞in. high. $255 £170

An unattributed jug with an incised green and brown scale pattern, r.m., 1884, 7in. high. $127 £85

An unattributed vase, the pale blue ground with carved green flowering plants, r.m., 1880, 14¼in. high. $255 £170

A pair of unattributed cylindrical vases, each with applied medallions of fish and a lobster, r.m., circa 1885, 10¼in. high. $315 £210

An unattributed vase decorated with natural coloured foliage, r.m., circa 1885, 11½in. high. $330 £220

A vase painted with plums against buff, purple and pink bands, c.m.l. & c., circa 1912, 7½in. high. $60 £40

A ribbed vase moulded with a cellular pattern and glazed olive-green, s.c.m., circa 1920, 6½in. high. $75 £50

A vase painted with stylised yellow chrysanthemums against a mottled pink ground, c.m.l. & c., circa 1912, 9in. high. $97 £65

CLARA BARKER

A vase by Clara Barker, with incised green scrolls on a hatched blue ground, r.m., 1884, 6in. high. $165 £110

A small tazza by Clara Barker, the stem moulded with eight blue dolphins, c.m., 1878, 3¾in. high. $180 £120

A vase by Clara Barker, the white ground with an incised continuous green foliate band, r.m., 1882, 6½in. high.
$165 £110

ARTHUR BARLOW

A jug with incised green, blue and brown leaves on a white background, o.m., 1875, 10in. high. $240 £160

A pair of vases decorated with incised blue and green stylised leaf designs on a buff ground, o.m., circa 1873, 8¾in. high.
$390 £260

A ewer with deeply incised foliage and geometric patterns, and applied flower heads, o.m., 1874, 10½in. high. $225 £150

A jug with incised green and brown scrolling foliage on a white ground, o.m., 1873, 8¾in. high. $270 £180

A candlestick with lightly incised leaves glazed brown and blue, and applied borders, o.m., 1874, 9½in. high.
$210 £140

A jug with incised blue foliate scrolls on a white ground, o.m., the silver mount hall-marked 1872, 8in. high.
$330 £220

ARTHUR BARLOW

A jug with incised pink and blue foliage on a pale green ground, o.m., 1874, 10¼in. high.
$232 £155

A flask with incised brown foliage on a ground impressed with stars, o.m., 1875, 8¼in. high. $165 £110

A pierced vase, the outer wall with foliage glazed dark brown on a buff ground, o.u.m., circa 1872, 7¼in. high. $195 £130

A pepper pot by Arthur Barlow, o.u.m., the silver cover hall-marked 1872, 3¼in. high.
$105 £70

A jug with carved scrolling foliage and applied flower heads and beads in brown, green and blue, o.m., 1874, 6¼in. high.
$180 £120

A large jug with incised brown foliage, applied bead decoration and blue flower heads, o.m., 1876, 12¼in. high. $435 £290

A ewer, the body with unusual leaf motifs incised in blue, white and green, assistants monogram: Mary A. Thomson, o.m., 1875, 10in. high.
$240 £160

A jug with incised mottled brown leaves on a pale buff ground, o.u.m., circa 1871, 7¼in. high. $180 £120

A vase with incised brown foliate scrolls and applied white flowers on a buff ground, o.m., 1874, 9½in. high. $210 £140

ARTHUR BARLOW

A vase with incised leaves glazed bright blue on a hatched ground, glazed brown, o.u.m., circa 1872, 9in. high. $330 £220

A mug by Arthur Barlow, the light buff body with an incised blue leaf band and applied shell motifs, o.u.m., the silver rim hallmarked, 1871, 4½in. high. $127 £85

A ewer with incised foliate scrolls in blue and green on a buff ground, o.m., 1873, 9¾in. high. $225 £150

A large jug with incised blue and green foliage below various incised and applied borders, o.m., 1874, 14¾in. high. $630 £420

A dish with incised concave flower heads surrounded by bands of leaves and basketwork in green, brown and blue, o.m., 1874, 10½in. diam. $195 £130

A ewer, the light buff body with incised stiff leaves glazed mottled brown, signed A. B. Barlow, o.u.m., circa 1872, 11in. high. $345 £230

A jug with incised dark brown foliage on a mottled pink ground, o.m., 1874, 10in. high. $225 £150

A beaker with applied bead decoration and blue flowerheads, c.m., 1876, 5¼in. high. $97 £65

A vase with finely incised blue and pale green foliage on a brown ground, o.m., 1874, 10in. high. $240 £160

FLORENCE BARLOW

A turkey vase painted in bright green and brown pâte-sur-pâte with a frieze of turkeys, r.m. & e., circa 1895, 14in. high.
$405 £270

A biscuit barrel with plate cover and mounts, the sides painted in pâte-sur-pâte with four cockatoos, r.m., 1886, 5½in. high. $195 £130

A double-handled vase with various incised leaf and scroll designs, c.m., 1878, 11¼in. high. $420 £280

A vase by Florence Barlow, with three panels of young birds amongst coloured grasses, DSL, 1885, 10½in. high. $390 £260

A pair of vases, the alternating panels with incised and cut out stylised flowers and foliage in various shades of blue, c.m., 1878, 10¾in. high. $345 £230

A pair of vases incised on the buff ground with finches amongst grasses, c.m., 1878, 11in. high. $480 £320

A vase with incised brown foliate scrolls on a buff ground, the base with incised green and blue leaves, c.m., 1878, 10in. high. $270 £180

An oil lamp, the stoneware stand modelled on both sides with fox-gloves and a field mouse in high relief, r.m., 1882, 15¼in. high. $480 £320

A vase decorated in pâte-sur-pâte, the four oval panels each with a garden bird, r.m., 1883, 8in. high. $330 £220

FLORENCE BARLOW

A jug, the stippled buff ground painted in pâte-sur-pâte with two green and white crested birds, r.m., circa 1885, 5½in. high. $180 £120

A tall vase, decorated with five pâte-sur-pâte tit-mice perched on a branch, r.m. & e., circa 1895, 16in. high. $330 £220

A jug with incised scrolling brown foliage and applied white bead work, c.m., 1876, 6¾in. high. $165 £110

A jug painted in pâte-sur-pâte with a hen and her chicks in a shaped panel, r.m., circa 1885, 9in. high, with a beaker en suite, 5½in. high. $270 £180

A pair of ewers, each with two shaped panels painted in pâte-sur-pâte with a parrot on a branch, r.m. & e., circa 1895, 10¼in. high. $570 £380

A tapering jug painted in white, with ducks amongst rushes on a buff ground, c.m., 1879, 9½in. high, with two beakers en suite, 5¼in. high. $330 £220

A jug with incised horses in blue and brown slip on a buff ground, c.m., 1877, 6¾in. high. $240 £160

A massive vase painted in green and white pâte-sur-pâte with garden birds amongst branches and numerous ducks amongst rushes, circa 1880, 26½in. high. $1020 £680

A jug decorated with a shaped panel containing two pâte-sur-pâte black swans reserved on a buff ground, r.m., 1884, 7¾in. high. $255 £170

FLORENCE BARLOW

A vase decorated with brown leaves and blue birds on a buff lace ground, impressed date for 1880 and Doulton Lambeth, 10in. high. $245 £165

A jug with incised squirrels on a buff ground, the base with incised stiff green and blue leaves, c.m., 1877, 7¾in. high, with a beaker en suite, 4½in. high. $375 £250

An early jug, incised in a white ground with herons standing in water, o.m., 1874, 7½in. high.
$255 £170

A pair of vases, each with incised horses and sheep in shaped panels with garden birds in pâte-sur-pâte, the animals by Hannah Barlow; the birds by Florence Barlow, r.m. & e., circa 1895, 16½in. high.
$1020 £680

Australiana, a tall vase painted in green and brown pâte-sur-pâte with cassowaries, r.m. & e., circa 1895, 28¼in. high.
$840 £560

A pair of vases, each painted in green and white pâte-sur-pâte with storks standing amongst grasses, c.m.l. & c., date letter for 1906, 14¼in. high.
$630 £420

A double-handled vase painted in pate-sur-pâte with a green and white titmouse perched on a branch, DLE, circa 1895, 9½in. high. $225 £150

A pair of covered vases with upright handles, c.m., 1878, 7¾in. high. $480 £320

A vase painted on either side with a swallow-tailed butterfly, c.m.l. & c., circa 1906, 11¾in. high. $375 £250

FLORENCE BARLOW

A large vase painted with herons fighting over a fish, the reverse side with herons and a bat against the moon, r.m. & e., circa 1895, 19¾in. high.
$450 £300

A large pair of vases, each with three shaped panels painted with garden birds amongst foliage, r.m. & e., circa 1895, 14½in. high. $825 £550

A vase, modelled in high relief, with two budgerigars perched on green leafy branches, r.m., 1886, 12¼in. high. $345 £230

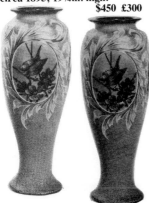

A pair of vases, each with three panels decorated in relief with garden birds perched amongst blossom, c.m.l. & c., date letter for 1903, 11½in. high.
$825 £550

A lavishly decorated vase commemorating the 1897 Jubilee, the central panel with painted white VR monograms and applied moulded portraits of the Queen, signed in full: F. E. Barlow, r.m. & e., circa 1897, 24¼in. high. $1035 £690

A small pair of vases painted in green and white pâte-sur-pâte with a frieze of ducks, r.m. & e., circa 1895, 6¾in. high.
$240 £160

A large vase with three stippled buff panels painted with garden birds, r.m., circa 1885, 25½in. high. $630 £420

A pair of vases with a frieze of ducks and grass, r.m. & e., circa 1895, 9¾in. high.
$480 £320

A vase painted in pâte-sur-pâte, with a green bunting perched on a branch, r.m. & e., circa 1895, 13¼in. high. $420 £280

HANNAH BARLOW

A pepper pot by Hannah
Barlow, o.u.m., the silver cover
hallmarked 1872, 3in. high.
$105 £70

A mug with an incised frieze of
running deer on a buff ground,
c.m., 1878, 3½in. high.
$135 £90

A cream jug with incised
puppies and blue and brown
leaves on a buff ground, o.m.,
1874, 4¾in. high. $195 £130

An early jug with incised stiff
leaves filled with blue and
brown slip on a buff ground,
o.m., silver mount hallmarked,
1872, 6¾in. high. $225 £150

A large pair of vases, each with
two quatrefoil panels, one of
cats and the other of dogs, the
birds by Florence Barlow, the
background by Eliza
Simmance, r.m. & e., circa
1895, 18in. high. $1275 £850

A cup and saucer with incised
sheep and lambs on a buff
ground, r.m., 1884, the cup 2in.
high. $165 £110

A vase with three shaped
panels, each painted with a cat
in pate-sur-pate, r.m., 1884,
9in. high. $270 £180

A jug with an incised white dog
wearing a ruff, DLE, circa
1895, 6½in. high. $240 £160

A vase with finely incised ponies
and goats in a landscape, c.m.,
1878, 8in. high. $360 £240

HANNAH BARLOW

A small jug with incised goats in pasture on a dark buff ground, o.m., 1874, 5¾in. high.
$195 £130

A tobacco jar and cover, the body with incised brown glazed cows frolicking amongst incised green foliage, r.m. & e., circa 1895, 6½in. high. $240 £160

A small jug with an incised bird on a branch and flowering plants, o.m., circa 1872, 6in. high. $210 £140

A tall jug with incised deer in a wreath of foliage below incised scrolls, o.m., 1873, 10¾in. high. $225 £150

A large pair of vases with a boldly incised frieze of goats, borders by Frank Butler, r.m. & e., circa 1895, 21½in. high.
$1425 £950

A jug with an incised pride of lions on a buff ground, DLE, circa 1895, 8½in. high.
$270 £180

A jug, the buff body incised with a dog and plants, titled 'Lost', o.u.m., circa 1871, possibly the work of Hannah Barlow, 6¾in. high. $240 £160

A tyg with three incised groups of rabbits in a landscape, the handles with incised flowers, o.m., 1873, 5¾in. high.
$225 £150

A jug with incised lions in a landscape, filled with a dark blue slip on a light buff ground, o.m., circa 1872, 8in. high.
$270 £180

HANNAH BARLOW

A small jug with an incised fox stalking a rabbit, filled with a blue slip on a buff ground, o.m., 1875, 6½in. high. $210 £140

A loving cup in buff glazed stoneware, with two boldly incised lions, o.m., silver rim hallmarked 1872, 6½in. high. $210 £140

A jug with incised cat and rabbits between incised stiff leaves, o.m., circa 1872, 8in. high. $255 £170

A jug with incised stiff leaves, scrolls, and a frieze of rabbits, o.m., circa 1872, 7½in. high. $255 £170

A terracotta picture, titled 'So near and yet so far', the animals modelled in high-relief in buff terracotta, 1890, 10 x 7in. $675 £450

A large vase with an incised frieze of frightened deer being pursued by wolves, o.m., circa 1872, 15¾in. high. $525 £350

A waisted beaker with an incised frieze of running dogs, o.m., 1873, 6¼in. high. $195 £130

A large tankard with incised water rats stealing eggs from an enraged swan, o.m., circa 1872, 6¾in. high. $195 £130

A tall tankard with an incised heron and ears of corn, filled with a bright blue slip, o.m., circa 1872, 10in. high. $225 £150

HANNAH BARLOW

A waisted beaker with incised
sheep and lambs above stiff
leaves, o.m., 1873, 6in. high.
$195 £130

A salt cellar by Hannah Barlow
of hexagonal trencher type,
o.u.m., circa 1872, 3in.
diameter. $127 £85

A vase with incised herons
flying amongst reeds, glazed
blue on a white ground, c.m.,
1876, 8¼in. high. $285 £190

A tapering jug with incised
sheep by a fence, filled with blue
slip on a white ground, c.m.,
1877, 9¼in. high. $225 £150

A massive vase, the white
ground impressed with blue
flower heads and with incised
lions in two shaped buff panels,
further decorated by Frank
Butler, r.m., 1886, 33in. high.
$5775 £3850

A jug with an incised band of
pheasants above blue and
brown leaves, o.m., 1873, 6in.
high. $210 £140

A two-handled vase with incised
horses between borders of stiff
blue leaves on a buff ground,
o.m., circa 1872, 10in. high.
$315 £210

A vase, the sides modelled in
high relief with wolves chasing
deer, o.m., circa 1872, 11¼in.
high. $975 £650

A jug with incised leaves and
flowers glazed dark blue on a
pale blue ground, r.m., 1880,
7in. high. $165 £110

361

HANNAH BARLOW

A vase with incised horses grazing in a field, filled with blue slip on a buff ground, r.m., circa 1882, 13½in. high.
$420 £280

A double-handled jardinière with an incised frieze of horses, r.m., 1880. 6¾in. high.
$390 £260

A vase with two modelled brown glazed dogs, the body with incised blue, green and brown leaves, r.m., 1889, 14in. high.
$630 £420

A jug with an incised frieze of cows in pasture on a white ground, c.m., 1878, 9in. high.
$210 £140

A pair of vases, one with incised children playing with puppies, the companion with a girl watching dogs chase a rabbit, r.m., 1885, 10¾in. high.
$690 £460

An amusing jug with an incised dog growling at a bristling cat defending its kittens playing on a tree, r.m., 1883, 9¼in. high.
$247 £165

A jug with incised gun dogs sniffing a scent and a fox hiding behind the handle in long grass, c.m., 1880, 9½in. high.
$240 £160

A tankard with incised farm horses in a landscape, one ploughing, o.m., silver rim hallmarked 1872, 6¾in. high.
$225 £150

A jug with incised herons amongst reeds, in a bright blue slip on a buff ground, c.m., 1877, 9in. high. $210 £140

HANNAH BARLOW

A two-handled vase with an incised frieze of kangaroos, filled with blue slip on a white ground, r.m., 1886, 14¼in. high. $525 £350

A jardinière with an incised frieze of deer in a landscape on a light buff ground, c.m., 1877, 6½in. high. $390 £260

An unusual vase, with an incised frieze of sheep in pasture, c.m.l. & c., circa 1905, 7¾in. high. $165 £110

A mounted jug with incised horses in a landscape on a white ground, c.m., 1878, 9¼in. high. $240 £160

A large pair of vases, each with an incised frieze of wolves and their cubs amongst foliage, r.m., 1885, 16½in. high. $780 £520

A large vase painted in green and white pate-sur-pâte with a frieze of cattle, r.m. & e., circa 1895, 18½in. high. $570 £380

A jug with the incised figure of a young girl behind a tree watching pigs, r.m., 1883, 8¾in. high. $345 £230

A jardinière with a frieze of incised lions, and borders with incised foliage, r.m., 1882, 9¾in. high. $450 £300

A vase with an incised frieze of horses, and foliate borders in green, blue and brown, r.m., 1883, 9in. high. $330 £220

HANNAH BARLOW

A vase decorated with incised goats grazing, with blue and brown slip designs on a brown ground, r.m., 13¾in. high.
$340 £225

A ewer decorated with incised goats grazing, leaves and bead designs on a stippled brown ground, DLE, 12in. high.
$240   £160

A vase decorated with incised goats, beads and foliage designs on a blue brown ground, r.m., impressed date for 1881, 9¾in. high. $290 £195

A tea-set, comprising a teapot, cream jug and sugar bowl, each piece with an incised frieze of goats on a buff ground, o.m., 1875, the teapot 4¼in. high. $525 £350

A vase decorated with incised lions, stiff leaves and beads on a blue ground, r.m. & e., 1891-1902, 10½in. high. $540 £360

A cream jug and sugar bowl with an incised frieze of rabbits above green and blue leaves, c.m., 1880, 1886, 4½in. high. $570 £380

A vase decorated with an incised frieze of goats and donkeys with slip design scroll borders on a brown and green ground, r.m. & e., 12in. high. $360 £240

A large pair of vases with an incised frieze of white deer in a mountainous landscape, borders by Florence Barlow, DLE, circa 1895, 17¼in. high.
$1125 £750

A jug with an incised farm worker and a donkey pulling a cart loaded with tree branches, r.m., 1887, 9¼in. high.
$255 £170

HANNAH BARLOW

A vase with three incised donkeys in a landscape on a buff ground, r.m. & e., circa 1892, 9in. high. $330 £220

A pair of ewers, each with incised lions in a landscape on a white ground, r.m., 1883, 11¾in. high. $720 £480

A vase with incised horses in a landscape, borders by Bessie Youatt, c.m., 1879, 10¼in. high. $375 £250

A tea-set, comprising a teapot, cream jug and sugar bowl, each piece with incised kangaroos and emus, c.m., 1878, the teapot 4½in. high. $570 £380

A vase decorated with incised moorland ponies, a band of stiff leaves and flowers on a blue green ground, impressed date 1880 and Doulton Lambeth, 9½in. high. $330 £220

A tea-set, comprising a teapot, cream jug and sugar bowl, each piece with an incised frieze of rabbits, borders by Lucy Barlow, r.m., 1883, the teapot 4½in. high. $525 £350

A jug with an incised frieze of goats in a rocky landscape, c.m., 1879, 10½in. high. $225 £170

A vase with a quatrefoil panel incised with two kittens, r.m. & e., circa 1895, 10in. high. $390 £260

A tapering jug with incised stags and does in a landscape, c.m., 1878, 9½in. high. $225 £170

JOHN BROAD

STONEWARE

"The Boer War Soldier", a buff glazed figure of an infantry man, r.m. & e., circa 1900, 12½in. high. $480 £320

A modelled group, on a circular base with a buff glazed donkey, c.m., 1879 6½in. high.
                    $420 £280

A terracotta statuette of King Edward VII standing against a column, the base inscribed ERI, c.m.l. & c., circa 1901, 16¾in. high. $975 £650

A slip-cast figure of "The Bather", the white glazed nude seated on a purple sphere, s.c.m., circa 1912, 13in. high.
          $1275 £850

Queen Victoria, a buff salt-glaze figure commemorating her life, incised Doulton Co. Ltd. Lambeth, circa 1901, 11¾in. high. $1125 £750

Pitt's Centenary, a grey terracotta portrait-bust of the statesman, the shaped based inscribed "William Pitt 1759-1806", Sc., c.m.l. & c., circa 1906, 13¾in. high.
                    $675 £450

ROSINA BROWN

A large vase with running green glaze by Rosina Brown, c.m.l. & c., 14½in. high. $75 £50

A jug by Rosina Brown, the shaded green ground with incised scrolls, r.m. & e., circa 1892, 7¼in. high. $150 £100

A pierced vase by Rosina Brown cut with geometric patterns, r.m., circa 1885, 7in. high.
                    $105 £70

366

FRANK BUTLER

A small early jug, the buff body
with deeply incised foliate
scrolls, o.u.m., silver mount
hallmarked 1873, 5in. high.
$195 £130

A candlestick with incised
geometric and leaf designs,
o.m., 1874, 5 in. high.
$135 £90

A flask of flattened circular
shape incised in green, brown
and purple, c.m., 1878, 8in.
high. $360 £240

A jug with incised stiff leaves
and scrolls in green, blue and
brown, o.m., 1873, 7in. high.
$180 £120

A jardinière decorated with a
frieze of applied moulded bust-
portraits representing Queen
Victoria, Victor Emmanuel of
Italy, Napoleon III, Empress
Eugenie and Kaiser Wilhelm of
Germany, o.m., 1874, 8¼in.
high. $480 £320

A jug with incised blue leaves on
a brown ground, o.m., 1874,
5¼in. high. $180 £120

A jug with deeply incised brown
and blue foliage, o.m., 1873, 9
in. high. $210 £140

A vase with shaped projections,
incised leaves in blue and
brown, o.m., 1874, 9½in. high.
$240 £160

A vase with incised blue leaves,
applied white beads on a sepia
ground, c.m., 1876, 7½in. high.
$165 £110

FRANK BUTLER

A vase modelled in relief with a stylised plant, r.m., circa 1890, 12in. high. $315 £210

A shaped bowl richly decorated on the inside and outside with incised leaves and foliate scrolls, c.m., 1880, 10¼in. diameter. $480 £320

An egg cup by Frank Butler with incised blue leaves on a buff ground, circa 1872, 3½in. high. $112 £75

A jug with carved and incised blue leaf patterns on a stippled buff ground, r.m., 1881, 13½in. high. $495 £330

A large pair of vases, the three panels with incised foliate scrolls in lovat, blue and ochre, r.m., 1882, 17½in. high. $1125 £750

A portrait jug, the dark blue ground with impressed flower motifs, c.m., 1877, 10½in. high. $390 £260

A vase with incised green and blue foliage and brown cross-hatched panels, r.m., 1884, 7¾in. high. $240 £160

An inscribed bowl with incised blue flowers and scrolls on an olive-green ground, 1894, 8¼in. diameter. $270 £180

A large vase, the central panel with carved brown scrolls on a hatched blue ground between incised leaf and scroll borders, r.m., 1884, 14¼in. high. $780 £520

FRANK BUTLER

A goblet-shaped vase, with applied stylised blue flowers on a brown panel, c.m.l. & c., circa 1905, 8½in. high.
$195 £130

A shallow dish with incised scrolls and the name K. B. Smallfield, 1897, on a green ground, r.m., 6½in. diameter.
$180 £120

A tall vase with incised dark green plants on a brown ground, c.m.l. & c., date letter for 1909, 17½in. high.
$465 £310

A large jug, ornately decorated with incised, applied and impressed work. o.m., 1874, 17in. high. $570 £380

A pair of vases, each with incised scrolls and leaves, c.m., 1876, 14¼in. high. $975 £650

A jug with a profusion of incised leaves in blue, green, pink and brown, o.m., 1875, 14½in. high. $420 £280

A jug with incised green and purple leaves on a brown ground, c.m., 1878, 10in. high. $255 £170

A shell-shaped bowl painted with white flowers on a green panel, r.m. & e., circa 1895, 4¾in. high. $480 £320

A jug, modelled in relief with depressed fan-shaped motifs, c.m., 1879, 8¼in. high. $495 £330

FRANK BUTLER

A vase with flowering plants against a brown background, r.m. & e., circa 1895, 13in. high. $630 £420

A pair of vases, modelled with stylised plants having green bulbs, brown stems and leaves, and blue flowers, DLE, circa 1895, 9¾in. high. $570 £380

A vase with stylised flowering plants in blue and brown, r.m. & e., circa 1895, 13¼in. high. $705 £470

A covered sprinkler, the squashed body with incised blue and green flowers, FAB., 1894, 10¼in. high. $315 £210

A pair of vases, modelled with projecting brown forms growing from a green ground, c.m.l. & c., date letter for 1906, 7in. high. $420 £280

An Art Nouveau vase with dark blue flowers and seed pods on a pale blue ground, DLE, circa 1900, 13in. high. $390 £260

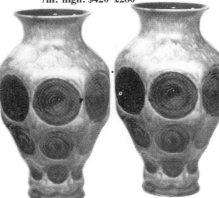

A shaped flask, each side decorated with pierced and carved green foliate scrolls, r.m. & e., circa 1895, 9½in. high. $390 £260

A pair of vases, the mottled green ground modelled with projections divided by graduated brown and blue circles, r.m. & e., circa 1895, 9¾in. high. $405 £270

A vase modelled with projecting flowers, with green leaves and brown stems, c.m.l. & c., date letter for 1909, 14¾in. $480 £320

LOUISA DAVIS

A mounted jug, the incised buff ground with impressed flowers, c.m., 1880, 9½in. high.
$255 £170

A jug, the brown ground with impressed flower motifs, c.m., 1876, 6in. high. $225 £150

A vase, the white ground with an incised spiral band of foliage with blue flowers, c.m., 1877, 11¾in. high. $262 £175

A vase, the buff ground with incised long lovat leaves, brown foliage, and blue flowers, c.m., 1877, 9¾in. high. $315 £210

A bowl, the brown ground with incised blue flowers and scrolling, c.m., 1878, 7½in. high. $480 £320

A vase decorated with incised blue leaves and flowers with bands of applied beads and florets, on a blue ground, impressed dated for 1878 and Doulton Lambeth, 9¼in. high. $125 £85

W. EDWARD DUNN

A small vase by W. Edward Dunn, painted in green and white pâte-sur-pâte with a dog's head, r.m., 1883, 5¼in. high. $142 £95

A pilgrim bottle by W. Edward Dunn, one side with incised sheep in a landscape glazed green, the other with women gleaning, r.m., 1883, 9in. high. $465 £310

A vase by W. Edward Dunn, each side with an incised blue bird on a buff panel, r.m., 1882, 12in. high. $480 £320

EMILY EDWARDS

A jug by Emily J. Edwards with a mottled brown glaze and applied flower heads within incised borders, o.u.m., circa 1872, 7in. high. $127 £85

A flower-shaped dish, the brown ground with incised lines and green and purple leaves, impressed Doulton Lambeth, 1876, 10½in. diameter.
$240 £160

A jug with incised green scrolls and blue leaves on a scored brown ground, o.m., 1873, 7¼in. high. $180 £120

LOUISA EDWARDS

A jug with incised dark brown leaf scrolls on a buff ground, c.m., 1878, 10¾in. high.
$270 £180

A jug with incised green and yellow plants with blue flowers, c.m., 1878, 7¼in. high.
$165 £110

A vase, the pale blue ground with finely incised foliage, r.m., 1881, 10in. high. $210 £140

A jug, the buff ground with fine incised lines and impressed flower heads, c.m., 1879, 9½in. high. $247 £165

A vase with incised blue flowering foliage on a pale blue ground, c.m., 1879, 11in. high.
$270 £180

A jug, the body with incised bands of stylised leaves in green and purple, c.m., 1879, 9½in. high. $210 £140

HERBERT ELLIS

STONEWARE

A cream coloured terracotta figure of a partly draped woman holding a plaque, impressed Doulton & Co., Lambeth, incised H. Ellis Sc., circa 1910, 13½in. high. $375 £250

An unglazed cream coloured terracotta figure of a nude woman kneeling on a net, incised H. Ellis Sc., circa 1910, 9½in. high. $375 £250

An unglazed moulded terracotta figure, the partly draped woman holding a branch of foliage. Impressed Doulton & Co., Lambeth, circa 1910, 11in. high. $375 £250

ELIZABETH FISHER

A jug, the brown ground with incised panels in green, purple and brown, c.m., 1876, 9in. high. $270 £180

A pair of vases with incised foliate scrolls in two shades of blue, r.m., 1883, 11in. high. $570 £380

A jug, the blue ground with incised leaves, buff panels with impressed flower heads, c.m., 1878, 8½in. high. $240 £160

A beaker, the brown ground with impressed flower heads, c.m., 1876, 5¼in. high. $135 £90

A pair of candlesticks with incised blue leaves and applied flower heads and bead work, c.m., 1877, 8½in. high. $435 £290

A jug, incised in blue and brown on a buff ground, r.m., 1881, 9¼in. high. $165 £110

A brown salt-glaze spirit flask modelled as John Burns, the Labour leader, DLE, circa 1912, 7¼in. high. $337 £225

A cast figure of Sairey Gamp, the light buff glaze, s.c.m., circa 1913, 8in. high. $525 £350

A brown salt-glaze spirit flask modelled as David Lloyd George, DLE, circa 1912, 7¾in. high. $337 £225

A vase by Leslie Harradine cast into a square section and moulded with laburnum, s.c.m., circa 1912, 8¾in. high. $112 £75

A brown terracotta bust of George V, the reverse stamped Doulton Lambeth, L. Harradine Sc., circa 1910, 7½in. high. $390 £260

A vase after a design by Leslie Harradine with moulded yellow flowers, s.c.m., circa 1910, 9¾in. high. $180 £120

A slip-cast figure of Mr. Pickwick in a light buff glaze, s.c.m., circa 1913, 8½in. high. $525 £350

A white glazed figure of a peasant woman wearing a blue checkered dress, RDE, circa 1905, 8½in. high. $525 £350

A moulded figure of a farm labourer holding a scythe, wearing a blue shirt, circa 1905, 7½in. high. $525 £350

LESLIE HARRADINE

A brown salt-glaze spirit flask modelled as President Roosevelt, DLE, circa 1912, 7½in. high.
$337 £225

"Motherhood", a white glazed figure of a mother cradling her baby, the dress with blue flowers, RDE, circa 1912, 6in. high. $525 £350

A brown salt-glaze spirit flask modelled in the traditional style with Austen Chamberlain, DLE, circa 1912, 7¾in. high.
$337 £225

A brown salt-glaze figure of Mr. Pecksniff, s.c.m., circa 1913, 9¼in. high $525 £350

A white slip-cast group modelled with two mermaids, s.c.m., circa 1910, length 7in.
$375 £250

Dickens, a moulded white glazed stoneware figure of Mr. Squeers, s.c.m., circa 1913, 9¼in. high. $525 £350

VERA HUGGINS

A large vase with incised green flowering foliage on a mottled blue ground, c.m. & l., circa 1925, 12¾in. high. $165 £110

A bowl painted with pink and blue flowers against a brown field, c.m. & l., 1926, 5in. high.
$105 £70

A vase glazed in green, blue and brown with incised and raised borders, c.m. & l., circa 1925, 11¼in. high. $127 £85

FRANCES LEE

A vase, the buff ground with impressed concentric circles, heightened with gold, c.m., 1886, 10in. high. $270 £180

A pair of vases, the panels with incised green leaves and bordered by purple leaves, c.m., 1877, 9¾in. high. $390 £260

A vase, the royal blue ground with four stippled buff panels painted with dolphins, c.m., 1883, 9¾in. high. $240 £160

A jug with four oval panels with incised green foliage, c.m., 1878, 5¼in. high. $165 £110

A shallow bowl with incised green and blue panels supported by three columns, c.m., 1884, 8¼in. high. $480 £320

A jug, the neck with incised blue flowers on a brown ground, c.m., 1879, 6¾in. high. $135 £90

A jug, the incised brown leaves with applied bead work and flower heads, c.m., 1877, 9¼in. high. $225 £150

A pair of vases, with finely incised foliage, painted overall in pâte-sur-pâte with blossom, c.m., 1882, 9in. high. $375 £250

A jug carved with green flower heads on a blue ground, c.m., 1881, 9½in. high. $195 £130

EDITH LUPTON

A jug with incised green, blue and brown leaves, o.m., 1875, 6½in. high. $150 £100

A large pierced vase with three shaped panels painted in pâte-sur-pâte with wild flowers, r.m., 1882, 14in. high.
$390 £260

A jug with incised stiff blue leaves and carved seed pods, c.m., 1876, 8¼in. high.
$195 £130

A small jug with incised green foliage on a brown ground, c.m., 1876, 7½in. high.
$195 £130

A pair of salt cellars with incised leaves, o.m., 1875, 3¼in. high.
$525 £350

A candlestick modelled with three buff cranes between incised green and blue columns, c.m., 1875, 8in. high. $210 £140

A mounted jug with incised blue and green leaves, o.m., 1875, 6¾in. high. $180 £120

A vase by Edith Lupton with chocolate panels painted with blue flowers, DSL, 1884, 9½in. high. $210 £140

A large vase by Edith Lupton, pierced overall with flowering plants and foliage, DSL, 1884, 15¼in. high. $390 £260

EDITH LUPTON

A large vase with incised
mottled foliage and seed pods,
r.m., 1886, 14in. high.
$330 £220

A vase with incised green leaves
and painted blossom and
berries, r.m., 1886, 6¾in. high.
$135 £90

A jug with incised blue and
white leaves on a brown ground,
c.m., 1876, 7½in. high.
$165 £110

An ecclesiastical vase modelled
in the form of a tower, and on
each corner the letters IHS in
brown shields, r.m., 1881,
13¾in. high $480 £320

A small pair of church vases, the
quatrefoil necks with incised
blue scrolls, r.m. & e., circa
1892, 6in. high. $390 £260

A jug with incised dark brown
scrolls on a royal blue ground,
c.m., 1880, 9in. high.
$240 £160

A tapering jug with incised green,
brown and blue scrolls, 9½in.
high, with two beakers en suite,
5½in. high, c.m., 1879. $285 £190

A globular vase, the stippled
buff ground with incised
fruiting vine, r.m., 1886, 10in.
high. $330 £220

A mounted jug with incised
foliate scrolls in shades of blue
and green, r.m., 1880, 9½in.
high. $210 £140

MARK V. MARSHALL

A large vase, one side modelled with a profile female portrait, the other with a bird amongst flowers, r.m. & e., circa 1895, 15in. high. $600 £400

A paperweight modelled as a smiling creature glazed brown, RDE, circa 1902, 2½in. high. $315 £210

A vase after a design by Mark V. Marshall with purple foliage and sepia fruit, c.m. & l., circa 1922, 8¼in. high. $135 £90

A vase with pink swirling panels painted with blue flowers and green leaves, c.m.l. & c., date letter for 1905, 12in. high. $330 £220

A pair of vases pressed from the inside with pink fruits against green foliage on a pale pink ground, c.m.l. & c., date letter for 1903, 10¾in. high. $375 £250

A vase painted with pink flowers and brown veined white leaves, c.m.l. & c., date letter for 1906, 11½in. high. $285 £190

A buff coloured vase with two modelled monkeys grasping the neck of the vase, r.m. & e., circa 1895, 6¾in. high. $375 £250

An unusual bowl of flattened disc shape painted with purple foliage in shaped sepia panels, c.m., circa 1890, 4in. height, 14½in. diameter. $330 £220

An elaborate jug with incised lip and blue neck, the base of the handle modelled with the head of a dark-skinned Arab wearing a kefiya, r.m. & e., circa 1895, 11¼in. high. $1320 £880

A tankard, the grey-green
ground indented with purple
foliate scrolls and a grotesque
mask, DLE, circa 1895, 6½in.
high. $195 £130

A jug modelled as a fabulous
fish with legs and cloven feet,
c.m., circa 1885, 9in. high.
                $780 £520

A vase pressed from the inside
with russet and lovat foliate
scrolls, r.m. & e., circa 1895,
10¾in. high. $330 £220

A paperweight modelled as a
duck with mottled blue
and green glaze, c.m.l. & c.,
circa 1902, 2¾in. high.
                $300 £200

An inkwell modelled as a
stylised bird glazed blue and
green, RDE, circa 1902, 2¼in.
high. $330 £220

A paperweight modelled as a
green glazed cat with grinning
features, RDE, circa 1902,
3¼in. long. $330 £220

A dark blue glazed vase, the
body modelled in high relief
with a sinuous dragon rising
from blue waves, c.m., 1880,
10in. high. $1275 £850

An Art Nouveau jug, the base
of the handle modelled with a
hare's head, c.m.l. & c., date
letter for 1909, 10¾in. high.
                $525 £350

A standing bowl attributed to
Mark V. Marshall, supported
by three moulded and modelled
heraldic beasts, c.m.l. & c.,
circa 1902, 9in. high. $675 £450

MARK V. MARSHALL

A gourd-shaped vase, incised and modelled in relief with fruiting foliage in brown and white, c.m.l. & c., date letter for 1904, 10½in. high.
$675 £450

An early grotesque bowl modelled as a fish, 8½in. high.
$720 £480

A vase, the glaze shading from white through purple to blue at the base, around which climbs a fabulous buff scaly creature, c.m.l. & c., date letter for 1904, 10½in. high. $975 £650

A salt cellar modelled as a frog glazed brown, DLE, circa 1900, 1¾in. high. $315 £210

A 'Borogove' vase modelled as a hedgehog-like creature, r.m., circa 1890, 8in. high. $750 £470

An unattributed model of a rabbit glazed light brown, c.m. & l., circa 1922, 2¾in. long.
$135 £90

A vase painted on either side with a stylised plant in shades of green, r.m. & e., circa 1895, 8¼in. high. $225 £150

An inkwell modelled with two fabulous beasts glazed ochre, blue and brown, r.m., 1884, 5¼in. high. $630 £420

A jug modelled in low relief with brown leaves against a royal blue ground, DLE, circa 1895, 8½in. high. $240 £160

MARK V. MARSHALL

A trumpet-shaped vase, incised overall and glazed blue, circa 1879, 10¼in. high. $570 £380

A paperweight modelled as a bird glazed brown, c.m.l. & c., circa 1902, 3in. high. $270 £180

A vase modelled in low relief, with purple and pink sea-weed on a claret ground, r.m. & e., circa 1895, 9in. high. $255 £170

A tall jug, decorated with rambling blue and pink roses on which perch garden birds, c.m., circa 1880, 19¼in. high. $870 £580

A pair of vases, each decorated with four ribbed panels in brown and pale green, c.m.l. & c., date letter for 1903, 12½in. high. $870 £580

A large covered vase, each side modelled in relief, one with a music conductor with human head and the body of a bird, the other with a lizard and flowering plants, c.m., circa 1885, 26¾in. high. $3750 £2500

A slender vase painted in outline with three long-tailed birds perched amongst foliage, c.m.l. & c., circa 1902, 10in. high. $225 £150

A pot-pourri bowl with pierced blue cover overlaid with green foliate scrolls in high relief, r.m. & e., circa 1895, 5½in. high. $180 £120

A shaped vase, the mottled blue ground with incised green markings and white neck, c.m., circa 1890, 8½in. high. $240 £160

ISABELLA MILLER

A vase by Isabella Miller, the mottled purple ground with incised green and blue scrolls, c.m., 1880, 7¼in. high.
$165 £110

A vase by Isabella Miller, the green and ochre ground with incised dark green scrolls and plants, r.m., 1884, 10¼in. high.
$210 £140

A ewer by Isabella Miller with incised green and blue leaves and flowers, c.m., 1880, 6½in. high. $195 £130

MARY MITCHELL

A vase by Mary Mitchell, with the incised figures of two girls playing with a ball, r.m., 1881, 10¾in. high. $420 £280

A jug by Mary Mitchell, with two oval panels, with incised children in a landscape, c.m., 1879, 9¼in. high. $240 £160

A vase by Mary Mitchell, the white ground with incised green foliage and purple flowers, c.m., 1879, 7in. high.
$135 £90

WILLIAM PARKER

A massive jug carved in high relief with green and brown flowers, c.m., 1879, 15¼in. high. $525 £350

A vase with incised flowers on a pale buff ground, r.m., 1883, 7½in. high. $210 £140

An inscribed jug with carved and incised pale green leaves, the neck with incised patterns and blue borders, c.m., 1881, 13¼in. high. $450 £300

WILLIAM PARKER

STONEWARE

A vase with incised foliate scrolls in shades of blue, c.m., 1879, 11¾in. high. $262 £175

A vase incised through the celadon ground with blue and white flowering plants, r.m., 1883, 7in. high. $135 £90

A vase with finely incised flowering plants in mottled blue and green, r.m., 1884, 8¼in. high. $165 £110

A vase with finely incised blue convolvulous, sweet-peas, and clover, r.m., 1883, 9½in. high. $180 £120

A pair of vases, with an incised continuous blue branch bearing yellow fruits, r.m., 1884, 9½in. high. $390 £260

A vase carved with a frieze of green foliage scrolls within blue and green incised borders, c.m., 1881, 13¼in. high. $480 £320

FRANCIS POPE

A bottle with applied handle, and incised blue and green foliage, c.m.l. & c., silver rim hallmarked 1913, 8¼in. high. $120 £80

A slip-cast vase of gourd-shape with projecting ribs and a mottled blue glaze, circa 1920, 5¾in. high. $90 £60

A vase painted with green flowers growing from black stems, c.m.l. & c., circa 1905, 10in. high. $142 £95

STONEWARE

An unusual vase, modelled in relief with a mermaid riding on a fish amongst underwater plants, c.m.l. & c., circa 1905, 11¾in. high. $135 £90

A pair of tall vases, each with incised mottled blue, pink and green leaves, c.m.l. & c., date letter for 1904, 15¼in. high.
$480 £320

A handled bottle or spirit decanter with incised green leaves, c.m.l. & c., silver hall-marked 1913, 7½in. high.
$135 £90

A slip-cast vase, the mottled blue body with brown ribs and pale blue scrolls in relief, s.c.m., circa 1920, 6¼in. high.
$120 £80

A slip-cast vase moulded with arched panels covered in a mottled ochre and pale blue glaze, s.c.m., circa 1920, 6¼in. high. $90 £60

A vase with deeply incised black and brown scrolls on a green ground, c.m.l. & c., 5½in. high. $105 £70

A vase modelled in relief with a white bird amongst white foliage, c.m.l. & c., circa 1905, 9¾in. high. $165 £110

A pair of slip-cast vases of hexagonal section with a mottled green glaze, s.c., circa 1910, 11in. high. $195 £130

A slip-cast vase of square section, moulded on each side with a blue bird, s.c.m., circa 1920, 8¾in. high. $105 £70

FLORENCE ROBERTS

A mug by Florence C. Roberts, the combed buff ground with impressed flowers, r.m., 1884, 5¼in. high. $90 £60

EDITH ROGERS

A pair of vases by Florence C. Roberts, the buff ground modelled in relief with green, blue and brown stylised flowers and leaves, r.m., 1884, 10¼in. high. $405 £270

A vase, the buff ground stippled and modelled in relief with blue flowers and mottled green foliage, r.m., 1885, 12in. high. $330 £220

A vase with incised blue flowers heightened with white, r.m., 1883, 7¾in. high. $225 £150

A jug, the silicon body painted in rust and blue, DSL, 1884, 7¼in. high. $210 £140

A vase, with finely incised blue flowering plants, the ground over-glazed in brown, r.m., 1883, 8in. high. $210 £140

A vase painted in green and white pâte-sur-pâte with foliate scrolls on an orange ground, r.m., 1881, 10½in. high. $255 £170

A pair of vases with overall incised white and buff scrolls, one with three plaques inscribed 'Burns, Scott and Keats', r.m., 1882, 11½in. high. $525 £350

A vase, the white ground with a thick dark olive-green glaze, r.m., 1882, 10¼in. high. $225 £150

MARTHA ROGERS

A vase, the buff ground with finely incised foliage, r.m., 1881, 7¾in. high. $225 £150

A vase, the buff ground with painted white foliage, r.m., 1881, 12¾in. high. $375 £250

A vase, the dark blue ground with incised pale blue foliage edged with gilt piping, r.m., 1884, 11in. high. $285 £190

A vase, the pale ground with incised brown foliate scrolls bordered by incised blue leaves, r.m., 1883, 12¼in. high. $270 £180

A pair of vases, the orange ground with painted white motifs, r.m., 1882, 8¾in. high. $330 £220

A vase by Martha M. Rogers, the stippled frieze glazed blue, with pale blue scrolls, DSL, 1883, 10½in. high. $142 £95

ELIZA SAYERS

A flask of flattened shape, each side with incised green berried foliage, c.m., 1880, 8½in. high. $270 £180

A jug with incised dark brown and blue stylised foliage enriched with white bead work, c.m., 1877, 9in. high. $255 £170

A jug with incised green foliage and applied beads on a brown ground, c.m., 1877, 7in. high. $202 £135

HARRY SIMEON

A vase painted with ears of corn in brown, green and purple against a mottled blue ground, c.m. & l., circa 1922, 9in. high. $105 £70

A vase painted with a parrot amongst green tropical foliage, c.m. & l., circa 1922, 10½in. high. $180 £120

A vase painted in polychrome colours with a cockerel and a blue pheasant, c.m. & l., circa 1922, 9¾in. high. $150 £100

ELIZA SIMMANCE

A jug painted with vine leaves and purple grapes against a pink ground, c.m.l. & c., date letter for 1910, 8½in. high. $150 £100

A ewer with incised brown foliage and impressed clusters of fruit, r.m. & e., circa 1895, 12in. high. $270 £180

A jug with incised yellow leaves and impressed brown berries against a mottled blue ground, c.m.l. & c., date letter for 1909, 9in. high. $180 £120

A vase with incised pale blue flowers and brown foliage edged in white, DLE, circa 1895, 14in. high. $435 £290

A waisted jar and cover painted with rings of white flowers, c.m.l. & c., date letter for 1907, 6½in. high. $180 £120

A large ribbed vase painted with blue leaves and pale blue flowers, c.m.l. & c., date letter for 1906, 15in. high. $375 £250

ELIZA SIMMANCE

A vase modelled with orange trees against a blue sky with birds, c.m.l. & c., date letter for 1905, 13in. high. $330 £220

A pair of vases with incised and painted pale blue cornflowers, r.m. & e., circa 1895, 11¼in. high. $525 £350

A vase painted with purple and green flowering plants, c.m.l. & c., date letter for 1915, 12¾in. high. $240 £160

A vase painted with purple berried trees against a pale blue background, c.m.l. & c., date letter for 1907, 13¾in. high. $330 £220

A pair of ribbed vases with incised green leaves, c.m.l. & c., date letter for 1910, 10in. high. $390 £260

A vase with a frieze of green trees edged in white, c.m.l. & c., circa 1907, 13½in. high. $390 £260

A vase painted with pink roses, the stems brown against a pale pink ground, c.m.l. & c., date letter for 1910, 11in. high. $150 £100

A pair of vases after Charles Rennie Mackintosh, with incised green roses, c.m.l. & c., date letter for 1910, 9in. high. $420 £280

A tall vase painted with pink pomegranates growing against a green ground, c.m.l. & c., date letter for 1910, 19¼in. high. $450 £300

ELIZA SIMMANCE

A vase with incised blue flowers against a buff panel of white scrolls, r.m. & e., circa 1895, 14in. high. $375 £250

A pair of vases by Eliza Simmance, the smooth cream ground with incised and painted flowering plants, r.m., circa 1890, 7¾in. high. $135 £90

A vase painted with green and white pâte-sur-pâte blossom on a stippled buff ground, r.m. & e., circa 1892, 8¼in. high. $210 £140

A vase painted with pale green foliate scrolls on a darker green ground, r.m., 1884, 8¼in. high. $195 £130

A stoneware bracket clockcase by Eliza Simmance, inspired by 18th century models, r.m. & e., circa 1895, 14½in. high. $1425 £950

A vase with shaped panels painted in pâte-sur-pâte natural colours with blackberries, r.m., 1881, 10¾in. high. $225 £150

A vase with shaped panels of incised stylised flowers in blue and green, r.m., 1884, 11in. high. $270 £180

A pair of vases with incised blue foliage and modelled green chrysanthemums, r.m. & e., circa 1895, 9¾in. high. $480 £320

A vase painted with pale green and blue leaf sprays, r.m., 1883, 9¼in. high. $240 £160

ELIZA SIMMANCE

A vase painted with blue dolphins and green sea-weed on a pale pink ground, c.m.l. & c., date letter for 1910, 10½in. high. $270 £180

A bowl painted with alternate floral panels in pale green and blue on a dark green ground, r.m., 1883, 7in. high. $330 £220

A vase with incised green and brown sea-weed on an undulating green ground, c.m.l. & c., circa 1905, 9in. high. $240 £160

A jug with incised green and blue leaves on a buff ground, silver mount hallmarked 1875, 8in. high. $255 £170

A pair of vases by Eliza Simmance, the light grey ground with incised and painted brown plants, DSL, 1884, 7¼in. high. $120 £80

A pepper pot attributed to Eliza Simmance with pottery sprinkler and pierced base, r.m., 1884, 3¼in. high. $112 £75

A vase by Eliza Simmance, the brown ground with three shaped panels, DSL, 1884, 8in. high. $120 £80

An octagonal plate painted with white pâte-sur-pâte flowers on a brown ground, c.m., 1878, 10in. diameter. $195 £130

An Art Union vase and cover painted with green and white pâte-sur-pâte blossom on a buff stippled ground, r.m. & e., circa 1895, 11½in. high. $675 £450

ELIZA SIMMANCE

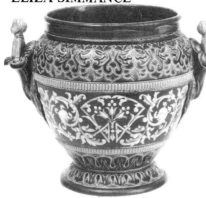

A cachepot with a broad pate-sur-pate band of Renaissance scrollwork and grotesques on an olive-green ground, dated 1882, 20cm. high. $525 £350

A vase by Eliza Simmance, the glazed buff ground with incised scrolls, r.m., 1881, 3¾in. high. $82 £55

A vase modelled with yellow apples growing from green branches, r.m., 1887, 9½in. high. $390 £260

A vase with incised royal blue flowers and leaves, r.m., circa 1887, 10in. high. $330 £220

A pair of cylindrical vases incised through the pale blue glaze onto the white body, c.m., 1879, 6¾in. high. $165 £110

One of a pair of vases with incised and modelled blue flowers, c.m.l. & c., date letter for 1909, 9¾in. high. $540 £360

A vase painted with green and white pâte-sur-pâte blossom on a Doulton and Slater buff lace ground, r.m., circa 1889, 6½in. high. $165 £110

A tazza, the surface with an incised blue and brown leaf pattern, c.m., 1877, 6½in. high. $240 £160

A vase with an incised foliate design in pale green and dark blue, c.m., 1876, 7¼in. high. $195 £130

ELIZA SIMMANCE

A small vase by Eliza Simmance, the brown ground painted with white blossom and dark brown leaves, DSL, 1884, 4in. high. $105 £70

A vase with incised blue and white flowers and green foliage on a dark green ground, r.m. & e., circa 1895, 14in. high. $345 £230

A three-handled loving cup with green and white pâte-sur-pâte flowering scrolls, r.m., 1881, 6in. high. $180 £120

A pair of vases painted with long-tailed blue birds, c.m.l. & c., date letter for 1916?, 15¾in. high. $525 £350

A mustard pot by Eliza Simmance, the handle and body with incised blue leaves, o.m., 1875, 2¼in. high. $112 £75

A pair of vases by Eliza Simmance, with incised and painted brown garden birds and white daisies, DSL, 1885, 10¼in. high. $345 £230

ELIZABETH SMALL

A vase, the mottled blue ground with incised bright blue flowering foliage, r.m., 1884, 12½in. high. $375 £250

A pair of vases with incised blue and brown berried foliage on a mottled pale blue ground, r.m., 1884, 10¼in. high. $375 £250

A beaker, the buff ground with incised blue foliage, the entwined panels painted with white flowers, r.m., 1882, 4¾in. high. $112 £75

EMILY STORMER

A pair of vases, each with incised brown foliage above stiff green leaves, c.m., 1877, 10¾in. high. $480 £320

A pair of flasks, with white bead work and an incised green, blue, and brown flower, c.m., 1878, 8¼in. high. $420 £280

A vase, the handles modelled as brown peacocks, the body with incised blue and yellow foliate scrolls, r.m. & e., circa 1892, 12½in. high. $450 £300

A candlestick, the base with carved green stylised leaves, r.m., 1886, 7in. high, $270 £180

A mounted jug with incised green flowers on a blue ground with incised brown scrolls, r.m., 1884, 6¾in. high. $225 £150

A jug, the buff body with impressed white circles and incised blue foliage and leaves, c.m., 1879, 9¼in. high. $225 £150

GEORGE H. TABOR

A vase by G. H. Tabor with carved blue oak branches and acorns, r.m., 1883, 9¼in. high. $202 £135

A pair of vases by G. H. Tabor, the green ground with overall incised blue masks, r.m., 1884, 9½in. high. $525 £350

A vase by G. H. Tabor, the buff stippled ground with incised brown masks, urns and foliate scrolls, r.m., 1881, 10¾in. high. $360 £240

GEORGE TINWORTH

A baluster vase, the mottled brown ground with incised blue foliate scrolls, r.m. & e., circa 1892, 12½in. high. $390 £260

A frog and mouse group with frogs riding mice over a water jump, o.m., circa 1875, 4½in. high. $1425 £950

A large jug, the hatched pale green ground with incised green and brown scrolls, o.m., 1874, 11¼in. high. $525 £350

A brightly glazed jug, the green ground with an incised shaped blue panel, c.m., 1876, 9¾in. high. $360 £240

The Menagerie, a stoneware clock case in the form of a circus building, with incised wild animals, the base inscribed The Wild Beast Show, o.m., circa 1875, 9¾in. high. $3300 £2200

A mounted jug, with an incised green foliate meander, c.m., 1877, 9½in. high $375 £250

An early pair of candlesticks glazed blue, with incised leaves each supported by two buff winged putti, o.m., 1875, 7in. high. $975 £650

A monkey group inscribed A United Family, sitting on a bench and sheltering under an ochre umbrella, r.m. & e., circa 1892, 5in. high. $1275 £850

An early vase, the burnt sienna ground with incised blue and pale green scrolls, o.u.m., circa 1871, 9¾in. high. $420 £280

GEORGE TINWORTH

A carpenter's bag attributed to George Tinworth, glazed in shades of brown, c.m., circa 1880, length 5in. $825 £550

The young carpenter, a brown salt-glaze model of a young boy planing at a bench, DLE, circa 1892, 5¼in. high. $1120 £750

A salt cellar, the bowl and stand glazed blue and brown, the moulded drummer boy glazed buff, r.m., circa 1885, 3½in. high. $525 £350

A jug, the lovat ground with an incised blue and buff fence decorated with pale blue bead work, c.m., 1879, 9½in. high. $405 £270

A blue glazed frog playing cricket with a brown bat, r.m., circa 1880, 4¾in. high. $1125 £750

A tapering jug, the dark brown ground with an incised spiral band, c.m., 1878, 9¾in. high. $420 £280

A jug, the light buff ground with incised scrolling blue foliage, o.u.m., circa 1872, 10½in. high. $420 £280

A blue glazed group of two frogs riding on the backs of two mice, o.m., circa 1875, 3¾in. high. $975 £650

One of a pair of vases, the buff ground with a painted white cellular pattern, c.m.l. & c., date letter for 1903, 10¾in. high. $675 £450

GEORGE TINWORTH

A candlestick with incised blue leaves on a brown ground, c.m., 1876, 8¼in. high. $675 £450

A quatrefoil inkwell with cover and liner, the body with incised blue leaves, c.m., 1879, 4in. high. $825 £550

Mr Pickwick, the modelled figure glazed green and standing on a brown chair inscribed Pickwick Bachelor, DLE, circa 1895, 5in. high.
$570 £380

A vase with a mottled blue ground with incised dark brown scrolls and applied flower heads, o.u.m., circa 1872, 9½in. high. $375 £250

A model of a green frog riding a yellow and brown penny farthing, r.m., circa 1880, 4½in. high. $1125 £750

A vase, the brilliant royal blue ground with incised mottled brown scroll-work, r.m. & e., circa 1892, 8in. high.
$330 £220

A standing salt cellar, supported by moulded blue and brown dolphins, incised Doulton & Co., Lambeth, with the monogram GT, 4in. high. $375 £250

A double vase, the moulded buff putti with a blue garland standing on a brown sphere, r.m., circa 1885, 5¼in. high.
$480 £320

The eagle and the fox, a fable group with a brown trumpet-shaped vase, incised Doulton & Co., Lambeth, circa 1882, 7in. high. $1425 £950

GEORGE TINWORTH

A letter rack, the stoneware compartments with incised leaves and flowers in brown, blue and green, r.m., circa 1885, length 14in.
$1225 £850

The drunken husband, a modelled fable group with an old man wearing a blue night-gown, sitting on the detachable lid of a coffin, r.m., 1881, length 7¾in. $1500 £1000

A brown salt-glazed group modelled with a frog painting and a country mouse holding an upturned basket of fruit, circa 1885, length 7in. $1800 £1200

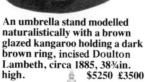

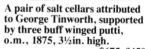

A pair of mantle ornaments, each moulded with a kneeling figure of a young Egyptian boy, r.m., circa 1885, 9in. high.
$675 £450

An umbrella stand modelled naturalistically with a brown glazed kangaroo holding a dark brown ring, incised Doulton Lambeth, circa 1885, 38¾in. high. $5250 £3500

A pair of salt cellars attributed to George Tinworth, supported by three buff winged putti, o.m., 1875, 3½in. high.
$675 £450

A brown glazed stoneware mirror frame carved in low relief with a head and shoulders portrait of a young girl, c.m., circa 1880, 18in. high.
$825 £550

The Fables Clock, the stone-ware case modelled with the interior of a house and numerous figures and animals, the base inscribed: H. Doulton & Co., Lambeth, and G. Tinworth, circa 1882, 11¼in. high. $3750 £2500

The vain jackdaw, a fable group with the peacock's display forming a fan-shaped vase, incised H. Doulton, Lambeth, circa 1882, 6in. high.
$1425 £950

GEORGE TINWORTH, MERRY MUSICIANS

A boy kicking a tambourine, DLE, incised Doulton Lambeth, circa 1895, 5in. high. $825 £550

A kneeling boy playing a harp, RDE, circa 1902, 3¾in. high. $825 £550

A moulded and modelled figure of a seated boy with a cittern, DLE, circa 1895, 4¾in. high.
$825 £550

A cello played by a seated boy, DLE, circa 1895, 4½in. high. $825 £550

A boy with a white face playing a cello, RDE, circa 1902, 4¾in. high.
$825 £550

An upright piano played by a boy seated on a stool, printed circle mark: Doulton Lambeth England, circa 1895, 4in. high. $825 £550

A brown glazed figure of a boy playing a rebec, DLE, circa 1895, 5¼in. high. $825 £550

A seated boy playing a harp, DLE, circa 1895, 4in. high. $825 £550

A cornet played by a seated cross-legged boy, RDE, circa 1902, 4½in. high. $825 £550

A boy leaning against a cylinder playing a concertina, DLE, circa 1895, 4½in. high. $825 £550

A boy playing a fiddle supported on his foot, DLE, circa 1895, 4¼in. high. $825 £550

A seated figure with a light buff face playing a French horn, RDE, circa 1902, 4¾in. high.
$825 £550

GEORGE TINWORTH, MOUSE FIGURES

A mouse group with a white mouse playing a tuba and a little mouse playing the cornet, o.m., circa 1875, 3¾in. high.
$1125 £750

A knight from a chess set glazed white, r.m., 1884, 3¼in. high.
$375 £250

Play Goers, the group glazed pale brown with a blue and brown shaped base, r.m., 1886, 5¼in. high. $1500 £1000

A mouse group with a green vase and pale green mice playing ochre double-basses, r.m., circa 1885, 5¼in. high.
$1425 £850

A tea party with pale green mice seated on brown chairs, the hollow oval base inscribed Tea-Time Scandal, r.m., circa 1885, 3½in. high. $1425 £950

A green vase on an oval base modelled with a pale green mouse playing a brown harp, and a little mouse playing a cornet, r.m., circa 1885, 5¼in. high. $1425 £850

A blue spill vase, with a mouse sleeping on the ground with a broom, r.m., circa 1885, 4in. high. $525 £350

A menu holder with a white mouse playing a harp and a little mouse playing a double bass, r.m., 1885, 3¾in. high.
$1125 £750

A bishop from a chess set, glazed white with a blue mitre, r.m., 1884, 3in. high. $375 £250

GEORGE TINWORTH, MOUSE FIGURES

A menu holder with two white mice playing a double-base and a cornet, inscribed Doulton Lambeth, circa 1880, 3¾in. high. **$1125 £750**

A brown glazed mouse-pawn holding an axe, r.m., 1884, 2½in. high. **$375 £250**

A tobacco jar, the lid with a green mouse sitting on a blue cushion smoking a brown pipe, r.m., circa 1885, 7in. high. **$525 £350**

A musical group with a blue vase and pale green mice, one playing an organ and the other a triangle, r.m., circa 1885, 5½in. high. **$1425 £850**

A mouse group moulded with three minstrels on a green mound, r.m., circa 1885, 3¾in. high. **$1275 £850**

A mouse-pawn glazed white, inscribed Pawn, r.m., 1884, 2½in. high. **$375 £250**

A model of a blue mouse eating a currant taken from the brown bun on which he sits, circa 1880, 2¾in. high. **$375 £250**

A blue spill vase modelled with a pale green mouse sitting comfortably in a brown chair, r.m. & e., circa 1895, 4½in. high. **$525 £350**

A menu holder with a little mouse about to steal an apple from a stall, r.m., circa 1885, 3¾in. high. **$1275 £850**

GEORGE TINWORTH, PLAQUES

A Guard's Chapel maquette glazed green, blue and brown, and modelled with the parable of the lost piece of silver, inscribed H. Doulton & Co., Lambeth, G. Tinworth, circa 1877, 12in. x 9in. $975 £650

A cream coloured terracotta self-portrait plaque inscribed G. Tinworth, circa 1913, 5¾in. x 4¾in. $570 £380

Tinworth's boyhood, a terracotta plaque modelled in high relief with George Tinworth as a young boy carving a small wooden bust in his father's wheelwright's workshop while his mother looks on, and a small boy watches for the possible arrival of his father, circa 1877, 8in. x 8in. $900 £600

A terracotta tile picture moulded and carved in low relief with Samson, DLE, circa 1880, 8½in. x 8½in. $525 £350

A terracotta tile picture moulded and carved in low relief with the Saviour and woman at the well, DLE, circa 1880, 8½in. x 8½in. $525 £350

A stoneware maquette with blue and brown glaze of David and Goliath, inscribed: H. Doulton & Co., Lambeth, G. Tinworth, with impressed oval stamps Doulton & Co., Lambeth London, circa 1877, 12in. x 9in. $975 £650

GEORGE TINWORTH, PLAQUES

A Station of the Cross, a terracotta plaque modelled in high relief with some free-standing figures, incised: H. Doulton & Co., Lambeth, G. Tinworth, circa 1878, 6in × 13in. $600 £400

The Four Seasons, a set of four plaques in salt-glaze stoneware carved in high relief and glazed in shades of brown and blue, circa 1875, 8½in. × 4in. $2400 £1600

Zacchaeus, a terracotta plaque modelled in high relief and inscribed Make Haste and Come Down for Today I Must Abide at Thy House and He Made Haste and Come Down, and Received Him Joyfully, in ebonised frame, circa 1878, 6in. × 13in. $600 £400

A religious plaque glazed in brown and blue and carved in high relief with the
Resurrection, circa 1880, 12¼in.×4½in.   **$600 £400**

A religious terracotta plaque modelled in high relief and inscribed When She Had
Heard of Jesus Came in the Press Behind and Touched His Garment, inscribed: H.
Doulton & Co., Lambeth, G. Tinworth, circa 1878, 6in.×13in.   **$600 £400**

John the Baptist, a terracotta plaque modelled in high relief with Salome demanding
the head of John the Baptist, circa 1878, 6in×13in.   **$600 £400**

GEORGE TINWORTH, PLAQUES

The Nativity, a terracotta plaque modelled in high relief and inscribed And They Came with Haste and Found Mary, and Joseph, and the Babe Lying in a Manger, the Poor of this World Rich in Faith, circa 1878, 5½in. x 12in. $600 £400

A small plaque, the stoneware glazed blue and brown on a white ground and carved in high relief, circa 1875, 8½in. × 4in. $600 £400

A Parable, a terracotta plaque modelled in high relief and incised And Jesus Called a Little Child Unto Him and Set Him in the Midst of Them, Humble Yourselves Therefore Under the Mighty Hand of God, circa 1878, 5½in. x 12in. $600 £400

A match striker advertising
Dewar's Whisky, c.m.l. & c.,
2½in. high.　　$45　£30

A tray glazed green and brown,
with a central blue horse's
head, c.m.l. & c., circa 1910,
4¼in. diameter.　　$112　£75

A match striker with Art
Nouveau designs, DLE, 4in.
high.　　　　　$27　£18

A moulded tray centred by a
brown mouse and a tree stump,
s.c.m., circa 1925, 4in. high.
　　　　　　　　$112　£75

The Suffragette Movement, an
inkwell modelled as a baby with
hinged head, R.D.E., circa
1905, 3¼in. high.　　$127　£85

A circular ring tray, slip-cast
with a glazed brown rabbit,
s.c.m., circa 1925, 3¼in. high.
　　　　　　　　$97　£65

An inkwell moulded with a
grumpy old lady, the green
apron inscribed 'Votes for
Women', c.m.l. & c., circa
1905, 3½in. high.　　$120　£80

A book-end glazed dark brown
and modelled with a monkey
clutching its young, DLE, circa
1900, 6½in. high.　　$165　£110

A moulded ring tray edged with
green leaves on which sits a
bird, DLE, Made in England,
circa 1925, 4in. high.　$120　£80

BIBELOTS

A group of two white ducklings squatting on a blue rockwork base, c.m.l. & c., circa 1920, 4¼in. high. $120 £80

An ash tray match holder, 'Queen Anne's Mansion', DLE. $45 £30

A ring tray attributed to Vera Huggins with a brown and buff owl. s.c.m., circa 1925, 4in. high. $97 £65

A trump indicator attributed to Leslie Harradine, RDE, circa 1910, 4in. high. $135 £90

A slip-cast ring tray modelled with a nymph seated on a ring of flowers, s.c.m., circa 1925, 4¼in. high. $112 £75

A match striker attributed to Harry Simeon, modelled with an old soldier seated next to a hollow drum, DLE, 4¾in. high. $120 £80

A shaped blue and brown ring tray on which perches a large billed bird, s.c.m., circa 1925, 4¼in. high. $97 £65

A match striker attributed to Harry Simeon with a toper wearing a blue coat, s.c.m., circa 1925, 3¾in. high. $165 £110

A whist booby attributed to Leslie Harradine, moulded with a skeleton, RDE, circa 1910, 4¼in. high. $135 £90

COMMEMORATIVE WARE   STONEWARE

A jug with white relief lettering 'Christopher Columbus sighted America Oct 12 1491', flanking a buff portrait of the explorer, r.m. & e., 6¼in. high.
$135 £90

A shallow bowl, with applied moulded celadon portraits of the young Queen Victoria, r.m., circa 1885, 6in. diameter.
$375 £250

A jug commemorating Benjamin Disraeli, the buff portrait in high relief flanked by a quotation, r.m., 6½in. high. $112 £75

A tankard designed by John Broad commemorating the 1897 Jubilee, DLE, circa 1897, 6½in. high. $135 £90

A bellarmine jug commemorating Queen Victoria's Golden Jubilee, r.m., 9in. high.
$225 £150

A coronation jug commemorating the accession of Edward VII and Queen Alexandra, DLE, circa 1902, 7½in. high. $142 £95

A jug with a portrait of H. M. Stanley below the inscription 'Emin Pasha Relief Expedition 1887-1889', r.m. & e., 7½in. high. $120 £80

A vase with a grey Doulton & Slater lace ground with an applied white bust of the Prince of Wales, r.m. & DSP., circa 1885, 6¼in. high. $195 £130

General Gordon, a jug commemorating his death at Khartoum in 1884, the buff ground with applied motifs and inscriptions, r.m., dated 1884, 7½in. high.
$120 £80

COMMEMORATIVE WARE

STONEWARE

A three-handled mug commemorating the coronation of King George V in 1911, moulded with relief portraits in pale green and blue, c.m.l. & c., 6¼in. high.　$135　£90

A jug commemorating the Golden Jubilee of Queen Victoria, with green glazed portraits of the Young and Old Queen on a blue ground, DLE, 9in. high.　$165　£110

A three-handled mug commemorating the hoisting of the flag at Pretoria, DLE, 6½in. high.　$127　£85

A jug commemorating the hoisting of the flag at Pretoria, DLE, circa 1900, 8¼in. high.　$165　£110

A double-handled tankard commemorating War in the Sudan, r.m., 1883, 6in. high.　$127　£85

An oviform vase made to commemorate the Coronation of Edward VII and Queen Alexandra in 1902, c.m.l. & c., 27.5cm. high.　$225　£150

William Ewart Gladstone, the jug printed with quotations below the title, 'England's Great Commoner', DLE, 7½in. high.　$127　£85

A small jug designed by John Broad commemorating the 1887 Jubilee, DL, 4½in. high.　$97　£65

A Nelson jug, moulded with a portrait of the famous admiral flanked by naval battle scenes, c.m.l. & c., 8in. high.　$315　£210

DOULTON & SLATER'S PATENT

A jug, overlaid with a grey and brown lace pattern on which mistletoe is applied, r.m. & DSP, circa 1888, 7¾in. high. $135 £90

A pair of ewers with rough brown lace ground decorated with floral sprays, Slater's Patent 'Chine', DLE, 8in. high. $87 £58

A dated vase with brown lion's head handles and applied green foliage on a brilliant blue ground, r.m. & DSP, 1886, 11in. high. $480 £320

A jug, the dark green elaborate lace ground overlaid with two celadon classical portraits, r.m. & DSP, circa 1888, 7½in. high. $135 £90

A jug, the blue lace ground with the impressions of large ferns and overlaid with bouquets of ochre flowers, r.m. & DSP, circa 1890, 7in. high. $120 £80

A jug, with a grey lace panel overlaid with moulded white and brown foliage enclosing six oval medallions, r.m. & DSP, circa 1888, 6in. high. $127 £85

A vase decorated with bands of applied stiff leaves on a blue ground, Slater's Patent 'Chine', DLE, 11¾in. high. $78 £52

A pair of vases, each with three panels of white flowering foliage, r.m. & e. & DSP, circa 1895, 10in. high. $300 £200

One of a pair of vases with rough brown lace ground decorated with floral sprays, Slater's Patent 'Chine', c.m.l. & c., 14¼in. high. $165 £110

410

DOULTON & SLATER'S PATENT

A vase with four moulded blue-glazed cupids and numerous stars superimposed on a plain dark green lace ground, r.m. & DSP, circa 1888, 10¼in. high.
$135 £90

A pair of vases moulded with celadon fish and dragon medallions, r.m. & DSP, 1885, 9¼in. high. $127 £85

A vase with rough brown lace ground decorated with floral sprays, Slater's Patent 'Chine', r.m. & e., 10¾in. high.
$45 £30

A jug with applied pale blossom in high relief and two moulded medallions, one of a snake and a mouse, r.m. & DSP, circa 1888, 7½in. high. $142 £95

A teapot with rough brown lace ground decorated with floral sprays, Slater's Patent 'Chine', r.m., 4¾in. high. $48 £32

A jug, with two impressed lace patterns and decorated round the centre with three white medallions, r.m. & DSP, circa 1888, 6¾in. high. $120 £80

A vase with blue handles and neck, the rough brown lace ground with incised brown and blue foliage, r.m. & e. & DSP, circa 1895, 12in. high.
$180 £120

A pair of oriental vases, applied flower head and brown dragons supporting beige lace impressed medallions, r.m. & DSP, circa 1888, 8in. high. $375 £250

A small vase with a blue lace frieze in which are the impressions of dark green ferns, r.m. & DSP, circa 1890, 5½in. high. $120 £80

411

Miniature Doulton Lambeth stoneware mug with silver hallmarked rim and decorated with applied toping scenes.
$16 £11

A narrow vase with incised blue leaves and bead work, c.m., 1877, 5in. high. $75 £50

Miniature Doulton Lambeth stoneware jug with applied toping scenes. $10 £7

A bowl by Alberta Green, the buff ground with white bead work, r.m., 1887, 3¼in. high.
$82 £55

A double-handled vase with incised blue and green flowers, r.m. & e., circa 1892, 5in. high.
$112 £75

Doulton Lambeth miniature stoneware mustard pot with 'Colman's' in relief and applied moulding. $15 £10

A handled bottle with overall applied pink, brown, and white fan-shaped patterns, r.m., 1882, 3¼in. high. $82 £55

A miniature Doulton Lambeth stoneware caster with plated lid and applied moulding.
$18 £12

A jug by Edith Lupton with green panels painted in pâte-sur-pâte, c.m., 1878, 4¾in. high. $97 £65

STONEWARE

NATURAL FOLIAGE WARE

A 'natural foliage-ware' vase with the impression of veined leaves glazed olive-green, c.m.l. & c., circa 1905, 8¾in. high.
$105 £70

A pair of 'natural foliage-ware' vases with the impression of veined leaves, r.m. & e., 16¼in. high. $360 £240

A 'natural foliage-ware' vase, the rough ochre ground impressed with two types of reddish-brown leaves, DLE, circa 1895, 12½in. high
$135 £90

SIMULATED WARE

A Doulton & Slater's patent mug, simulating brown leather with stitched panels, r.m. & e. & DSL, the silver rim hall-marked 1893, 6¼in high.
$105 £70

A silicon jug, the dark brown body simulating leather with stitched joints, 9¾in. high, with two beakers en suite, hallmarked 1899, 4¼in. high, DSL & e. $247 £165

A stoneware jug simulating a black jack, the dark brown leather with stitched joints, DLE, the silver rim hallmarked 1897, 9in. high. $112 £75

Cast iron, a covered box in silicon ware, simulating an iron 14 lb. weight, DSL & e., the silver handle hallmarked 1898. 5in. high. $77 £55

A jug, the silicon body with a copper-colour glaze and imitation joints, rivets and dents, 7in. high, with two beakers en suite, 4¼in. high, DSL & e. $262 £175

A jug, the silicon body with copper coloured glaze and imitation joints, 7in. high, DSL & e., 1900. $105 £70

A small vase of hexagonal section inscribed on either side 'The Waning of the Honey-Moon', supported on an oval base with two hares sitting defiantly at either end, r.m., 1880, 4¾in. high. $420 £280

A pair of ewers decorated with applied slip flower, leaf and bead designs, DSL, circa 1891, 7¼in. high. $50 £34

A jug with impressed flower and leaf motifs, and applied blue flower heads, DSL, 1884, 5½in. high. $75 £50

A jardiniere decorated with applied and incised flower and leaf designs on a blue ground, 'DSL, 7½in. high. $72 £48

A modelled owl with brown wings and feet, the detachable head and the body decorated with applied blue, green and white motifs, DSL, circa 1880, 7½in. high. $390 £260

A jardiniere decorated with blue floret and incised designs on a buff ground, DLE, impressed date for 1884, 6¾in. high. $50 £34

A water filter with incised, carved and applied decoration on a buff ground, DSL, 14½in. high. $180 £120

A tobacco jar decorated with applied blue and white beads, r.m., impressed date for 1888, 4¼in. high. $27 £18

A tapering jug with overall incised diamond patterns, DSL, circa 1880, 8in. high. $90 £60

SPORTING SUBJECTS

A cricketing jug printed in dark brown, with portraits of George Griffin, W. G. Grace and K. S. Ranjitsinhji on the buff ground, DLE, 7in. high. $210 £140

A silver mounted cycling jug and two beakers, DLE, circa 1900, the jug 8in. high, the beakers 4¾in. high. $270 £180

A sporting jug commemorating the untimely death of F. J. Archer, the champion jockey in 1886, r.m., 6½in. high. $180 £120

A golfing jug, sprigged in white, with the panels of the 'Last Ball', 'Putting' and 'Driving', impressed Lambeth mark, circa 1880, 20cm. high. $420 £280

A waisted mug applied with moulded white figures of a bowler, wicket keeper, and a batsman, DLE, circa 1900, 6in. high. $180 £120

A cricketing jug, the moulded relief figures against the buff salt glaze ground within stylised floral borders outlined in white slip and coloured in blue and green, DLE, circa 1900, 9¼in. high. $255 £170

A silver mounted sporting tyg, DLE, circa 1900, 6in. high, the silver rim maker's mark H. W., Sheffield. $240 £160

A cricketer's mug applied with moulded white figures of a bowler, wicket keeper and a batsman, circa 1880, 15.5cm. high. $180 £120

A cricketing tyg, impressed Registration mark, r.m., and dated 1884, 6¼in. high. $360 £240

STONEWARE

A mug with applied moulded golfing vignettes of 'the drive', and 'the lost ball', DLE, circa 1900, 5in. high. $345 £230

A beaker with relief white figures of a shot putter, a runner, and a long-jumper, DLE, the silver rim hallmarked 1900, 5in. high. $90 £60

A cycling mug with three applied white figures inscribed Military, Road, and Path, DLE, circa 1900, 4¾in. high.
$130 £85

A cycling jug with three white vignettes, inscribed Military, Road and Path, DLE, circa 1900, 7¼in. high. $180 £120

A sporting jug with three moulded white vignettes, a man running, men playing football, and a man putting the shot, DLE, circa 1900, 8in. high.
$135 £90

A cricket jug with applied vignettes of a bowler, wicket keeper and a batsman, DLE, circa 1900, 7in. high. $240 £160

A rugby football jug with vignettes of two men kicking a ball, a scrummage and two of the men running with a ball, r.m., 1883, 7½in. high. $195 £130

A cricket mug with three applied figures of batsmen in high relief, registration mark of 1880, r.m., 1882, 5¼in. high.
$210 £140

A golfing jug with three applied white vignettes of 'the lost ball', 'putting', and 'driving', DLE, circa 1900, 7¾in. high.
$390 £260

TOBY JUGS

CHARLIE CHAPLIN
Designer: Unknown
Size: Large 11in., 28cm.
Issued: c.1918
Price: $6000 £4000

FALSTAFF D6062
Designer: C. Noke
Size: Large 8½in., 21.5cm.
Issued: 1939-
Price: $82 £33

FALSTAFF D6063
Designer: C. Noke
Size: Small 5¼in., 13.5cm.
Issued: 1939-
Price: $41 £17

GEORGE ROBEY
Designer: Unknown
Size: Large 10½in.,
26.5cm.
Issued: c.1925
Price: $5250 £3500

HAPPY JOHN D6031
Designer: H. Fenton
Size: Large 8¾in., 22cm.
Issued: 1939-
Price: $82 £33

HAPPY JOHN D6070
Designer: H. Fenton
Size: Small 5½in., 14cm.
Issued: 1939-
Price: $41 £17

HONEST MEASURE D6108
Designer: H. Fenton
Size: Small 4½in., 11.5cm.
Issued: 1939-
Price: $41 £17

HUNTSMAN D6320
Designer: H. Fenton
Size: Large 7½in., 19cm.
Issued: 1950-
Price: $82 £22

JOLLY TOBY D6109
Designer: H. Fenton
Size: Medium 6½in.,
16.5cm.
Issued: 1939-
Price: $54 £22

OLD CHARLEY D6030
Designer: H. Fenton
Size: Large 8¾in., 22cm.
Issued: 1939-1960
Price: $82 £55

FALSTAFF

HAPPY JOHN

HONEST MEASURE

HUNTSMAN

JOLLY TOBY

OLD CHARLEY

TOBY JUGS

GEORGE·ROBEY·

·CHAPLIN·

GEORGE ROBEY who lived between 1869 and 1954 was nicknamed 'The Prime Minister of Mirth' because of his huge popularity as a music hall artist.

He was born George Wade in Herne Hill, the son of a civil engineer who gave him an expensive education at Dresden, Leipzig and Cambridge, but the young George changed his name to Robey and went on the stage at the age of 22. Music hall audiences loved his Rabelaisian humour and his first hit was in a musical called 'The Bing Boys' but he went on to become an highly individual comedian and also played Falstaff in his one venture into Shakespeare.

In private he was a lonely and aloof figure, reserving his slapstick humour for the stage. In 1953, one year before his death, he was knighted.

The Toby Jug of Robey was produced by Doulton's between 1910 and 1925 when he was at the peak of his fame. The jugs were ten and a half inches high and were faithful representations of Robey's stage persona with heavily painted eyebrows, wrinkled suit and bowler hat. In the jug the hat doubled as a lid.

CHARLIE CHAPLIN lived between 1889 and 1979. Like George Robey he was knighted shortly before his death, the accolade being bestowed on Chaplin in 1977.

When he was eight years old Chaplin went on the stage. In 1914 he emigrated to Hollywood where he joined the famous Karno troupe and made a staggering thirty-five films in his first year in America.

In his characteristic 'Little Man' dress and make-up of toothbrush moustache, out-turned broken shoes, baggy suit, walking cane and, like Robey, a bowler hat, Chaplin became one of the greatest stars Hollywood every produced. His list of credits as actor, writer and director ranges from 'The Gold Rush' to 'Mister Verdoux' and 'Limelight'.

Doulton produced a limited number of Toby Jugs of Chaplin in 1918. They were inscribed 'Charlie' on the base and his bowler hat formed the lid. The jugs stood ten and a half inches high and there is no note of the designer but they are today very rare because less than ten are known to be in private collections.

OLD CHARLEY D6069
Designer: H. Fenton
Size: Small 5½in., 14cm.
Issued: 1939-1960
Price: $52 £35

SHERLOCK HOLMES D6661
Designer: R. Tabbenor
Size: Large 8¾in., 22cm.
Issued: 1981-
Price: $82 £33

SIR FRANCIS DRAKE D6660
Designer: M. Abberley
Size: Large 9in., 23cm.
Issued: 1981-
Price: $82 £33

SHERLOCK HOLMES   SIR FRANCIS DRAKE

SQUIRE D6319
Designer: H. Fenton
Size: Medium 6in., 15cm.
Issued: 1950-1969
Price: $135 £90

THE BEST IS NOT TOO GOOD D6107
Designer: H. Fenton
Size: 4½in., 11.5cm.
Issued: 1939-1960
Price: $60 £40

TOBY XX D6088
Designer: H. Fenton
Size: 6½in., 16.5cm.
Issued: 1939-1969
Price: $105 £70

SQUIRE   THE BEST IS NOT TOO GOOD

WINSTON CHURCHILL D6171
Designer: H. Fenton
Size: Large 9in., 23cm.
Issued: 1941-
Price: $82 £33

WINSTON CHURCHILL D6172
Designer: H. Fenton
Size: Medium 5½in., 14cm.
Issued: 1941-
Price: $54 £22

WINSTON CHURCHILL D6175
Designer: H. Fenton
Size: Small 4in., 10cm.
Issued: 1941-
Price: $41 £17

TOBY XX   WINSTON CHURCHILL

THE DOULTONVILLE TOBIES

Designer: W. Harper
Size: 4in., 10cm.

MR LITIGATE D6699
Issued: 1983-
Price: $35 £14

MISS NOSTRUM D6700
Issued: 1983-
Price: $35 £14

MR FURROW D6701
Issued: 1983-
Price: $35 £14

REV. CASSOCK D6702
Issued: 1983-
Price: $35 £14

MR TONSIL D6713
Issued: 1984-
Price: $35 £14

MADAME CRYSTAL D6714
Issued: 1984-
Price: $35 £14

MRS LOAN D6715
Issued: 1984-
Price: $35 £14

BETTY BITTERS D6716
Issued: 1984-
Price: $35 £14

SERGEANT PEELER D6720
Issued: 1985-
Price: $35 £14

CAPTAIN SALT D6721
Issued: 1985
Price: $35 £14

DR. PULSE D6723
Issued: 1985-
Price: $35 £14

MISS STUDIOUS D6722
Issued: 1985-
Price: $35 £14

FRED FLY D6742
Issued: 1986
Price: $35 £14

MR BRISKET D6743
Issued: 1986
Price: $35 £14

MAJOR GREEN D6740
Issued: 1986
Price: $35 £14

MIKE MINERAL
Issued: 1986
Price: $35 £14

MADAME CRYSTAL

MRS LOAN

SERGEANT PEELER

CAPTAIN SALT

DR. PULSE

MISS STUDIOUS

TOBY JUGS

MR LITIGATE

MISS NOSTRUM

MR FURROW

REV. CASSOCK

MR TONSIL

BETTY BITTERS

SMALL SEATED TOBIES

Designer: H. Fenton
Size: 4½in., 11.5cm.

MR PICKWICK D6261
Issued: 1948-1960
Price: $98 £65

MR MICAWBER D6262
Issued: 1948-1960
Price: $98 £65

SAIREY GAMP D6263
Issued: 1948-1960
Price: $98 £65

FAT BOY D6264
Issued: 1948-1960
Price: $98 £65

SAM WELLER D6265
Issued: 1948-1960
Price: $98 £65

CAP'N CUTTLE D6266
Issued: 1948-1960
Price: $98 £65

MR PICKWICK

MR MICAWBER

SAIREY GAMP

FAT BOY

SAM WELLER

CAP'N CUTTLE

ARTISTS & ASSISTANTS

Adelaide **AARON**	aO	
Christine **ABBOT**	CA	
Elizabeth J. **ADAMS**	LA	
Ella H. **ADAMS**	aa A	
Matilda S. **ADAMS**	MsA	
Margaret **AITKEN**	AM	
Mary **AITKEN**	MA	
Emily **ALLEN**	EEA	
Fannie J. **ALLEN**	AE	
E. **ARCHER**	A	
Helen A. **ARDING**	A	
Mary M. **ARDING**	M.M.A	
Margaret M. **ARMSTRONG**		
A. **ASKEW**	:: a	
Elizabeth **ATKINS**	EA	
N. **ATKINS**		
Lizzie **AXFORD**	a:	
Louisa **AYLING**	a	
Agnes E. M. **BAIGENT**	AEB	
Clara **BAKER**	bbb	
Emily **BAKER**	b:b	
Edith H. **BALL**	B̄ bq	
E. **BANFIELD**	bd	
Eliza S. **BANKS**	EfB	
Alice M. E. **BARKER**	b: B AMB	
Clara S. **BARKER**	CSB	
G. **BARKER**	-//-	
Arthur B. **BARLOW**	AB	
Florence E. **BARLOW**	FEB	
Hannah B. **BARLOW**	HB	
Lucy A. **BARLOW**	AL	
Harry **BARNARD**	B	
V. **BARNES**	V	
W. **BARON**	W3	
Mary A. **BARRETT**	bbO MAB	
Ethel **BEARD**	EB	
George W. **BEARNE**	B	
Acidalia E. C. **BECK**	AB	
N. **BEEDEN**		
Arthur **BEERE**	AB	
G. **BENSON**		
A. **BENTLEY**		
Augusta M. **BIRNIE**	b̄ AB	
Florence M. **BIRT**	qb	
Ernest R. **BISHOP**	B	
Eborah **BISSMIRE**	bOO	
F. **BLACKSTAFFE**	)-(	
H. **BLAKE**	b	
O. **BOUCHER**	br	
Maud **BOWDEN**	MB	
Florence **BOWDITCH**	:b:	
Jessie **BOWDITCH**	B	
Eliza **BOWEN**	bb:	
L. F. **BOWEN**	LfB	
Winnie **BOWSTEAD**	W.B	
Jessie **BOYCE**	J.B	

N.	BRAKE	
Daisy	BRIANT	D.B
John	BROAD	B
D.	BROND	F
F.	BROOKE	F
Rosina	BROWN	RB
Alice E.	BUDDEN	ACB. b
Mary	BUDDEN	obo
C.	BUNN	tU
Alice L.	BURLTON	ALB. B
Georgina	BURR	b+ G.D.B
Eleanor	BURRELL	ⓑ
Emma A.	BURROWS	ob
Frank A.	BUTLER	FB
Mary	BUTTER	bb M.B
Mary	BUTTERTON	MB
Alice	CAFFIN	A
Alice	CAMPBELL	A.C.
Bertha M.	CAPES	B
Mary	CAPES	M
Annie M.	CASTLE	AG.
Kate J.	CASTLE	c
M.	CAUTY	c c m.l.
Margaret M.	CHALLIS	MM
Emily M.	CHANDLER	C I
J.	CHANDLER	C
Clara	CHURCHER	▪c▪
Emily	CLARK	E.C.
Fanny	CLARK	FC
L.	CLARK	C
E.	CLARKE	S
Frances	CLEMENTS	E

Miss	COCKS	CO
Edith M.	COLEMAN	EG
F.M.	COLLINS	CM
Rose	COLLINS	RC
Miss	CONGDON	c▪▪
Alice	COOKE	ccO
D.	CORDERO	
Joan	COWPER	Joan Cowper
Minna L.	CRAWLEY	M CM
D.	CROFTS	
Ellen	CROSBY	E
Emily	CROSBY	cOO
James R.	CRUICKSHANK	¢
Annie	CUPIT	cc
Lilian	CURTIS	L.C. C c▪
Lizzie M.	DAINTREE	dO
Olive	DALE	d▪
A.	DANIELS	
Kate M.	DAVIS	KD.
Louisa J.	DAVIS	
Mary A.	DAVIS	MB d+
W.	DAVISON	D
Elizabeth	DAYTON	ⓓ
Mary	DENLEY	M
Ada	DENNIS	AD AD d▪
Florence	DENNIS	≢ dd▪
Miss	DOUTHWAITE	ddd
Amelia A.	DRAKE	A.D.
M.	DRIVER	
A.	DUNCAN	
Edward	DUNN	ED
W. Edward	DUNN	wED

ARTISTS & ASSISTANTS

M.	DUNTON	
Beatrice M.	DURTNALL	D
Josephine A.	DURTNALL	J.D
L. Imogen	DURTNALL	ĿD dd
Alice K.	EARL	
Florence	EARL	
Alice	ECKENSTEIN	e A.E.
Lottie	ECKENSTEIN	eeO
M.	EDERMANIGER	
Emily J.	EDWARDS	
Louisa E.	EDWARDS	
Edward E.	EGGLETON	
Fanny	ELLIOTT	
Herbert	ELLIS	HE
Sarah	ELLIS	SE
C.	EMERTON	E
Bertha	EVANS	E e
Kate	EVERETT	ee
John	EYRE	JEyu
Miss	FELTON	
Ada E.	FIMISTER	
Elizabeth	FISHER	
Sarah	FISHER	SF f
Emily A.	FORSEY	fO E.A.F
Minnie	FORSTER	ff
E.	FORSYTH	
Constance	FOSTER	ff
M.	FOX	M.F.
D.	FRAMPTON	
Catherine	FRANCIS	F
L.	FRANCIS	f
May	FREAKES	fr

Lizzie	FRENCH	ff
A. E.	FRENCH	ÆF
M.	FRICKER	
Elizabeth A.	GADSDON	gg
Jessie	GANDY	JG go
Walter	GANDY	WG
Nellie	GARBETT	g EG
Ellen	GATHERCOLE	NGgg
Sarah P.	GATHERCOLE	g
Annie	GENTLE	AG
Kate R.	GIBLIN	G go
Elizabeth M.	GILLMAN	g
Emily J.	GILLMAN	
L.	GOLDSACK	LG
Mary A.	GOODE	g g
Laura	GOODERHAM	ggo
M.	GOODING	g
E.	GRAVER	M
M.	GRAY	
Alberta L.	GREEN	AG
Edith	GREEN	G
Laura	GREEN	g
Lydia	GREIG	OgO
A.	GRIGGS	g
Alice E.	GROOM	AG .G.
Jessie	GUEST	gOO
Alice	HALL	
Elizabeth	HAMILTON	E.H.
J. B.	HARDING	BH
B.	HARMAN	h
A. Leslie	HARRADINE	LH
Edith	HARRINGTON	hOO

Name	Monogram	Name	Monogram
Rosina HARRIS	ℛℋ	Florence L. HUNT	J.H.
Emma C. HARRISON	H	Jane S. HURST	H
Nellie HARRISON	hn	John HUSKINSON	H
W. HASTINGS	W	Ernest JARRETT	[symbol]
Lizzie HAUGHTON	H	E. JESSETT	[symbol]
Ethel HAWKINS	h k	Doris JOHNSON	DJ
Emily M. HAWKSBY	hh▪ E.M.H.	Florrie JONES	FJ
Emily HAYNES	hh	Gladys JOYCE	J
A. HAYS	AH	Ivy JOYCE	J
E. Violet HAYWARD	hd	Rosa KEEN	RK
L. HAYWARD	[symbol]	Edith KELSEY	J
Rosetta HAZELDINE	▪h▪	Edith L. KEMP	K EK
O. HEATH	hOh	Harriette E. E. KNIGHT	k
Alice G. HELLIS	h̄	Alice LACY	[symbol]
E. HENDERSON	(·)	Charlotte LAMB	CL
Alice M. HERAPATH	H h▪ A.M.H	Ulrique LARCHER	UL
Edith HERAPATH	hh	J. LASHAM	[symbol]
F. HEWITT	hhh	Marion LAYZELL	11
K. HEYWOOD	[symbol]	Francis E. LEE	FEL
E. HIBBERD	[symbol]	Harriette E. LEE	L 11
Harriett E. HIBBUT	HEH	Nellie LEGGE	[symbol]
Jessie HINCHLIFF	(h)	Esther LEWIS	[symbol]
Marion HOLBROOK	MH	Florence E. LEWIS	[symbol]
Eliza J. HOLLIS	hhO E.H.	Isabel LEWIS	[symbol]
Joan HONEY	JH	Ada C. LILLEY	11▪
Agnes S. HORNE	hO H̄	Mary M. S. LILLEY	1▪
Annie HORTON	ho▪	Frances M. LINNELL	[symbol]
Agnete HOY	AH	Ada LONDON	l
Eliza L. HUBERT	ELH	Emily A. LONDON	L EA
Vera HUGGINS	v.H ℋ YH	Alice LONGHURST	l::
Kate HUGHES	h:: K.H	Jessie LORD	1d
Annie M. HULFORD	H.x.	Edith D. LUPTON	EDL

ARTISTS & ASSISTANTS

Annie	LYONS	_A.L._	Annie	NEAL		n
W. W.	MACKAY	M	Minnie	NEAL		Z
B.	MACNAE	/X	William J.	NEATBY		WJN
Matilda	MARLYN	m▪m	Bessie	NEWBERY		8N
Emma	MARRIOTT	⊞⊟	Josephine E.	NEWNHAM		N
L.	MARRIOTT	÷	Mary	NEWSON		mn
Alice	MARSHALL	A.M.	E.	NOBLE		▪n▪
Mark V.	MARSHALL	M·Y·M	Lilla	NOTTINGHAM		N
Susan	MARSHALL	m	E.	NORRIS		x⁊
Eliza	MARTIN	m m	F.	NORRISH		⌒c
Emma	MARTIN	ЄM.	W. J. W.	NUNN		𝕎
M.	MARTIN	m▪m	Gertrude	NYE		𝓧
Matilda	MARTYN	_mmm_	A.	ORCHIN		Ⓐ
F.	MASKELL	☥	Lizzie	PADBURY	P	LP
Louisa	MATTERSON	mO	D.	PAINTER		P
Ada	MAYCOCK	m▪	Ellen	PALMER		Op
Emily	MAYES	m	L.	PARKER		◇
Emily W.	MAYNE	EM.	William	PARKER		ωp
John H.	McLENNAN	JHMᶜ	Emily J.	PARTINGTON		EP
L.	MEAR	♯C	Lily	PARTINGTON		LP
Miss	MEDLICOTT	mt	Annie	PARTRIDGE		P▪
Miss	MIDDLEMISS	mi	Arthur E.	PEARCE	A℘	R
Alice	MILBORROW	▪▪m	Georgina	PEARSON		P▪P
Isabella	MILLER	M ℳ	S.	PEARSON		P.
A.	MILLS	⅄	Helena M.	PENNETT		PP
Annie	MILNE	ⓜ	F.	PERRIN		⅄x
Mary	MITCHELL	MM	E.	PHEBY		▪P▪
Ada	MORGAN	mOO	E.	PICKERSGILL		Pᴘ
Joseph H.	MOTT	JHM	F.	POMEROY		FP
Iza M.	MUNDAY	EM	Francis C.	POPE	.P.	F·C·P
E.	NAISH	⊼	A.	POTTERTON		⅃z
H.	NAISH	ⓝ	R.	PRITCHARD		℞

427

Name	Mark	Name	Mark
M. PRYCE	[symbol]	Agnes D. SANDES	A.S.
Jane RABBIT	rrO	F. SAWYER	[symbol]
Emily RANDALL	E.R.	A. SAYERS	sO AS
L. RAWLINGS	rg	Elizabeth A. SAYERS	EAS
Frank W. READER	R FR	Fanny SAYERS	sOO
Constance E. REDFORD	R r:	Rosalie SCOTT	ssO
George W. RHEAD	[symbol]	G. SHARPE	[symbol]
S. RICKARDS	r:	G. SHEARS	sr
Alice M. RITCHIN	AR	Elizabeth SHELLEY	E.S
Emma ROBERTS	ER	Annie SHELTON	ss:
Florence C. ROBERTS	FER	Lizzie SHETTLEWORTH	[symbol]
Emily L. ROBINSON	R	F. SHIPMAN	[symbol]
Alice ROBJENT	(r)	A. SHUTE	ss:
Edith ROGERS	EER	Emma SHUTE	ES.
Isabel ROGERS	R:	Harry SIMEON	HS
Kate ROGERS	R	Eliza SIMMANCE	S ES
L. ROGERS	[symbol]	Alice M. M. SKIDMORE	OsO
Martha M. ROGERS	MMR	Mary SLATTER	M.S.
A. ROHSS	[symbol]	Elizabeth M. SMALL	EMS
Letitia ROSEVEAR	r	Katherine B. SMALLFIELD	KBS [symbol]
William ROWE	WR	Mildred B. SMALLFIELD	MBS
M. RUCKSTUHL	mr	Alice G. SMITH	A.S.
E. RUDDOCK	E.R	Ellen B. SMITH	E.B.S S. ss
Agnes M. RUFF	[symbol]	E. SMITH	[symbol]
Ellen RUMBOL	ER RO	Frances SMITH	F.S.
Jane RUMBOL	rOO	Georgie SMITH	GS
Alice RUSSELL	:r:	Gertrude SMITH	S S
F. RUSSELL	[symbol]	Catherine A. SPARKES	CAS
Kate E. RUSSELL	rɹ	E. SPONG	(S)
Louisa RUSSELL	[symbol] R LR	A. SPURRELL	[symbol]
Clara RYMER	rO	Fanny STABLE	F.S.
Susanna M. SANDERSON	S.S	Mary STAREY	SMS s:

ARTISTS & ASSISTANTS

Eliza	STOCK	s	Bessie M.	VARNEY	v
Emily E.	STORMER	EES	C.	VIGOR	C.V.
N.	STRAKER		Emily M.	VINER	E.Y.
Emilie M.	STRATFORD	s■s	E.	WAKELY	w■
E.	STRATTON	st	Louisa	WAKELY	w LW
Katherine	STURGEON		K.	WALKER	
George Hugo	TABOR	GTH	Helen	WALTERS	X
Winifred	TALBOT	tl	L.	WATERS	L.W.
N.	TAYLOR		Linnie	WATT	Watt
Florence	TEGETMEIER	tO	Minnie	WEBB	MW
A. Euphemia	THATCHER		Jenny F.	WEEKES	wO
Elsie S.	THOMAS	tt	Emily M. R.	WELCH	EW
Margaret E.	THOMPSON	TM	M.	WELSBY	
Marie E.	THOMPSON	tx	Georgina	WHITE	G.W.
Minnie G.	THOMPSON	MGT	Onslow E.	WHITING	O.W.
Mary Ann	THOMSON	M	K.	WHITTON	
Walter	THORNEMAN		H.	WILKINSON	
M.	THORNTON		Arthur	WILLCOCK	W
George	TINWORTH		A.	WILSON	
H.	TOLAND		Edgar W.	WILSON	
Louisa E.	TOMKINS	F	Louie	WILSON	
F.	TOMLYN		R.	WILSON	
Ada	TOSEN	AT	Ada M.	WOOD	wOO
A.	TOSEN		Christina	WOOD	C.W
Eleanor	TOSEN	ttt	Emily	WOOD	ww
Ellen C.	TOWNSEND	t■■	Edith H.	WOODINGTON	W
A.	TRANTER		Rosetta S.	WOODS	RW
Ethel	TRANTER	tOO	Ada L.	WORTHEY	A.W.
A.	TURNER		C. M.	WRAY	
M.	UNWIN	U■	Bessie J.	YOUATT	
C.	VARGAS		L.	YOUNG	y
R.	VARGAS		A.	ZURCHER	Z

MARKS

DOULTON & WATTS — Impressed or incised mark used on stoneware, 1827–1858.

 Circular mark impressed with date, used on Doulton Ware and Lambeth Faience, 1876–1880.

DOULTON & WATTS LAMBETH POTTERY LONDON — Impressed or incised mark used on stoneware, 1827–1858.

 Impressed or printed mark used on stoneware, with England added after 1891, 1879–1902.

 Impressed or incised mark used on stoneware, 1827–1858.

 Rosette Mark impressed or printed on Doulton Ware and Lambeth Faience, 1880-1891.

(r.m. – rosette mark)

DOULTON LAMBETH — Impressed or printed mark used on stoneware, with England added after 1891, 1858–1910.

H. DOULTON & CO. — Incised on panels and plaques by George Tinworth.

 Oval undated mark impressed on early Doulton Ware, 1869–1872.

(o.u.m. – oval undated mark)

DOULTON & SLATERS PATENT — Doulton and Slater's Patent, 1885–1939.

(DSP – Doulton & Slater's Patent)

 Oval mark impressed and dated used on Doulton Ware, 1872–1876.

(o.m. – oval mark)

 Doulton Silicon Lambeth, with England added after 1891, 1880–1932.

(DSL – Doulton Silicon Lambeth)

Circular mark, impressed or printed, and sometimes dated in the centre, used on Lambeth Faience, 1873–1914.

(c.m. – circular mark)

Rosette mark with England added, used on Doulton Ware and Lambeth Faience, 1891–1902.

(r.m. & e. – rosette mark and England)

Impressed or printed mark, with England added after 1891, used on Lambeth Faience, 1873–1914.

DOULTON LAMBETH ENGLAND — Impressed or printed on small objects of Doulton Ware, 1891–1956.

 Doulton Lambeth England, used on Doulton Ware and Lambeth Faience, 1891–1956.

(DLE – Doulton Lambeth England)

 Impressed or printed mark used on Crown Lambeth Ware, 1891–1905.

 Impressed or printed mark used on Impasto Ware, often dated in the centre and with England added after 1891, 1879–1914.

 Used on objects with a metallic coating, circa 1900.

 Printed mark used on Faience, with England added after 1891, 1880–1914.

 Printed on Morrisian Ware, 1901–1924.

 Impressed or printed on Marqueterie Ware, with England added after 1891, 1887–1906.

 Printed mark used on Brangwyn Ware.

 Impressed or printed on Marqueterie Ware, with England added after 1891, 1887–1906.

 Circle mark, lion and crown used on Doulton Lambeth and Burslem Ware, 1902–1956.

(c.m.l. & c. – circle mark, lion and crown)

 Impressed or printed on Marqueterie Ware, with England added after 1891, 1887–1906.

 Circle mark used on small objects of Doulton Lambeth and Burslem Ware, 1902–1956.

(RDE – Royal Doulton England)

 Impressed or printed on Marqueterie Ware, with England added after 1891, 1887–1906.

 Printed mark used on Royal Doulton Flambe, with 'Made in England' added from 1930, 1902–1930.

Impressed or printed mark used on Carrara Ware, 1891–1924.

ROYAL DOULTON FLAMBE Royal Doulton Flambe mark used on small pieces, 1904–1930.

Printed on Velluma Ware, 1911–1914.

Impressed or printed mark used on Persian Ware, 1920–1936.

Impressed or printed mark used on Doulton Ware, 1912–1956.

(s.c.m.–slip cast mark)

Printed mark used on Burslem stoneware, 1922–1927.

Printed mark used on Royal Doulton Titanian Ware, 1916–1929.

Circle mark and lion, impressed or printed on Doulton Ware, 1922–1956.

(c.m. & l. – circle mark and lion)

Printed mark used on Royal Doulton Titanian Ware, 1916–1929.

Printed mark used on Chang Ware with the monogram of H. Nixon, 1925–1940.

Printed mark used on hard-paste figures, 1918–1933.

Printed mark used on Chinese Jade, 1920–1940.

Mark used mainly on wall plaques, 1925–1939.

Printed mark used on Burslem earthenware, 1932 –present day.

Printed Flambe mark with Sung in script, 1920–1940.

Mark in current use, 1959–present day.

INDEX

433

Q

R